THE VARIATIONAL METHOD IN ENGINEERING

THE
VARIATIONAL
METHOD IN
ENGINEERING

R. S. SCHECHTER

Professor of Chemical Engineering
The University of Texas

McGRAW-HILL BOOK COMPANY

NEW YORK   ST. LOUIS   SAN FRANCISCO   TORONTO   LONDON   SYDNEY

THE VARIATIONAL METHOD IN ENGINEERING

Library of Congress Catalog Card Number 66-25488

55187

1234567890 M P 7432106987

TO MY PARENTS

"He that dwelleth in the secret place of the most High shall abide under the shadow of the Almighty."

PSALMS: 91:1

PREFACE

The number of engineering research papers making use of that body of mathematics generally classified as the calculus of variations has seemingly grown at an exponential rate in the past few years. Associated with this accelerated activity is the need to introduce both senior and beginning graduate students to the essential concepts governing the reported applications. This pressure will certainly result in the formation of new courses or the revamping of existing courses in order to make room for this important body of knowledge. This book is intended to serve as an introduction to the methods of variational calculus for engineering students. It is also hoped that the existence of this book, which emphasizes the applications, provides numerous examples, and is understandable to students having no mathematics beyond calculus, will help to stimulate interest in teaching this important field of applied mathematics to young engineers.

The applications of variational calculus can be divided into two broad categories. On the one hand, we find problems which require the determination of some best design or strategy, where "best" has a well-defined sense. A classic example is Newton's study of the shape of the body of revolution giving the least frictional drag when translated through a quiescent fluid. Such problems, related to optimal policy, often find their expression in the format of variational calculus. In this application the mathematical apparatus serves to define a differential equation, the Euler-Lagrange equation, which must be satisfied if an optimal policy is to exist. Such problems have been termed *natural problems* because one is lead directly from the statement of the problem to a variational formulation. Such problems are treated in Chap. 2.

In Chap. 3, we demonstrate the methods of approximating certain differential equations by direct calculations based on the variational "analog" to the differential equation. These direct methods, for example, the Ritz method, are shown to be simple in their application and are often extremely effective. Thus it is desirable to represent the balance equations in variational form so that direct calculations can be used to approximate these important equations. The variational formulation of these equations, which provide the framework for many engineering calculations, is discussed in Chap. 4. The principle of minimum entropy production is shown to have certain limitations, and, in its place, we propose the local potential which has been recently introduced by Glansdorff and Prigogine. This general variational principle is applicable to all continuum systems and permits the application of the methods introduced in Chap. 3 with very little modification. The local potential does not fall within the realm of classical variational calculus, and one loses the means of exacting bounds, which is the price for preserving the other desirable features of variational formulations such as compactness of expression, straightforward treatment of the boundary conditions, and use of the direct methods.

Example problems, which make use of both the principle of minimum entropy production and the local potential, are studied in Chap. 5.

In Chap. 6, a brief survey of other variational techniques used to treat continuum systems are considered. In the final chapter, time-dependent processes are shown to be represented within the framework of the local potential, and this structure is shown to be suited to studies in hydrodynamic stability.

In general, the book has been written so that the methods are illustrated by example. Some of these examples have appeared in the literature, but for the most part, they have been developed for this text. However, in every case examples have been used in place of complex and abstract arguments. It is hoped that the reader will be able to translate from the examples to forms suited to his purposes.

As always, a book cannot be the product of an individual, but is influenced by the writings of admired and respected persons in the field, by discussions with colleagues, and by the response of the students. It is never possible to recognize all of these contributors. However, I should like to thank Profs. I. Prigogine and P. Glansdorff of the University of Brussels for their advice and assistance. Indeed, my interest in variational calculus was aroused by my discussions with Professor Prigogine about the method of the local potential. He has also been a source of encouragement throughout the ordeal of writing. My interest was first directed to the potential of variational methods while working with Dr. R. J. Blackwell of the Esso Production Research Company on problems of flow in porous media. Professor G. S. G. Beveridge, of the University of Edinburgh, first called my attention to problems in optimal reactor design and participated in many of the calculations presented here. Also, much of the analysis of hydrodynamic stability has been done in collaboration with Prof. D. M. Himmelblau of the University of Texas. His contributions are greatly acknowledged. I cannot name all of the students who have aided me in making calculations; however, the work of Charles Loeffler and John Ball has been notable.

Finally, it is with pleasure that I acknowledge the efforts of my wife. She has done much of the editing, some of the typing, and performed other tasks, too numerous to mention. Without her efforts, this work would not yet have been complete.

R. S. SCHECHTER

CONTENTS

Preface vii

CHAPTER 1
THE
CALCULUS
OF
VARIATIONS

1.1 INTRODUCTION Variational principles have played an important role in the development of many branches of physics, the most notable examples being mechanics, both classical and quantum, and thermodynamics. It is well known that the problems of particle mechanics are expressible in a variational form known as Hamilton's principle (see Sec. 1.3), as well as by Newton's equation of motion. Although there is a correspondence between the two modes of expression, physical insight into complicated physical systems can often be acquired more easily using the energy concept (Hamilton's principle) than by studying the Newtonian equations of motion. In addition to this advantage, variational principles are also valuable in determining approximate solutions. Finally, it is noted that the variational principles are independent of the coordinate system. These advantages have motivated researchers to retain both modes of expression in studies of particle mechanics.[1]

In this book our primary concern is to investigate applications of variational calculus to a broad class of engineering problems. We have chosen to classify these problems into two groups. The descriptive title, *natural* problems, has been used to characterize one of the groups. As we shall see, a variational format has the structure of an integral to be rendered stationary (usually either a maximum or a minimum) by an appropriate choice of the function appearing in the integrand of the integral. As often happens in engineering endeavors, the task of determining an optimal policy is encountered, and it is *natural* to give the mathematical statement of the problem in variational form. For example, suppose we have the reaction system

$$A \rightarrow B \rightarrow C \tag{1.1.1}$$

where the rates at which each reaction progresses are a function of the concentrations of the reactants and of the temperature. The task is to program the reaction temperature as a function of time such that the production of B in a batch reactor is maximized at the time the reaction is terminated. Thus the production of B is to be maximized at the end of a time interval T. The integral I is therefore to be maximized

$$I = \int_0^T r_B \, dt \tag{1.1.2}$$

where r_B is the rate of reaction of B and t represents time. The rate r_B is a function of the temperature, and the temperature must be established as a function of time in order to maximize I. This is a variational problem.

[1] See, for example, A. G. Webster, "The Dynamics of Particles," 2d ed., Dover Publications, Inc., New York, 1959.

The formulation of the variational integral followed from the statement of the task to be accomplished, and is thus classified as a natural problem. It should now be clear that many economic and design considerations lead directly to a variational problem. Further, the calculus of variations is also a useful tool in thermodynamic studies, where the state of the system is often determined by the maximum or minimum of some thermodynamic variable (for example, the Helmholtz free energy is minimized at equilibrium for systems at constant temperature and volume). The application of the calculus of variations to this class of problems is studied in Chap. 2.

The mathematical descriptions of many systems studied by engineers find their expression in the form of differential equations. Superficially, we might be inclined to state unequivocally that such problems are outside the realm of variational calculus. However, we can again refer to the structure of particle mechanics in which both Newton's laws and Hamilton's principle offer alternate, but equivalent, formulations of the problem. Since alternate computational methods exist for the determination of particle trajectories, why should not a variational formulation for continuous systems (those most often arising in engineering) exist also? Indeed, in many cases we shall find that a variational formulation is possible for many of the continuum balance equations. The means of finding the variational principle can be frequently based on the postulate of minimum entropy production at the stationary state. In any event we have chosen to term such problems *synthetic* problems, since their natural mode of expression is in the form of differential equations.

Finally, we have noted that variational formulations are useful in finding approximate solutions. These approximate techniques are discussed in Chap. 3, and detailed examples are presented in Chap. 5, the emphasis being placed on synthetic problems.

With this brief introduction, we first began the task of acquainting ourselves with the methods of variational calculus. This chapter is basic to the understanding of all the material to follow. There are several good books[2] which the student can use to supplement this material and thereby achieve a better insight into the basic mathematical problems. However, the subject matter presented in Chap. 1 is complete in the sense that no further information is required to understand the remaining material.

1.2 EULER-LAGRANGE EQUATIONS

Extremal problems have been of great interest throughout the ages, for man has always sought the "best" course of action when there are alternate

[2] A. R. Forsyth, "Calculus of Variations," pp. 30–36, Dover Publications, Inc., New York, 1960; R. Weinstock, "Calculus of Variations," pp. 74–75, McGraw-Hill Book Company, New York, 1952.

methods of accomplishing a necessary task. The calculus of variations is that branch of mathematics which treats the selection of an unknown function appearing in the integrand of an integral such that the value of the integral is made either a maximum or a minimum. This type of problem, which is termed a *variational* problem, often arises in many phases of engineering endeavor. Newton, for example, sought to determine the shape of the solid body of revolution which encountered the least resistance in being translated through a fluid. This and other pertinent examples are discussed in Chap. 2.

To give formal definition to our problem, consider the integral

$$I = \int_{x_2}^{x_1} F[x, y(x), y_x(x)]\, dx \tag{1.2.1}$$

where F, the integrand, is, in general, both an implicit and explicit function of x, since F depends on the function $y(x)$ and its first derivative $y_x(x)$. For the moment we consider that the limits x_1 and x_2 are fixed. The problem is to select the function $y(x)$ such that the integral defined by Eq. (1.2.1) is minimized (or maximized).

To clarify the nature of the problem somewhat, let us consider a simple example. Suppose that we wish to determine the curve of minimum length connecting two points (of course, our intuition has already given us the solution to this problem). Several possible curves connecting the points (x_1, y_1) and (x_2, y_2) are shown in Fig. 1.2.1. We know from elementary considerations that the length of the curve connecting the two points is

$$I = \int_{x_1}^{x_2} (1 + y_x^2)^{\frac{1}{2}}\, dx \qquad ds = \sqrt{1 + \left(\frac{dy}{dx}\right)^2}\, dx \tag{1.2.2}$$

The task is to find the function $y(x)$ which minimizes I. Comparing this specific form with the general structure given in Eq. (1.2.1), we see that

$$F[x, y(x), y_x(x)] \equiv (1 + y_x^2)^{\frac{1}{2}} \tag{1.2.3}$$

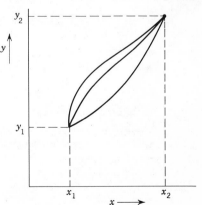

Fig. 1.2.1   Alternate paths connecting two points.

We note that I is called a functional, since its value is dependent on the choice of the function $y(x)$ used in the integration. Thus we inquire about the conditions which $y(x)$ must satisfy to insure that I is as small as possible. It will be shown in the work to follow that a necessary, but not sufficient, condition is that $y(x)$ satisfy the differential equation

$$\frac{\partial F}{\partial y} - \frac{d}{dx}\frac{\partial F}{\partial y_x} = 0 \qquad (1.2.4)$$

Equation (1.2.4) is called the Euler-Lagrange equation to honor two of the great mathematicians who investigated this problem. To demonstrate the assertion that Eq. (1.2.4) is a necessary condition which must be imposed on $y(x)$ to insure that I is a minimum, it is necessary to digress from the example problem and to introduce the concept of a variation.

Suppose $y(x)$ is indeed the function of x which gives I the smallest possible value when used in Eq. (1.2.1), and $y^*(x)$ is a second function of x which is at most infinitesimally different from $y(x)$ at every point x within the open interval (x_1,x_2). Define

$$\delta y = y^*(x) - y(x) \qquad (1.2.5)$$

The operator δ is called the variation symbol. The variation of a function should be understood to represent an infinitesimal change in the function at a given value of x. The change is arbitrary; that is, it is a virtual change. We should stress that the variation differs from the usual differentiation, which gives a measure of the change of a function resulting from a specified change in the independent variable (in this case x). It is well to keep this difference in mind, since both the operation of variation and the operation of differentiation will often appear in the same equation. Equation (1.2.5) can be represented as

$$\delta y(x) = y^*(x) - y(x) = \epsilon\phi(x) \qquad (1.2.6)$$

where $\phi(x)$ is an arbitrary continuous and differentiable function of x and the variable parameter ϵ tends to zero. It is useful to develop several properties of the variation operator. Since we have agreed that the variation operator imparts an infinitesimal change to a function at fixed x, we have

$$\delta x = 0 \qquad (1.2.7)$$

so that the independent variable does not participate in the variation process. Further we note that the variation operator commutes with both the operations of differentiation and integration. These two valuable properties can easily be demonstrated in the following way. First compute the derivative of a variation

$$\frac{d}{dx}\delta y = \frac{d}{dx}\epsilon\phi(x) = \epsilon\frac{d\phi}{dx} \qquad (1.2.8)$$

Next take the variation of a derivative

$$\delta \frac{dy}{dx} = \frac{dy^*}{dx} - \frac{dy}{dx} = \frac{d}{dx}(y^* - y) = \epsilon \frac{d\phi}{dx} \tag{1.2.9}$$

Since we obtain the same result from both computations, we conclude

$$\frac{d}{dx} \delta y = \delta \frac{dy}{dx} \tag{1.2.10}$$

which demonstrates that the operations of differentiation and variation commute. Integration and variation also commute. For

$$\delta \int_{x_1}^{x_2} y(x)\, dx = \int_{x_1}^{x_2} y^*(x)\, dx - \int_{x_1}^{x_2} y(x)\, dx = \int_{x_1}^{x_2} [y^*(x) - y(x)]\, dx$$
$$= \int_{x_1}^{x_2} \delta y(x)\, dx$$

Thus

$$\delta \int_{x_1}^{x_2} y(x)\, dx = \int_{x_1}^{x_2} \delta y(x)\, dx \tag{1.2.11}$$

and we have verified the assertion that the two operators are commutative.

We have developed a few of the properties of the operation of variation. We now return to our original task of determining the function $y(x)$ which minimizes the I of Eq. (1.2.1). The concept of a variation will prove invaluable in this search. To obtain some "feel" for the task facing us, let us recall some of the principles developed in differential calculus which guided the search for a local minimum (or a maximum) of a function of one or more independent variables. In this search, a kind of "mathematical experiment" is performed to establish the possible existence of a minimum at a specified point. The "mathematical experiment" consists of studying the function in an infinitesimal region about the specified point to determine if the function is the same (to the first order) at all neighboring points. This condition, the vanishing of the first derivative with respect to all of the independent variables, is necessary for the function to be a minimum at the point in question. However, it is clear that the vanishing of the first derivative is not a sufficient condition to insure a minimum, since the function can also be a maximum or a saddle point at the specified point. If the rate of change of a function vanishes in every possible direction, then that function is said to have a *stationary value* at the point. Further investigation of the second derivatives is required to establish the existence of a minimum at the point in question. To be a minimum the sign of the second derivative must be positive for all infinitesimal displacements. If the sign of the second derivative is positive for some displacements and negative for others, then the stationary point is neither a maximum nor a minimum.

This brief description of the principles of minimization is not intended to be mathematically precise, for it has been assumed that the reader is already well acquainted with the material which we have just discussed. However, the discussion was included in this section, since our development follows these principles rather closely. We shall define the I of Eq. (1.2.1) to be *stationary* if

$$\delta I = 0 \tag{1.2.12}$$

This condition is analogous to that of finding the stationary value of a function; however, in this case we should remember that we are investigating the change of I with respect to changes in the functional relationship; that is, we are varying $y(x)$ rather than varying a function with respect to changes in an independent variable.

Using the commutative property, Eq. (1.2.11), we write

$$\delta I = \int_{x_1}^{x_2} \delta F \, dx \tag{1.2.13}$$

where

$$\delta F = F(y^*, y_x^*, x) - F(y, y_x, x) = F(y + \epsilon\phi, y_x + \epsilon\phi_x, x) - F(y, y_x, x)$$

The quantity δF can be expanded into a Taylor series to give

$$\delta F = \epsilon\left(\frac{\partial F}{\partial y}\phi + \frac{\partial F}{\partial y_x}\phi_x\right) \tag{1.2.14}$$

where terms of higher order in ϵ have been omitted, since ϵ is presumed to be small.

If I is to be stationary, then we require

$$\delta I = 0 = \epsilon\int_{x_1}^{x_2}\left(\frac{\partial F}{\partial y}\phi + \frac{\partial F}{\partial y_x}\phi_x\right) dx \tag{1.2.15}$$

for all functions $\phi(x)$.

The second term in the integrand of Eq. (1.2.15) can be integrated by parts as follows:

$$\int_{x_1}^{x_2}\frac{\partial F}{\partial y_x}\phi_x \, dx = \phi\frac{\partial F}{\partial y_x}\Big|_{x_1}^{x_2} - \int_{x_1}^{x_2}\phi\frac{d}{dx}\frac{\partial F}{\partial y_x} dx \tag{1.2.16}$$

The first term, evaluated at the limits of the integration, vanishes if we assume that the boundary conditions are specified so that the function $y(x)$ is fixed at the end points. In this case the function $\phi(x)$ must vanish on the boundary, since variations in $y(x)$ are not permitted at the boundaries. Of course, if other boundary conditions are imposed or if the boundary conditions are free (unspecified), further consideration must be given to the evaluation of the first term. For the moment we shall assume that the function is specified on the boundary and no variation is permitted at the end points; however, the general question of boundary conditions is examined in Sec. 1.6. Using the result expressed in Eq. (1.2.16), Eq. (1.2.15) becomes

$$\frac{\delta I}{\epsilon} = \int_{x_1}^{x_2} \left(\frac{\partial F}{\partial y} - \frac{d}{dx} \frac{\partial F}{\partial y_x} \right) \phi(x) \, dx = 0 \tag{1.2.17}$$

The integration by parts was a very essential step in the analysis of the problem. For now we have rearranged the integral so that the arbitrary function $\phi(x)$† is multiplied by a grouping of terms which are dependent on the true solution but not on the choice of $\phi(x)$. Since $\phi(x)$ is arbitrary, we assert that if Eq. (1.2.17) is to be satisfied for all possible $\phi(x)$, then

$$0 = \frac{\partial F}{\partial y} - \frac{d}{dx} \frac{\partial F}{\partial y_x} \tag{1.2.4}$$

For if Eq. (1.2.4) is not satisfied at every point within the interval (x_1, x_2), then the right side of Eq. (1.2.4) must be either positive or negative in some finite range of x. Since $\phi(x)$ is arbitrary, it is always possible to construct a $\phi(x)$ such that its sign is always the *same* as that of the right-hand side of Eq. (1.2.4). Thus all of the contributions to the value of the integral over the range of integration would be positive, giving Eq. (1.2.17) a positive result and violating the equality sign expressed by Eq. (1.2.17). Hence Eq. (1.2.4) is to be satisfied for all values of x. As noted above, this differential equation is called the Euler-Lagrange equation, and the Euler-Lagrange equation must be satisfied if the integral defined by Eq. (1.2.1) is to be stationary.‡

Let us apply the Euler-Lagrange equation to the problem of determining the path giving the shortest distance between two points. Applying Eq. (1.2.4) to the integrand of Eq. (1.2.2) we see that

$$\frac{\partial F}{\partial y} = \frac{\partial}{\partial y} (1 + y_x^2)^{\frac{1}{2}} = 0 \tag{1.2.18}$$

and

$$\frac{\partial F}{\partial y_x} = \frac{\partial}{\partial y_x} (1 + y_x^2)^{\frac{1}{2}} = \frac{y_x}{(1 + y_x^2)^{\frac{1}{2}}}$$

so that the Euler-Lagrange equation becomes

$$0 = -\frac{d}{dx} [y_x (1 + y_x^2)^{-\frac{1}{2}}] \tag{1.2.19}$$

---

† The function $\phi(x)$ is not completely arbitrary, for there are three restrictions which must be imposed on this function—the function must be continuous, have a continuous first derivative, and vanish at the end points to be an admissible function.
‡ Of course, an extremal may not exist and Eq. (1.2.1) will not have a solution.

Thus

$$\frac{y_x}{\sqrt{1 + y_x^2}} = \text{const}$$

which implies that y_x is a constant. Thus the shortest path connecting the two points is a straight line. Of course, to insure that the function $y(x) = a$ constant is actually a minimizing function, we must test the second variation to see if this quantity is positive for all possible variations. The second variation can be found by applying the variation operator a second time; that is,

$$\delta^2 F = \delta(\delta F) = \delta\left[\epsilon\left(\phi\frac{\partial F}{\partial y} + \phi_x\frac{\partial F}{\partial y_x}\right)\right]$$

$$= \epsilon\left[\phi(x)\frac{\partial F(y + \epsilon\phi, y_x + \epsilon\phi_x, x)}{\partial y} + \phi_x(x)\frac{\partial F(y + \epsilon\phi, y_x + \epsilon\phi_x, x)}{\partial y_x}\right.$$

$$\left. - \phi(x)\frac{\partial F(y, y_x, x)}{\partial y} - \phi_x(x)\frac{\partial F(y, y_x, x)}{\partial y_x}\right] \tag{1.2.20}$$

As before, we expand the differences into a power series in powers of ϵ and ignore all but the second power of ϵ. This expansion gives

$$\delta^2 F = \epsilon^2\left(\phi^2\frac{\partial^2 F}{\partial y^2} + 2\phi\phi_x\frac{\partial^2 F}{\partial y_x\,\partial y} + \phi_x^2\frac{\partial^2 F}{\partial y_x^2}\right) \tag{1.2.21}$$

Thus

$$\delta^2 I = \int_{x_1}^{x_2} \delta^2 F\,dx \tag{1.2.22}$$

If

$$\delta^2 I > 0$$

for all possible admissible variations, then the stationary value is a minimum. On the other hand, we also note that

$$\delta^2 I < 0 \tag{1.2.23}$$

implies that the stationary value is a maximum, and if $\delta^2 I$ is positive for some variations and negative for others, the stationary state is not an extremal.

To show that the path $y_x = \text{const}$ is a path of minimum length, it is sufficient to show that $\delta^2 I$ is positive for all possible $\phi(x)$. Let us check to see if this is the case. Substituting Eq. (1.2.3) into Eq. (1.2.21) we see that

$$\delta^2 F = \epsilon^2\phi_x^2\frac{1}{(1 + y_x^2)^{3/2}}$$

or

$$\delta^2 I = \epsilon^2 \int_{x_1}^{x_2} \phi_x{}^2 \frac{1}{(1 + y_x{}^2)^{3/2}} \, dx \tag{1.2.24}$$

which is positive for all admissible $\phi(x)$. Hence the path $y_x = \text{const}$ is a path of minimum length.

EXAMPLE 1.2.1 Let us determine the function $y(x)$ which passes through the points (x_1, y_1) and (x_2, y_2) and gives the minimum surface of revolution when rotated about the x axis. This surface of revolution is depicted in Fig. 1.2.2. It is not difficult to show that the surface area of the surface of revolution is given by

$$S = 2\pi \int_{x_1}^{x_2} y(1 + y_x{}^2)^{1/2} \, dx \tag{1.2.25}$$

We note that the $y(x)$ must satisfy the Euler-Lagrange equation if a minimum is to exist. If the integrand does not depend on x explicitly, the Euler-Lagrange equation can be put into the form (see Example 1.2.2)

$$\frac{d}{dx}\left(F - y_x \frac{\partial F}{\partial y_x}\right) = 0 \tag{1.2.26}$$

If a minimum surface area exists, then $y(x)$ must satisfy the following differential equation:

$$\frac{d}{dx}\left[y(1 + y_x{}^2)^{1/2} - y_x{}^2 y(1 + y_x{}^2)^{-1/2}\right] = 0 \tag{1.2.27}$$

Equation (1.2.27) can be written in the form

$$\frac{y}{(1 + y_x{}^2)^{1/2}} = a \tag{1.2.28}$$

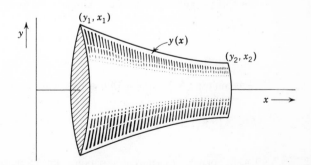

Fig. 1.2.2 Surface of revolution.

where a is a constant of integration. Integrating Eq. (1.2.28) we obtain

$$y = a \cosh \left(\frac{x}{a} + b\right) \tag{1.2.29}$$

where b is a second constant of integration. The two constants of integration are determined from the specified end points of the curve. Equation (1.2.29) represents a catenary. For a more complete and detailed solution of the problem the reader is referred to Forsyth.[1]

EXAMPLE 1.2.2   If the integrand of a variational integral does not depend explicitly on x, prove that the Euler-Lagrange equation can be written as

$$\frac{d}{dx}\left(F - y_x \frac{\partial F}{\partial y_x}\right) = 0 \tag{1.2.26}$$

To demonstrate this identity, differentiate the above expression to obtain

$$\frac{dF}{dx} - y_{xx}\frac{\partial F}{\partial y_x} - y_x \frac{d}{dx}\frac{\partial F}{\partial y_x} = 0 \tag{1.2.30}$$

Since F is presumed not to depend on x explicitly [but only through $y(x)$ and the first derivative of $y(x)$], we can write

$$\frac{dF}{dx} = \frac{\partial F}{\partial y}y_x + \frac{\partial F}{\partial y_x}y_{xx} \qquad \text{Chain Rule.} \tag{1.2.31}$$

which when substituted into Eq. (1.2.30) gives

$$\frac{\partial F}{\partial y} - \frac{d}{dx}\frac{\partial F}{\partial y_x} = 0 \tag{1.2.4}$$

This is the Euler-Lagrange equation and the proof is complete.

PROBLEM 1.2.1   In all of our calculations thus far we have assumed that the integrand is a functional of $y(x)$ and its first derivative $y_x(x)$. Develop the Euler-Lagrange equation which is necessary for the integral

$$I = \int_{x_1}^{x_2} F(y, y_x, y_{xx}, x)\, dx$$

to be stationary, given that both y and y_x are fixed at the end points.

PROBLEM 1.2.2   Show that a necessary condition for the functional

$$I = A \int_{x_1}^{x_2}\int K(z,x)y(z)y(x)\, dx\, dz - \int_{x_1}^{x_2}[y(x)]^2\, dx + 2\int_{x_1}^{x_2} y(x)G(x)\, dx$$

[1] A. R. Forsyth, "Calculus of Variations," pp. 30–36, Dover Publications, Inc., New York, 1960.

to be stationary is that the integral equation

$$y(x) = G(x) + A\int_{x_1}^{x_2} K(z,x)y(z)\,dz$$

be satisfied.   In these equations A is a constant, $G(x)$ is specified function of position, and $K(z,x)$ is a specified *symmetric* kernel [$K(z,x) = K(x,z)$].

I.3 SEVERAL DEPENDENT VARIABLES

In the remaining sections of this chapter we shall generalize the result of the preceding section; however, the analytical tools required to effect these generalizations are the same as those used in that section.   In this section we shall admit a second dependent function into the integrand of the variational integral and again inquire about the functions $y(x)$ and $z(x)$ which render the following integral stationary.

$$I = \int_{x_1}^{x_2} \{F[y(x),y_x(x),z(x),z_x(x),x]\}\,dx \tag{1.3.1}$$

where again we define I to be stationary if

$$\delta I = 0 \tag{1.3.2}$$

Now the definition of a variation remains unchanged and thus

$$\delta y = y^*(x) - y(x) = \epsilon\phi(x)$$
$$\delta z = z^*(x) - z(x) = \kappa\mu(x)$$

Then

$$\delta I = \int_{x_1}^{x_2} \delta F\,dx$$
$$= \int_{x_1}^{x_2} [F(y + \epsilon\phi(x), y_x + \epsilon\phi_x, z + \kappa\mu, z_x + \kappa\mu_x, x) - F(y,y_x,z,z_x,x)]\,dx \tag{1.3.3}$$

Expanding into a power series in ϵ and κ, we obtain

$$\delta I = \epsilon\int_{x_1}^{x_2}\left(\frac{\partial F}{\partial y}\phi + \frac{\partial F}{\partial y_x}\phi_x\right)dx + \kappa\int_{x_1}^{x_2}\left(\frac{\partial F}{\partial z}\mu + \frac{\partial F}{\partial y_x}\mu_x\right)dx \tag{1.3.4}$$

if terms of the first order are retained.   We now wish to arrange the integrand so that the variation is multiplied by a coefficient which does not depend on the variation.   To achieve this arrangement, we integrate by parts as before [see Eq. (1.2.16)] to obtain

$$\delta I = 0 = \epsilon\int_{x_1}^{x_2}\phi\left(\frac{\partial F}{\partial y} - \frac{d}{dx}\frac{\partial F}{\partial y_x}\right)dx + \kappa\int_{x_1}^{x_2}\mu\left(\frac{\partial F}{\partial z} - \frac{d}{dx}\frac{\partial F}{\partial z_x}\right)dx \tag{1.3.5}$$

Since $\mu(x)$ and $\phi(x)$ are restricted only by continuity requirements and by the boundary conditions and since the two dependent functions are entirely independent of one another, it is asserted that Eq. (1.3.5) can be satisfied for all admissible variations $\mu(x)$ and $\phi(x)$ if and only if the coefficient of the variations vanish at every point in the interval (x_1,x_2). Thus we have

$$\frac{\partial F}{\partial y} - \frac{d}{dx}\frac{\partial F}{\partial y_x} = 0$$

$$\frac{\partial F}{\partial z} - \frac{d}{dx}\frac{\partial F}{\partial z_x} = 0$$
(1.3.6)

These two equations are the necessary and sufficient conditions for I to be termed stationary. To determine if the stationary value is a maximum, a minimum, or neither, one must investigate the second variation.

It should be quite obvious that as additional dependent variables appear in the integrand of the variational integral, an additional Euler-Lagrange equation will be obtained.

Variational calculus has played a significant role in the development of particle mechanics. The Newtonian laws of motion provide a mathematical structure which describes the motion of a system of rigid interacting particles. Although the formulation of Newton is most widely studied in elementary physics and mechanics, there is a second and alternate method of expressing the behavior of mechanical systems. This alternate mathematical description is called Hamilton's principle, and states[1] that the motion of an arbitrary mechanical system occurs in such a way that the definite integral I, defined as

$$I = \int_{t_1}^{t_2} \mathscr{L}\, dt$$
(1.3.7)

becomes stationary for arbitrary possible variations of the configuration of the system, provided the initial and final configurations of the system are prescribed.

The integrand $\mathscr{L}$ is called the Lagrangian and is defined as

$$\mathscr{L} = T - V$$
(1.3.8)

where T is the kinetic energy of the system and V is its potential energy. It is indeed remarkable that the scalar function $\mathscr{L}$ determines the motion of the system.

EXAMPLE 1.3.1 Consider a particle moving in a potential field $V(x_1,x_2,x_3)$. The kinetic energy of the particle is given by

$$T = \frac{m}{2}\left[\left(\frac{dx_1}{dt}\right)^2 + \left(\frac{dx_2}{dt}\right)^2 + \left(\frac{dx_3}{dt}\right)^2\right]$$

[1] R. Weinstock, "Calculus of Variations," pp. 74–75, McGraw-Hill Book Company, New York, 1952.

and Eq. (1.3.7) is

$$I = \int_{t_1}^{t_2} \left\{ \frac{m}{2}\left[\left(\frac{dx_1}{dt}\right)^2 + \left(\frac{dx_2}{dt}\right)^2 + \left(\frac{dx_3}{dt}\right)^2 \right] - V(x_1,x_2,x_3) \right\} dt$$

[handwritten: acceleration in z direction]

Applying Eq. (1.3.6) to the integrand, we find

$$m\frac{d^2x_i}{dt^2} = -\frac{\partial V}{\partial x_i} \qquad i = 1, 2, \text{ or } 3 \qquad (1.3.9)$$

[handwritten: $V = \int m \frac{d^2x}{dt^2} dz$]

Equation (1.3.9) is clearly the Newtonian equation of motion describing the trajectory of the particle in a force field.

EXAMPLE 1.3.2   An important advantage of Hamilton's principle stems from the ease with which the Newtonian laws of motion can be developed in coordinate systems other than rectangular coordinates. For example, let us consider the motion of a particle constrained to move over the surface of a horizontal cylinder. If the acceleration due to gravity is g, then the potential energy is

$$V = mgx$$

where x is the height above a horizontal plane containing the axis of the cylinder. Let R be the radius of the cylinder, θ the angular displacement of the particle from the horizontal plane, and z the displacement along the axis of the cylinder. What are the equations which describe the motion of this particle? The potential energy can be written as

$$V = mgR\sin\theta$$

[handwritten diagram: R, R sin θ]

and the kinetic energy is

$$T = \frac{m}{2}\left[R^2\left(\frac{d\theta}{dt}\right)^2 + \left(\frac{dz}{dt}\right)^2 \right]$$

Thus Hamilton's principle takes the form

$$I = \int_{t_1}^{t_2} \left\{ \frac{m}{2}\left[R^2\left(\frac{d\theta}{dt}\right)^2 + \left(\frac{dz}{dt}\right)^2 \right] - Rmg\sin\theta \right\} dt$$

Using Eq. (1.3.6), we see that the necessary condition for I to be stationary is that

$$mR\frac{d^2\theta}{dt^2} = -mg\cos\theta$$

$$m\frac{d^2z}{dt^2} = 0$$

These are the Newtonian equations of motion describing the trajectory of the constrained particle.

1.4 SEVERAL INDEPENDENT VARIABLES

In many problems we shall encounter situations in which the integrand is a function of more than one independent variable. Thus, we ask what is the necessary and sufficient condition for the integrand

$$I = \int_V \{F[x,y,z,u,u_x(x,y,z),u_y(x,y,z),u_z(x,y,z)]\}\, dV \tag{1.4.1}$$

to be stationary. Here the integration is meant to be throughout some fixed volume V which is bounded by a surface S. For our purposes it is sufficiently general to develop the necessary conditions for a volume which is simply[1] connected and for a continuous function $u(x,y,z)$ possessing continuous derivatives in the volume V. Moreover, we shall assume that the function $u(x,y,z)$ is specified on the surface S, and, as a consequence, $u(x,y,z)$ is not subject to variations on this surface. We shall relax this latter restriction in Sec. 1.6 where more general boundary conditions are discussed. We now extend the definition of a variation as follows:

$$\delta u = u^* - u = \epsilon\eta(x,y,z) \tag{1.4.2}$$

Again we define u as the function which forces I to be stationary, and u^* as a function which is but infinitesimally different from u in the volume V. It is necessary for η to be continuous and to have continuous derivatives, but apart from these restrictions, η is arbitrary. Here ϵ is a small constant. Finally, we note that η must vanish on the boundary, since u is not subject to variations on S; however, as noted, this restriction will be relaxed in Sec. 1.6. Using this extended definition of a variation, we have

$$\delta I = \int_V \delta F\, dV = \int_V [F(x,y,z,\, u + \epsilon\eta,\, u_x + \epsilon\eta_x,\, u_y + \epsilon\eta_y,\, u_z + \epsilon\eta_z)$$
$$- F(x,y,z,u,u_x,u_y,u_z)]\, dV \tag{1.4.3}$$

As before, we expand the difference appearing in the integrand into a Taylor series in powers of ϵ. Ignoring terms of second order and higher, we find

$$\delta I = \epsilon\int_V \left(\frac{\partial F}{\partial u}\eta + \frac{\partial F}{\partial u_x}\eta_x + \frac{\partial F}{\partial u_y}\eta_y + \frac{\partial F}{\partial u_z}\eta_z \right) dV \tag{1.4.4}$$

We can rewrite this expression as

$$\frac{\delta I}{\epsilon} = \int_V \left(\frac{\partial F}{\partial u} - \frac{\partial}{\partial x}\frac{\partial F}{\partial u_x} - \frac{\partial}{\partial y}\frac{\partial F}{\partial u_y} - \frac{\partial}{\partial z}\frac{\partial F}{\partial u_z} \right)\eta\, dV$$
$$+ \int_V \left(\frac{\partial}{\partial x}\frac{\partial F}{\partial u_x}\eta + \frac{\partial}{\partial y}\frac{\partial F}{\partial u_y}\eta + \frac{\partial}{\partial z}\frac{\partial F}{\partial u_z}\eta \right) dV \tag{1.4.5}$$

[1] I. S. Sokolnikoff, "Advanced Calculus," p. 196, McGraw-Hill Book Company, 1939.

The second volume integral on the right-hand side can be transformed into a surface integral with the aid of the divergence theorem (sometimes called Green's or Gauss' theorem) which states[2]

$$\int_V \left(\frac{\partial P}{\partial x} + \frac{\partial Q}{\partial y} + \frac{\partial R}{\partial z} \right) dV = \int_S (P\, dy\, dz + Q\, dx\, dz + R\, dx\, dy) \qquad (1.4.6)$$

where P, Q, and R and $\partial P/\partial x$, $\partial Q/\partial y$, $\partial R/\partial z$ are continuous single-valued functions in the region V. Thus Eq. (1.4.5) can be written in the form

$$\frac{\delta I}{\epsilon} = \int_V \left(\frac{\partial F}{\partial u} - \frac{\partial}{\partial x}\frac{\partial F}{\partial u_x} - \frac{\partial}{\partial y}\frac{\partial F}{\partial u_y} - \frac{\partial}{\partial z}\frac{\partial F}{\partial u_z} \right) \eta\, dV$$

$$+ \int_S \left(\frac{\partial F}{\partial u_x}\, dy\, dz + \frac{\partial F}{\partial u_y}\, dx\, dz + \frac{\partial F}{\partial u_z}\, dx\, dy \right) \eta \qquad (1.4.7)$$

However, η vanishes on S and the surface integral then vanishes. Moreover, δI must vanish for all possible admissible variations, and hence

$$0 = \int_V \left(\frac{\partial F}{\partial u} - \frac{\partial}{\partial x}\frac{\partial F}{\partial u_x} - \frac{\partial}{\partial y}\frac{\partial F}{\partial u_y} - \frac{\partial}{\partial z}\frac{\partial F}{\partial u_z} \right) \eta\, dV \qquad (1.4.8)$$

Equation (1.4.8) must be satisfied for all admissible η, and again we can conclude that the integrand must vanish at each point in the region V. Hence

$$\frac{\partial F}{\partial u} - \frac{\partial}{\partial x}\frac{\partial F}{\partial u_x} - \frac{\partial}{\partial y}\frac{\partial F}{\partial u_y} - \frac{\partial}{\partial z}\frac{\partial F}{\partial u_z} = 0 \qquad (1.4.9)$$

which is an extended form of the Euler-Lagrange equations. This expression represents the condition for I to be stationary.

EXAMPLE 1.4.1   Consider the integral

$$I = \int_V \left[\left(\frac{\partial u}{\partial x} \right)^2 + \left(\frac{\partial u}{\partial y} \right)^2 + \left(\frac{\partial u}{\partial z} \right)^2 - 2u\psi(x,y,z) \right] dV \qquad (1.4.10)$$

What condition must u satisfy to render I stationary? To answer this question, we need only apply Eq. (1.4.9) to the integrand of Eq. (1.4.10) and find

$$\frac{\partial^2 u}{\partial x^2} + \frac{\partial^2 u}{\partial y^2} + \frac{\partial^2 u}{\partial z^2} + \psi = 0 \qquad (1.4.11)$$

The reader will readily recognize Eq. (1.4.11) as the differential equation governing the flow of heat in a solid body under such conditions that the process is no longer time dependent. The function $\psi(x,y,z)$ is directly proportional to the rate of internal heat generation and u plays the role of a

---

[2] I. S. Sokolnikoff, "Advanced Calculus," pp. 167–170, McGraw-Hill Book Company, 1939.

temperature. Thus the function $u(x,y,z)$ which makes I stationary also satisfies the steady-state heat-conduction equation with internal heat generation. There is a correspondence between the differential equation and the variational formulation. Indeed the two are mathematically equivalent statements governing the process of heat conduction. This correspondence will be of practical value, as is demonstrated in Chap. 3.

The variational formulation has the advantage of being valid in any coordinate system and, as a consequence, can often be used to facilitate the transformation to other coordinate systems. For example, suppose that it is desirable to represent the heat-conduction equation in spherical coordinates. It is necessary to recognize that Eq. (1.4.10) is essentially

$$I = \int_V (\nabla u \cdot \nabla u - 2u\psi) \, dV \tag{1.4.12}$$

where ∇ is the gradient operator. Then we can write

$$I = \int_V \left[\left(\frac{\partial u}{\partial r}\right)^2 + \frac{1}{r^2}\left(\frac{\partial u}{\partial \theta}\right)^2 + \frac{1}{r^2 \sin^2 \theta}\left(\frac{\partial u}{\partial \phi}\right)^2 - 2\psi u \right] r^2 \sin \theta \, d\theta \, d\phi \, dr \tag{1.4.13}$$

where r, θ, and ϕ are a set of spherical coordinates, the gradient has been expressed in spherical coordinates,[3] and the volume element is given for the spherical coordinate system.

Applying Eq. (1.4.9) gives

$$0 = \frac{1}{r^2}\frac{\partial}{\partial r} r^2 \frac{\partial u}{\partial r} + \frac{1}{r^2 \sin \theta}\frac{\partial}{\partial \theta} \sin \theta \frac{\partial u}{\partial \theta} + \frac{1}{r^2 \sin^2 \theta}\frac{\partial^2 u}{\partial \phi^2} + \psi(r,\theta,\phi) \tag{1.4.14}$$

which is the equation of heat conduction in spherical coordinates.

1.5 CONSTRAINED EXTREMALS

In our work thus far we have been content to establish the conditions necessary for the existence of an extremal without regard for any other facts which may be at our disposal or for any restrictions which might be imposed on our answer. Of course, it is not uncommon in the analysis of applied problems to be faced with the task of finding an optimal within the framework of a certain number of restrictions. This section is devoted to a study of the variational problem which is constrained by auxiliary conditions. This type of variational problem is often called the isoperimetric problem.

In particular we shall be concerned with the search for a function $y(x)$ which causes the integral

$$I = \int_{x_1}^{x_2} F[x, y(x), y_x(x)] \, dx \tag{1.5.1}$$

[3] H. Margenau and G. M. Murphy, "The Mathematics of Physics and Chemistry," pp. 172–178, 2d ed., D. Van Nostrand Company, Inc., Princeton, N.J., 1956.

to be an extremal with the auxiliary condition that $y(x)$ also satisfy the equation

$$J = \int_{x_1}^{x_2} G[x, y(x), y_x(x)] \, dx \tag{1.5.2}$$

where the constant J is given.   It is clear that we need not test all possible functions in Eq. (1.5.1) to determine the function which causes I to be the largest (or the smallest).   For any *admissible* function $y(x)$ must first satisfy Eq. (1.5.2) before we need consider the function as a possible extremalizing function.   Thus, we state that Eq. (1.5.2) must be satisfied by all admissible functions.

The variational problem stated above can be treated most conveniently using the method of Lagrangian multipliers.   Before proceeding with the analysis of the problem, we shall review this powerful method here for the sake of completeness.

To introduce the method of Lagrangian multipliers, let us consider the problem of finding the coordinates $x_1, x_2, \ldots, x_n$ which cause the function

$$f(x_1, x_2, \ldots, x_n) \tag{1.5.3}$$

to be an extremal subject to the condition that

$$g(x_1, x_2, \ldots, x_n) = J \tag{1.5.4}$$

be satisfied.   Here J is a constant.   If f is to be an extremal, then we require that

$$df = \frac{\partial f}{\partial x_1} \delta x_1 + \frac{\partial f}{\partial x_2} \delta x_2 + \cdots + \frac{\partial f}{\partial x_n} \delta x_n = 0 \tag{1.5.5}$$

However, the variations $\delta x_1, \delta x_2, \ldots, \delta x_n$ are not independent, for, by differentiating Eq. (1.5.4), we see that

$$0 = \frac{\partial g}{\partial x_1} \delta x_1 + \frac{\partial g}{\partial x_2} \delta x_2 + \cdots + \frac{\partial g}{\partial x_n} \delta x_n \tag{1.5.6}$$

It is possible to eliminate one of the variations in terms of all the others by using this equation.   But which variation should we eliminate?   The method of Lagrangian multipliers avoids that choice.   Multiply Eq. (1.5.6) by an arbitrary constant which we shall call the Lagrangian multiplier and denote it by the symbol λ.   Then add the resulting expression to Eq. (1.5.5) to obtain

$$df = 0 = \left(\frac{\partial f}{\partial x_1} + \lambda \frac{\partial g}{\partial x_1} \right) \delta x_1 + \left(\frac{\partial f}{\partial x_2} + \lambda \frac{\partial g}{\partial x_2} \right) \delta x_2 +$$
$$\cdots + \left(\frac{\partial f}{\partial x_n} + \lambda \frac{\partial g}{\partial x_n} \right) \delta x_n \tag{1.5.7}$$

It is now asserted that each of the variations may now be treated as being independent, and thus the coefficient of each variation must vanish identically. Thus we require that

$$\frac{\partial f}{\partial x_i} + \lambda \frac{\partial g}{\partial x_i} = 0 \qquad i = 1, 2, \ldots, n \tag{1.5.8}$$

and we must also have

$$g(x_1, x_2, x_3, \ldots, x_n) = J \tag{1.5.4}$$

These equations form a system of $n + 1$ equations and $n + 1$ unknowns—the values of the x's and the Lagrangian multiplier. Thus the introduction of the undetermined multiplier permits us to treat the $x_1, x_2, \ldots, x_n$ in a symmetric manner and, in essence, gives rise to a structure which permitted each of the variables to be considered as being independent even though an auxiliary condition is imposed.

It is also interesting to note that since λ is a constant with respect to the x_i, we can summarize the above conclusions by asserting that a necessary condition for an extremal of $f(x_1, x_2, \ldots, x_n)$ with respect to the variables $x_1, x_2, \ldots, x_n$ that satisfy

$$g_k(x_1, x_2, \ldots, x_n) = J_k \qquad k = 1, 2, \ldots, L, L < n \tag{1.5.9}$$

where the J_k are constants, is

$$\frac{\partial F_s}{\partial x_1} = \frac{\partial F_s}{\partial x_2} = \frac{\partial F_s}{\partial x_3} = \cdots = \frac{\partial F_s}{\partial x_n} = 0 \tag{1.5.10}$$

in which F_s is

$$F_s = f + \sum_{k=1}^{L} g_k \lambda_k \tag{1.5.11}$$

The constants $\lambda_1, \lambda_2, \ldots, \lambda_L$, which are undetermined Lagrangian multipliers, are evaluated together with x_1, x_2, x_n by the $n + L$ equations expressed by Eqs. (1.5.9) and (1.5.10).

EXAMPLE 1.5.1   Consider the minimum of the function

$$f = x_1^2 + x_2^2 = f(x_1, x_2) \tag{1.5.12}$$

subject to the restriction

$$x_1 x_2 = J \tag{1.5.13}$$

Now it is clear that in this simple example one of the variables x_1 or x_2 could be eliminated from Eq. (1.5.12) by using Eq. (1.5.13). However, in more complex problems the process of elimination may not be as simple as it is here. Thus, we do not attempt to reduce the problem to one of a single independent variable but instead use the method of Lagrangian multipliers. From F_s as prescribed by Eq. (1.5.11), differentiate partially to obtain

$$2x_1 + \lambda x_2 = 0$$
$$2x_2 + \lambda x_1 = 0$$

(1.5.14)

which, together with Eq. (1.5.13), gives three equations and three unknowns— x_1, x_2, and λ. The solution is

$$\left. \begin{array}{l} x_1 = J^{\frac{1}{2}} \\ x_2 = J^{\frac{1}{2}} \\ \lambda = -2 \end{array} \right\} \quad \text{for } J > 0$$

(1.5.15)

which is the result we would have obtained by eliminating one of the variables from Eq. (1.5.12). Thus, we have an extremal at the point indicated in Eq. (1.5.15).

Let us now turn back to the variational problem expressed by Eqs. (1.5.1) and (1.5.2). As before, suppose that the true minimizing function is $y(x)$ and define a variation as

$$\delta y(x) = y^*(x) - y(x) = \epsilon_1 \phi_1(x) + \epsilon_2 \phi_2(x)$$

(1.5.16)

where both $\phi_1(x)$ and $\phi_2(x)$ are continuous differentiable functions of x but otherwise arbitrary. Two parameters have been introduced in order to insure the admissibility of the test function. For had we used a single parameter as before, then it is clear that we could not satisfy Eq. (1.5.2) for *all* values of the parameter and hence the test function would not be an admissible function except for values of the parameter for which Eq. (1.5.2) is satisfied. The point is that we must devise a scheme of changing the $y(x)$ by an infinitesimal amount and at the same time insure that Eq. (1.5.2) is satisfied. By introducing two parameters in Eq. (1.5.16), we have achieved this goal, for now one of the parameters, say ϵ_1, can be changed freely and ϵ_2 manipulated so that Eq. (1.5.2) is satisfied for each value of ϵ_1. Thus, the two parameters are not independent. Recalling Eq. (1.2.12), we write the necessary condition for the existence of an extremal

$$\delta I(\epsilon_1, \epsilon_2) = \int_{x_1}^{x_2} \delta F \, dx = 0$$

(1.5.17)

and in this case we must impose the restriction

$$\delta J(\epsilon_1, \epsilon_2) = \int_{x_1}^{x_2} \delta G \, dx = 0$$

(1.5.18)

The structure of these two equations is identical to that of Eqs. (1.5.5) and (1.5.6). But Eqs. (1.5.5) and (1.5.6) were the starting point for the development of the method of undetermined multipliers. It is then clear that

Eqs. (1.5.17) and (1.5.18) are amenable to the same treatment without any modification of the method. Thus, following the steps in the previous development, we write

$$0 = \delta I + \lambda \, \delta J \qquad (1.5.19)$$

Or, defining I_s as

$$I_s = I + \lambda J \qquad (1.5.20)$$

Eq. (1.5.19) represents

$$\delta I_s = 0 \qquad (1.5.21)$$

The parameters ϵ_1 and ϵ_2 are treated as independent variables just as the variations of x_1 and x_2 were treated in Eq. (1.5.7). Thus we can write

$$\delta I_s = \int \delta F_s \, dx = \epsilon_1 \int_{x_1}^{x_2} \left[\frac{\partial F_s}{\partial y} \phi_1(x) + \frac{\partial F_s}{\partial y_x} \phi_{1x}(x) \right] dx$$
$$+ \epsilon_2 \int_{x_1}^{x_2} \left[\frac{\partial F_s}{\partial y} \phi_2(x) + \frac{\partial F_s}{\partial y_x} \phi_{2x}(x) \right] dx \qquad (1.5.22)$$

where $F_s = F + \lambda G$. This equation results from a Taylor expansion of the integrand in powers of ϵ_1 and ϵ_2 using the same techniques applied in the development of Eq. (1.2.15). Integrating by parts, as before, we have

$$\delta I_s = \epsilon_1 \int_{x_1}^{x_2} \left(\frac{\partial F_s}{\partial y} - \frac{d}{dx} \frac{\partial F_s}{\partial y_x} \right) \phi_1(x) \, dx + \epsilon_2 \int_{x_1}^{x_2} \left(\frac{\partial F_s}{\partial y} - \frac{d}{dx} \frac{\partial F_s}{\partial y_x} \right) \phi_2(x) \, dx$$
$$(1.5.23)$$

where it has been assumed that the variation vanishes on the boundary. Since ϵ_1 and ϵ_2 are independent, the coefficient of each of the parameters must vanish; thus,

$$\int_{x_1}^{x_2} \left(\frac{\partial F_s}{\partial y} - \frac{d}{dx} \frac{\partial F_s}{\partial y_x} \right) \phi_1(x) \, dx = 0 \qquad (1.5.24)$$

$$\int_{x_1}^{x_2} \left(\frac{\partial F_s}{\partial y} - \frac{d}{dx} \frac{\partial F_s}{\partial y_x} \right) \phi_2(x) \, dx = 0 \qquad (1.5.25)$$

Since $\phi_1(x)$ and ϕ_2 are arbitrary, both Eq. (1.5.24) and (1.5.25) give the differential equation

$$\frac{\partial F_s}{\partial y} - \frac{d}{dx} \frac{\partial F_s}{\partial y_x} = 0 \qquad \qquad F_s = f - \sum_{k=1}^{L} g_k \lambda_k \qquad (1.5.26)$$

which is the necessary condition for the existence of an extremal. Note that the Lagrangian multiplier appears in the differential equation as a parameter, and hence $y(x)$ will depend on the numerical value of the undetermined multiplier.   The numerical value of λ must be chosen so that

$$J = \int_{x_1}^{x_2} G[x,y(x),y_x(x)] \, dx \tag{1.5.2}$$

The problem is complete, since a necessary condition for $y(x)$ to give an extremal for the isoperimetric problem is that the differential Eq. (1.5.26) be satisfied and that λ be chosen so that Eq. (1.5.2) is satisfied.

EXAMPLE 1.5.2   To illustrate the preceding discussion, let us determine the way in which a perfectly flexible rope which is fixed at both ends will hang in a gravitational field.   The rope has a uniform mass per foot and this mass is denoted by β.   We now propose that the rope will hang in such a way that the potential energy of position will be a minimum with the constraint that the length of the rope remain constant.   The potential energy of a length of rope above a datum plane at $y = 0$ is given by

$$I = \int_{x_1}^{x_2} y\beta g \, ds = \int_{x_1}^{x_2} y\beta g (1 + y_x^2)^{\frac{1}{2}} \, dx \tag{1.5.27}$$

where (x_1,y_1) and (x_2,y_2) are the fixed end points of the rope and g is the acceleration due to gravity.   The total length of the rope is clearly

$$J = \int_{x_1}^{x_2} ds = \int_{x_1}^{x_2} (1 + y_x^2)^{\frac{1}{2}} \, dx \tag{1.5.28}$$

We now seek the function $y(x)$ which causes I to be stationary with the additional constraint that Eq. (1.5.28) be satisfied for all possible $y(x)$.   This is an isoperimetric problem of the type that we have discussed.   The applicable Euler-Lagrange equation is given by Eq. (1.5.26).   For the present example we can write†

$$\frac{d}{dx} \frac{g\beta y + \lambda}{(1 + y_x^2)^{\frac{1}{2}}} = 0 \tag{1.5.29}$$

which is the differential equation which determines the shape of the curve. The integration of this equation yields

$$y(x) = \frac{-\lambda}{\beta g} + c_1 \cosh \frac{x - c_2}{c_1} \tag{1.5.30}$$

There are three conditions which remain to be satisfied, and these determine the two constants of integration and the value of the undetermined multiplier. These conditions are: (1) the curve must pass through the point (x_1,y_1); (2) the curve must pass through the point (x_2,y_2); and (3) the length of the

† Actually, this result stems from application of Eq. (1.2.26), which is applicable since the integrand does not depend explicitly on x.

curve as computed by Eq. (1.5.28) must be the prescribed value. The computation of the constants from the three conditions is quite difficult. The shape of the hanging rope is called a catenary.

1.6 BOUNDARY CONDITIONS

In all of the preceding work we have tacitly assumed that the variation vanishes on the boundary.   This assumption is equivalent to asserting that the function is specified on the boundary and is not subject to variation.   However, we shall encounter many problems in the course of our work where the function to be varied is not specified on the boundary, but other equally valid boundary conditions are imposed.   Indeed in some instances, such as an interface between phases, no boundary conditions at all may be specified.   It is important to understand that the boundary conditions are an integral part of the variational investigation, and any alteration of the boundary condition produces a corresponding change in the minimizing (or maximizing) function.   Furthermore, if the function is not specified on the boundary, then an appropriate number of boundary conditions will be supplied during the course of the variational analysis.   This is one of the particularly elegant features of the variational problem.   To emphasize this point, let us consider a specific example.   Consider the variational problem defined by the following equation:

$$I = \int_a^b [\tfrac{1}{2} y_x^2 - y\psi(x)] \, dx \tag{1.6.1}$$

where $\psi(x)$ is a specified function of x and $y(x)$ is the function to be selected to produce a stationary value for I.   For the present, let us leave the question of boundary conditions open.   Thus, in the definition of a variation in $y(x)$,

$$\delta y = y^* - y = \epsilon\phi(x) \tag{1.6.2}$$

we have no reason to presume that $\phi(x)$ vanishes on the boundaries ($x = a$ and $x = b$).   *It is only in those cases for which $y(x)$ is specified on the boundary that we can assert that the variation vanishes on the boundary.*   The first variation of Eq. (1.6.1) gives

$$\frac{\delta I}{\epsilon} = \int_a^b [y_x\phi_x - \phi\psi(x)] \, dx \tag{1.6.3}$$

Integrating by parts the first term in the integrand, we obtain

$$\frac{\delta I}{\epsilon} = y_x\phi \Big|_{x=a}^{x=b} - \int_a^b \left[\frac{d}{dx} y_x + \psi(x) \right] \phi(x) \, dx \tag{1.6.4}$$

If δI is to be zero for all admissible variations (restricted only by continuity requirements since we have imposed no boundary conditions), we must have both

$$\frac{d^2y}{dx^2} + \psi(x) = 0 \tag{1.6.5}$$

and

$$\frac{dy}{dx}\phi\Big|_{x=b} = \frac{dy}{dx}\phi\Big|_{x=a} = 0 \tag{1.6.6}$$

which implies that the derivative must vanish on the boundary if the variation is free.   Equation (1.6.5) is the usual Euler-Lagrange equation applied to the integrand of Eq. (1.6.1).   Note that this particular Euler-Lagrange equation is a second-order differential equation and requires the specification of two boundary conditions to achieve a unique solution.   It is interesting to note that the condition for I to be stationary has supplied precisely two boundary conditions as expressed in Eq. (1.6.6).

Before proceeding with this discussion, it is instructive to give physical meaning to these mathematical expressions.

Equation (1.6.5) represents the mathematical model governing the conduction of heat in a solid slab in which there is internal generation of heat. The system is depicted in Fig. 1.6.1.   The function $y(x)$ plays the role of temperature in the physical analog, and $\psi(x)$ is proportional to the rate of internal heat generation per unit volume.

Since we have not specified any boundary conditions and since Eq. (1.6.6) must be valid for all values of $\phi(x)$ on the boundary, we must have

$$\frac{dy}{dx} = 0 \qquad \text{at } x = a, x = b \tag{1.6.7}$$

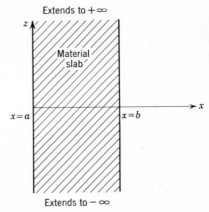

Fig. 1.6.1   System with internal heat generation.

These are the *natural boundary conditions* for the particular example under consideration and are evolved directly from the variational problem. These conditions represent perfectly insulated surfaces of the slab, and hence, in this case, the natural boundary conditions give rise to a solution of the problem in which no heat is dissipated from the system. Intuitively we may feel that this state of affairs will lead to some difficulty, since heat is being generated and none is being dissipated to the surroundings. We would expect a solution to exist only under very special circumstances. Let us pursue this point somewhat further. Integrate Eq. (1.6.5) and obtain

$$\frac{dy}{dx} = -\int_a^x \psi(\lambda)\, d\lambda \qquad (1.6.8)$$

We see immediately that the condition

$$\frac{dy}{dx} = 0 \qquad \text{at } x = a$$

is satisfied. However, to satisfy the conditions at $x = b$, we must have

$$0 = \int_a^b \psi(\lambda)\, d\lambda \qquad (1.6.9)$$

This condition is necessary for the existence of a solution compatible with the boundary conditions which have been naturally imposed on the problem. We can interpret Eq. (1.6.9) as a restriction on the rate of heat generation requiring that there be a *volume-weighted equality of sources and sinks* of thermal energy. In other words, the heat which is generated in certain regions of the slab must be absorbed in others. Under these circumstances a solution to the differential equation exists.

We have seen that leaving the boundary conditions unspecified gives rise to a set of natural boundary conditions which are derived from the variational statement of the problem. Furthermore, we found the correct number of boundary conditions required to solve the Euler-Lagrange equation. It is also clear that the specification of $y(x)$ on one boundary, say at $x = a$, would permit us to use the restriction of a vanishing $\phi(x)$ on that boundary $(x = a)$ and would leave only one natural boundary condition. This boundary condition would be selected such that Eq. (1.6.6) is satisfied with

$$\phi(x) = 0 \qquad \text{at } x = a, \ \phi(x) \text{ arbitrary at } x = b$$

We may wonder about the possibility of imposing other types of boundary conditions on the solution. For example, we frequently encounter boundary conditions of the type

$$-\frac{dy}{dx} + \alpha y = 0 \qquad \text{at } x = a \qquad (1.6.10)$$

in heat-conduction problems. Here α is a constant and Eq. (1.6.10) represents the radiation boundary condition. Thus, the question arises of how one can construct a variational principle which has the heat-conduction equation as its Euler-Lagrange equation and which is applicable with Eq. (1.6.10) as one of the boundary conditions. This type of problem can usually be handled by altering the variational problem. Consider

$$I = \int_a^b [\tfrac{1}{2}y_x^2 - \psi(x)y]\,dx + \frac{\alpha}{2}y^2 \Big|_{x=a} \tag{1.6.11}$$

where α is the same constant that appears in Eq. (1.6.10). Note that a term involving only the function evaluated at the boundary has been added to Eq. (1.6.1) to obtain Eq. (1.6.11). The variation of Eq. (1.6.11) is

$$\frac{\delta I}{\epsilon} = -\int_a^b \left(\frac{d^2y}{dx^2} + \psi(x)\right)\phi(x)\,dx + \phi(x)\frac{dy}{dx}\Big|_{x=b} - \phi(x)\frac{dy}{dx}\Big|_{x=a} + \alpha y\phi(x)\Big|_{x=a}$$

The last term of this equation is easily derived if we recall that the variation is defined as an infinitesimal change of the function $y(x)$ *at a given value of x.* Since we require δI to vanish for all variations, we can conclude that one of the natural boundary conditions is

$$-\frac{dy}{dx} + \alpha y = 0 \qquad \text{at } x = a \tag{1.6.10}$$

which is the desired result. Thus, we have shown that the function $y(x)$ which results in a stationary state for the functional I defined by Eq. (1.6.11) must satisfy the heat-conduction equation, the boundary condition expressed by Eq. (1.6.10), and have a zero derivative at $x = b$. Hence we have modified the natural boundary conditions for the variational problem by artificially adding a term to the statement of the variational problem. It is not difficult to visualize other possible modifications which give rise to different boundary conditions.

The example which we have just completed is a rather simple one, but the essential features remain unchanged when more complex problems are considered. To emphasize this important point, we shall consider a second example.

$$I = \int_V [\nabla u \cdot \nabla u - 2\psi(x,y,z)u]\,dV + \int_S [2uf(x,y,z) + u^2 g(x,y,z)]\,dS \tag{1.6.12}$$

where $f(x,y,z)$ and $g(x,y,z)$ are prescribed functions of position and the integrations are subject to the same restrictions and definitions stated in Sec. 1.4. The boundary conditions are not specified, so we must retain the following terms in the first variation.

$$\frac{\delta I}{\epsilon} = -2\int_V [\nabla^2 u + \psi(x,y,z)]\eta\,dV$$

$$+ \int_S [2\nabla u \cdot \mathbf{n} + 2f(x,y,z) + 2ug(x,y,z)]\eta\,dS \tag{1.6.13}$$

where **n** is the unit outward normal to the surface.   With the usual arguments we have

$$0 = \nabla^2 u + \psi(x,y,z) \tag{1.6.14}$$

and

$$0 = \nabla u \cdot \mathbf{n} + f(x,y,z) + ug(x,y,z) \qquad \text{on } S \tag{1.6.15}$$

This latter expression is a rather general *boundary condition,* since the functions $f(x,y,z)$ and $g(x,y,z)$ can be selected to match the requirements of the physical problem.

The essential result of our work in this section is the recognition that the answer derived from a variational formulation is dependent on the nature of the boundary conditions.   In the absence of fixed boundary conditions the variational problem will furnish itself with a sufficient number of restrictions to permit the solution of the Euler-Lagrange equation.   Furthermore, suitable boundary conditions can often be built into the problem by artificially adding terms to the variational problem.   We have examined examples of these important features but have avoided giving general proofs or prescriptions, since these tend to become rather lengthy.   In the following section a catalog of results will be developed for future use.

PROBLEM 1.6.1   Determine the natural boundary conditions to be imposed on the function which minimizes

$$I = \int_a^b F\left(x,y,y_x, \int_a^x y \, d\lambda\right) dx$$

PROBLEM 1.6.2   Suppose you wish to find the variational problem which corresponds to the physical problem of heat transfer from the plate shown in

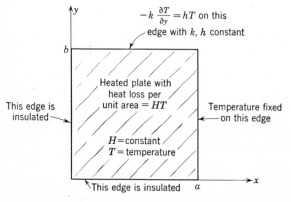

Fig. 1.6.2   Heated plate.

Fig. 1.6.2. From the surface of the plate, heat is lost to the ambient at a rate per unit area given by *HT*. Develop a variational principle which "corresponds" to this physical problem.

I.7 WORKING EQUATIONS

In this section we intend to present a kind of "catalog" of equations which will be used in the analysis to follow. The proof of the relationships given in Table 1.7.1 requires the use of the divergence theorem as expressed in Eq. (1.4.6) or, alternately, in the equivalent forms [Eqs. (1.7.1) and (1.7.2)]

$$\int_V \left(\frac{\partial P}{\partial x} + \frac{\partial Q}{\partial y} + \frac{\partial R}{\partial z} \right) dV = \int_S [P \cos (n,x) + Q \cos (n,y) + R \cos (n,z)] \, dS$$

$$(1.7.1)$$

where $\cos (n,x)$, $\cos (n,y)$, and $\cos (n,z)$ are the cosines of the angles between the positive x, y, and z directions, respectively, and the outward-drawn normal to the surface S, and

$$\int_V \mathbf{\nabla} \cdot \mathbf{a} \, dV = \int_S \mathbf{a} \cdot \mathbf{n} \, dS \tag{1.7.2}$$

in which $\mathbf{a}$ is the vector field

$$\mathbf{a} = \mathbf{i}P + \mathbf{j}Q + \mathbf{k}R$$

and $\mathbf{n}$ is

$$\mathbf{n} = \mathbf{i} \cos (n,x) + \mathbf{j} \cos (n,y) + \mathbf{k} \cos (n,z)$$

with $\mathbf{i}$, $\mathbf{j}$, and $\mathbf{k}$ being the three unit vectors along the positive x, y, and z axes, respectively.

Also needed to establish some of the equations given in Table 1.7.1 is Stokes' theorem (two dimensions), which can be written in the following form:

$$\iint_S \left(\frac{\partial P}{\partial x} + \frac{\partial Q}{\partial y} \right) dx \, dy = \int_C (Pt_2 - Qt_1) \, ds \tag{1.7.3}$$

where S = region of xy plane bounded by the closed curve C
  ds = an element of arc length measured along C
  $$t_1 = \frac{dx}{ds}$$
  $$t_2 = \frac{dy}{ds}$$

Here the integration is carried out along C in the sense that an observer walking along C has the region S to his left.

TABLE 1.7.1 EXTREMALS AND THE CORRESPONDING DIFFERENTIAL EQUATIONS

	Extremal	Euler-Lagrange Equation	Boundary Conditions
(a)	$I = \int_a^b F(x,w,w_x)\,dx$ $+\, g_b(x,w)\big|_{x=b} - g_a(x,w)\big|_{x=a}$	$\dfrac{\partial F}{\partial w} - \dfrac{d}{dx}\dfrac{\partial F}{\partial w_x} = 0$	$\left(\dfrac{\partial F}{\partial w_x} + \dfrac{\partial g_a}{\partial w}\right)\delta w\Big|_{x=a} = 0$ $\left(\dfrac{\partial F}{\partial w_x} + \dfrac{\partial g_b}{\partial w}\right)\delta w\Big|_{x=b} = 0$
(b)	$I = \int_a^b F(x,w,w_x,w_{xx})\,dx$ $+\, g_b(x,w,w_x)\big|_{x=b}$ $-\, g_a(x,w,w_x)\big|_{x=a}$	$\dfrac{\partial F}{\partial w} - \dfrac{d}{dx}\dfrac{\partial F}{\partial w_x} + \dfrac{d^2}{dx^2}\dfrac{\partial F}{\partial w_{xx}} = 0$	$\left(\dfrac{\partial F}{\partial w_{xx}} + \dfrac{\partial g_a}{\partial w_x}\right)\delta w_x\Big|_{x=a} = 0$ $\left(\dfrac{\partial F}{\partial w_{xx}} + \dfrac{\partial g_b}{\partial w_x}\right)\delta w_x\Big|_{x=b} = 0$ $\left(\dfrac{\partial F}{\partial w_x} - \dfrac{d}{dx}\dfrac{\partial F}{\partial w_{xx}} + \dfrac{\partial g_a}{\partial w}\right)\delta w\Big|_{x=a} = 0$ $\left(\dfrac{\partial F}{\partial w_x} - \dfrac{d}{dx}\dfrac{\partial F}{\partial w_{xx}} + \dfrac{\partial g_b}{\partial w}\right)\delta w\Big|_{x=b} = 0$
(c)	$I = \int_S F(x,y,w,w_x,w_y)\,dS$ $+ \int_C [g_1(x,y,w)t_2$ $-\, g_2(x,y,w)t_1]\,ds$	$\dfrac{\partial F}{\partial w} - \dfrac{\partial}{\partial x}\dfrac{\partial F}{\partial w_x} - \dfrac{\partial}{\partial y}\dfrac{\partial F}{\partial w_y} = 0$	$\left[\left(\dfrac{\partial F}{\partial w_x} + \dfrac{\partial g_1}{\partial w}\right)t_2 - \left(\dfrac{\partial F}{\partial w_y} + \dfrac{\partial g_2}{\partial w}\right)t_1\right]\delta w = 0$ on curve C
(d)	$I = \int_V F(x,y,z,w,w_x,w_y,w_z)\,dV$ $+ \int_S [g_1(x,y,z,w)\cos(n,x)$ $+\, g_2(x,y,z,w)\cos(n,y)$ $+\, g_3(x,y,z,w)\cos(n,z)]\,dS$	$\dfrac{\partial F}{\partial w} - \dfrac{\partial}{\partial x}\dfrac{\partial F}{\partial w_x} - \dfrac{\partial}{\partial y}\dfrac{\partial F}{\partial w_y} - \dfrac{\partial}{\partial z}\dfrac{\partial F}{\partial w_z} = 0$	$\left[\left(\dfrac{\partial F}{\partial w_x} + \dfrac{\partial g_1}{\partial w}\right)\cos(n,x) + \left(\dfrac{\partial F}{\partial w_y} + \dfrac{\partial g_2}{\partial w}\right)\cos(n,y) + \left(\dfrac{\partial F}{\partial w_z} + \dfrac{\partial g_3}{\partial w}\right)\cos(n,z)\right]\delta w = 0$ on surface S

A number of integrals to be extremalized and the corresponding Euler-Lagrange equations, together with the boundary conditions, are given in Table 1.7.1. These boundary conditions can be satisfied in two ways. First of all, one can require δw to vanish on the boundary, but this means that w is specified on the boundary. If w is not specified on the boundary, then the term in brackets must vanish. In this case the boundary conditions are called the *natural boundary conditions*.

CHAPTER 2
NATURAL
PROBLEMS

2.1 INTRODUCTION The principles of variational calculus have been discussed in the first chapter, and even the reader studying these principles for the first time has undoubtedly imagined a variety of problems which fall within this framework. There is an entire class of engineering problems which pose such questions as What is most . . . ? Where is minimum . . . ? or How can we best . . . ? In this class of optimization problems, one finds a subclass which is formulated in the language of variational calculus. These problems have been termed natural problems to mark them as being expressible only as variational problems and to emphasize that the Euler-Lagrange equations associated with the extremal problem give new differential equations. This state of affairs is contrasted with our work in Chap. 4 in which the differential equation is known and we seek to find an extremal principle to match the particular differential equation—the synthetic problems.

Thus natural problems are simply those problems which are so stated that the mathematical formulation has a variational structure. This chapter consists, in fact, of a series of examples intended to show how the calculus of variations can be employed to develop the appropriate differential equations. Although these differential equations are solved for some simple cases, our goal in this chapter is the development of the appropriate differential equation. The solutions are offered as a means of achieving an understanding of the behavior of the system.

2.2 MINIMUM PRESSURE DRAG

Since Newton innovated his pioneering studies on the determination of the best shape for a solid body being translated through a fluid, there has been a continuing interest among design engineers in optimal streamlining. Before embarking on such a study, one must first establish the mechanism of interaction between the solid body and the fluid. In the general problem, the forces exerted on the solid body are dependent on the shape of the solid body and the relative velocity in a very complex fashion, and we have no hope of describing the general case with any but very approximate considerations. However, if the density of the gas becomes so small that the mean free path of the gas molecules is large compared with the characteristic dimension of the solid body, then those molecules which strike the surface and are remitted will, in general, be far from the solid body before they encounter another molecule. In this case the molecules incident on the body are essentially undisturbed by the presence of the body. Moreover, if we assume that these molecules are reflected from the surface of the body specularly, then the

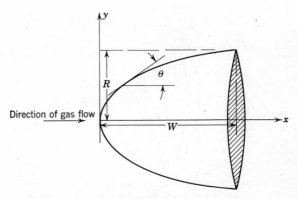

Fig. 2.2.1 Body of revolution.

normal pressure on the body is given by the simple expression[1]

$$p = 2\rho v^2 \sin^2 \theta \tag{2.2.1}$$

It should be noted for the sake of clarity that specular reflections refer to the interactions with the surface which leave the tangential component of the molecular velocity unchanged. The normal component of the molecular velocity is reversed during the course of such interactions. In the equation above, the angle given refers to the angle between the velocity and the tangent to the surface, ρ refers to the fluid density, and v is the speed of the fluid relative to the body. The problem we shall consider in this section concerns a body of revolution which is being translated with zero angle of attack, as depicted in Fig. 2.2.1. The pressure is normal to the surface, so we can write the x component of force acting on a ribbon of width $(1 + y_x^2)^{1/2}\, dx$ and radius $y(x)$ as

$$dF = 2\rho v^2 \sin^2 \theta [2\pi y(1 + y_x^2)^{1/2}] \sin \theta \, dx \tag{2.2.2}$$

The ribbon on which the force is acting is shown in Fig. 2.2.2. The total force acting in the positive x direction is

$$F = \int_0^W 4\pi \rho v^2 \sin^3 \theta y (1 + y_x^2)^{1/2} \, dx \tag{2.2.3}$$

To make the problem tractable, we shall assume

$$\sin \theta = \frac{y_x}{(1 + y_x^2)^{1/2}} \simeq y_x \qquad \text{or} \qquad y_x \ll 1$$

so that the force becomes

$$F = 4\pi \rho v^2 \int_0^W y_x^3 y \, dx \tag{2.2.4}$$

[1] Samuel A. Schaaf and Lawrence Talbot, "Handbook of Supersonic Aerodynamics," vol. 5, sec. 16, Mechanics of Rarefied Gases, Subsec. 16-2.2, p. 3, Government Printing Office, Washington, D.C., 1959.

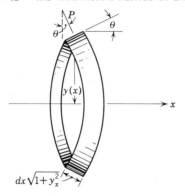

Fig. 2.2.2 An element of area acted on by pressure.

The problem is to determine the $y(x)$ which makes F as small as possible subject to the restriction that $y(x)$ pass through the following points on the boundary:

$$y(0) = 0$$
$$y(W) = R \tag{2.2.5}$$

Of course we recognize immediately that our task is reduced to the application of the calculus of variations. This is a natural problem, since the nature of the task to be performed leads us directly to a variational formulation and there is no alternate means of stating the problem. This is contrasted with the problems which will be studied in Chap. 4, where synthetic problems are considered, and we shall seek methods of finding variational principles which describe the same physical processes naturally described by differential equations. Let us continue our search for the shape giving the least pressure drag on the body of revolution. The Euler-Lagrange equation corresponding to the functional F is

$$y_x^3 - 3 \frac{d}{dx} y y_x^2 = 0 \tag{2.2.6}$$

Here we have used Eq. (1.2.4). Since this equation must be satisfied for all x and pass through the terminal points, $y = 0$ for all x is not an acceptable solution. We can write Eq. (2.2.6) as

$$y_x^3 + 3 y y_x y_{xx} = 0 \tag{2.2.7}$$

Integrating once, we obtain

$$y_x^3 y = C_1^3 \tag{2.2.8}$$

in which C_1 is a constant of integration. A second integration gives

$$y = (C_1 x + C_2)^{3/4} \tag{2.2.9}$$

Applying the boundary conditions expressed by Eq. (2.2.5), we find

$$\frac{y}{R} = \left(\frac{x}{W}\right)^{3\!/\!4} \tag{2.2.10}$$

which shows that the contour having the minimum drag for fixed end points is a parabola satisfying the ¾ power.

We shall not pursue the problem further; however, the reader can find an excellent discussion of this particular topic by Miele.[2]

PROBLEM 2.2.1   Derive the differential equation which gives the minimum pressure drag on a body of fixed volume.   The body is translated through a gas in free molecule flow.   (*Hint:* The method of Lagrangian Multipliers will be of value in solving this problem.)

2.3   OPTIMIZATION OF A THERMOELECTRIC GENERATOR

If a series of thermocouples are connected to a heat source and sink as shown in Fig. 2.3.1, the result will be a flow of heat from the reservoir to the thermocouples.   A portion of the heat from the source will be converted to electric power, as indicated by the $+$ and $-$ signs at the terminals shown in Fig. 2.3.1, and the remaining part of this heat will be rejected to the sink. The amount of power generated by a differential heat input from the source is given by

$$dp = \theta(T_h - T_c)\,dQ \tag{2.3.1}$$

where θ is some measure of the efficiency of conversion which depends in part on the materials of construction, and T_h and T_c are the hot and cold junction temperatures, respectively.

To put the principles illustrated in Fig. 2.3.1 into practical usage, Swanson and Somers[1] have suggested a configuration such as one shown in Fig. 2.3.2.

[2] Angelo Miele, "Optimization Techniques," George Leitmann, ed., Chap. 4, Academic Press Inc., New York, 1962.

[1] B. V. Swanson and E. K. Somers, "Optimization of a Conventional Fuel Fired Thermoelectric Generator," *J. Heat Transfer*, vol. 81, p. 245, 1959.

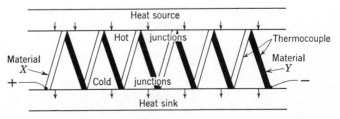

Fig. 2.3.1   Thermoelectric generator—fundamental construction.

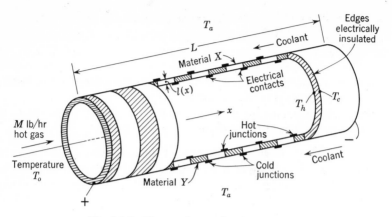

Fig. 2.3.2   Hot gas thermoelectric generator.

Here we see a duct which is constructed by alternating the use of material X with the use of material Y.   The heat source stems from the internal energy of a hot gas flowing through the center of the duct, and the heat sink is provided by a coolant flowing in a jacket about the outside of the duct. The temperature of the coolant is essentially that of the ambient and is constant, but the gas temperature decreases as the gas flows through the duct.

The amount of energy transferred from the gas to the wall over some incremental axial distance depends on the heat-transfer coefficients defining the rate of heat flow from the gas to the wall h_g and from the wall to the coolant h_a, as well as the conductance of the wall itself.   This wall conductance depends on the thermal conductivity of the materials of construction k and the wall thickness $l(x)$, which is a design variable.   Thus when the duct geometry is fixed, the inlet temperature and mass flow rate are given, and the temperature of the coolant is specified, the axial gas temperature can still be varied by changing the wall thickness as a function of axial position.   We then inquire whether a "best" distribution of gas temperature exists—that is, one which will produce more power for specified conditions than any other distribution.   Once we find the best distribution of temperatures, we intend

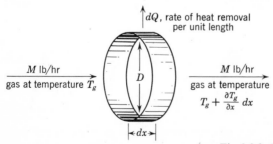

Fig. 2.3.3   Differential cross-section of duct.

to achieve these temperatures by appropriately varying the tube-wall thickness. This is clearly a problem in variational calculus—a *natural* problem, since we are required to produce the *most* possible power.

We begin our analysis by making an energy balance over the differential section shown in Fig. 2.3.3. If we neglect axial conduction, this balance is

$$-dQ = MC_p \frac{dT_g}{dx} dx \tag{2.3.2}$$

where Q = rate of heat removal from gas
  T_g = gas temperature
  C_p = gas heat capacity
  M = mass flow rate

The heat flow through the walls is approximated by the expression

$$dQ = \frac{k(T_h - T_c)}{l} dA \tag{2.3.3}$$

with the differential area being given by

$$dA = \pi D \, dx \tag{2.3.4}$$

Equation (2.3.3) is recognized as an approximation which is valid when the wall thickness is small compared with the tube diameter. Moreover, we shall assume that the dQ of Eq. (2.3.2) is the same as that of Eq. (2.3.3). However, it should be noted that these two heats are not strictly equal, since a fraction of the heat leaving the gas is adsorbed at the hot junction. We shall ignore this difference and assume that the efficiency θ of the machine is low. Within the framework of these assumptions, an alternate expression for dp is

$$dp = \frac{\theta l}{k \, dA} dQ^2 \tag{2.3.5}$$

We have eliminated the hot and cold junction temperatures from the expression defining the power. However, for our purposes it is desirable to express the power as a function of the gas temperature, since this is the variable which can be manipulated. This can be accomplished in two steps. We note that the rate of heat transfer is given by

$$dQ = U(T_g - T_a) \, dA \tag{2.3.6}$$

if the over-all heat-transfer coefficient is defined as[2]

$$U = \frac{1}{1/h_g + l/k + 1/h_a} \tag{2.3.7}$$

[2] R. B. Bird, W. E. Stewart, and E. N. Lightfoot, "Transport Phenomena," p. 285, John Wiley & Sons, Inc., New York, 1960.

In these equations T_a represents the constant coolant temperature. Substituting Eqs. (2.3.6) and (2.3.7) into Eq. (2.3.5) gives

$$dp = \frac{\theta l}{k} \left(\frac{T_g - T_a}{1/h_g + l/k + 1/h_a} \right)^2 dA \tag{2.3.8}$$

The l depends on x. This quantity is also related to the gas temperature by Eqs. (2.3.2), (2.3.6), and (2.3.7). After a little algebraic manipulation, one can show that

$$l(x) = - \frac{k\pi D(T_g - T_a)}{MC_p \, dT_g/dx} - k\left(\frac{1}{h_g} + \frac{1}{h_a} \right) \tag{2.3.9}$$

Substituting this expression for $l(x)$ into Eq. (2.3.8) gives, after integrating,

$$p = \int_0^L \theta \left[-MC_p \frac{dT_g}{dx} (T_g - T_a) - \frac{1}{\pi D}\left(\frac{1}{h_g} + \frac{1}{h_a} \right)\left(MC_p \frac{dT_g}{dx} \right)^2 \right] dx \tag{2.3.10}$$

This is the desired result, for we have p as a functional of $T_g(x)$, and we wish to select the $T_g(x)$ which will maximize the production of thermoelectricity. Of course, this is a problem in variational calculus, and if p is to be an extremal, $T_g(x)$ must satisfy the Euler-Lagrange equation

$$\frac{d^2 T_g}{dx^2} = 0 \tag{2.3.11}$$

and the natural boundary condition

$$A_1(T_g - T_a) + 2A_2 \frac{dT_g}{dx} = 0 \qquad \text{at } x = L \tag{2.3.12}$$

At the inlet $\delta T_g = 0$, since this temperature is fixed as a design parameter. The constants are defined as

$$A_1 = -\theta MC_p \tag{2.3.13}$$

and

$$A_2 = - \frac{\theta}{\pi D}\left(\frac{1}{h_g} + \frac{1}{h_a} \right)(MC_p)^2 \tag{2.3.14}$$

Equations (2.3.11) and (2.3.12) are a result of applying the equation given in row (a) of Table 1.7.1 to the integrand of Eq. (2.3.10). The optimal temperature distribution is found by integrating Eq. (2.3.11) twice, which gives

$$T = T_0 + \beta x \tag{2.3.15}$$

where the β is to be determined so that the natural boundary condition is satisfied and T_0 is the inlet temperature of the gas. Substituting Eq. (2.3.15) into Eq. (2.3.12), we find

$$\beta^* = -\frac{T_0 - T_a}{L + (2MC_p/\pi D)(1/h_a + 1/h_g)} \tag{2.3.16}$$

with the asterisk denoting β as the optimal value of the temperature gradient.

Let us now determine the power that we can expect from our optimal design. Using a linear temperature profile, the power is

$$p = \int_0^L -\theta \left[MC_p(T_0 - T_a + \beta x)\beta + \frac{1/h_g + 1/h_a}{\pi D}(MC_p\beta)^2 \right] dx \tag{2.3.17}$$

Integrating,

$$p = -\theta \left[MC_p\beta(T_0 - T_a)L + MC_p \frac{\beta^2 L^2}{2} + \frac{1}{\pi D}\left(\frac{1}{h_g} + \frac{1}{h_a}\right)(MC_p\beta)^2 L \right] \tag{2.3.18}$$

Putting β^* for β, the optimal power is

$$p^* = \frac{\theta MC_p(T_0 - T_a)^2}{2 + (1/h_g + 1/h_a)(4MC_p/\pi DL)} \tag{2.3.19}$$

This result is satisfying. As we would expect, the power increases with increasing efficiency θ, heat transfer coefficients h_g and h_a, and temperature difference $T_0 - T_a$.

As a last exercise, let us determine the variation in the direct wall thickness required to achieve the optimal linear temperature distribution. If the temperature $T_g = T_0 + \beta x$ is substituted into Eq. (2.3.9), the following expression is determined:

$$l(x) = -\left[\frac{k\pi D(T_0 - T_a)}{MC_p\beta} + k\left(\frac{1}{h_a} + \frac{1}{h_g}\right) \right] - \frac{k\pi D}{MC_p} x \tag{2.3.20}$$

Thus $l(x)$ is a decreasing linear function of x.

This study provides an interesting application of variational calculus to a typical engineering problem. There are several tasks left undone. Most of these points are illustrated in the problem set associated with this section. It is suggested that the reader study this set carefully.

PROBLEM 2.3.1   Given that

$$\left(\frac{1}{h_g} + \frac{1}{h_a}\right)MC_p \frac{4}{\pi DL} = 1$$

show that the temperature profile

$$T_g = T_a + (T_0 - T_a) \cos \frac{\pi x}{2L}$$

gives a smaller power-generation rate than does the optimal one, as determined by Eq. (2.3.19). This proves that the optimal power-generation rate is not a minimum!

PROBLEM 2.3.2 Prove that the power generation rate defined by Eq. (2.3.19) is a maximum. (*Hint:* see Sec. 1.2.)

PROBLEM 2.3.3 In the limit, as h_a and h_g both become very large relative to the value of $MC_p/D\pi$, the power is expressed by

$$p = -MC_p\theta \int_0^L \frac{dT_g}{dx} (T_g - T_a) \, dx$$

Show that this equation has no extremal by applying the Euler-Lagrange equations to the integrand. Interpret this result by integrating this expression for the power and show that all gas temperature distributions which give a temperature of T_0 at $x = 0$ and the coolant temperature at $x = L$ give rise to the same power-generation rate. Thus we would not expect to find an optimal temperature distribution if the heat-transfer coefficients h_g and h_a become very large.

2.4 EQUILIBRIUM CONFIGURATION OF AN INTERFACE

At thermodynamic equilibrium a virtual change in the Helmholtz free energy along a path of constant temperature and volume must vanish. This principle follows directly from the basic postulates of thermodynamics.[1] Thus we see that the equilibrium state is determined by an extremal principle. In this section we shall invoke the principle of minimum free energy to determine the equilibrium configuration of an interface. Two particular examples will be studied. First we shall study the shape of an interface near a solid boundary, and second we shall determine the relationship of the surface tension to the difference in pressure across a fluid-fluid boundary.

The first problem to be studied is depicted in Fig. 2.4.1. The plate is infinite in extent. To formulate the free energy for this system, both the surface free energies and the potential energy of the system must be considered. All other contributions can be ignored, however, since the variation will be taken at constant temperature and volume and the phases A and B are assumed to be immiscible.

---

[1] H. B. Callen, "Thermodynamics," pp. 3–47, John Wiley & Sons, Inc., New York, 1961.

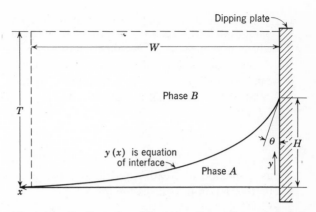

Fig. 2.4.1   Configuration of liquid interface at flat vertical plate.

If σ_{AB} is defined as the free energy per unit area of the AB interface, then the contribution to the free energy owing to the AB contact is given by

$$\sigma_{AB}\int_0^W (1 + y_x{}^2)^{1/2}\, dx \tag{2.4.1}$$

in which $y(x)$ defines the shape of the interface as a function of x and W is a large distance measured in the x direction.   Equation (2.4.1) represents the surface energy of the interface per unit of width.   The free energy resulting from phases A and B contacting the solid plate is given by

$$H\sigma_{AS} + (T - H)\sigma_{BS} \tag{2.4.2}$$

where σ_{AS} and σ_{BS} are the surface energies of the solid surface in contact with phases A and B, respectively.   The dimension T is selected such that it is greater than H, the height of liquid rise along the plate.

The contribution of the gravitational field to the free energy can be formulated as

$$\rho_A g \int_0^W y\left(\frac{y}{2}\right) dx + \rho_B g \int_0^W (T - y)\frac{T + y}{2}\, dx \tag{2.4.3}$$

since this portion of the free energy is simply the total potential energy of a given configuration relative to some arbitrary datum level (here taken to be $y = 0$).   Summing the individual contributions, the total free energy is found to be

$$F = F_0 + T\sigma_{BS} + \frac{\rho_B g W T^2}{2} + g(\rho_A - \rho_B)\int_0^W \frac{y^2}{2}\, dx$$
$$+ H(\sigma_{AS} - \sigma_{BS}) + \sigma_{AB}\int_0^W (1 + y_x{}^2)^{1/2}\, dx \tag{2.4.4}$$

where F_0 is a function of composition, temperature, and volume.

In accordance with the thermodynamic principle enunciated in the first paragraph of this section, the physically observable configuration will be that which minimizes F at constant temperature and volume. The problem is then one of classical variational calculus, and the tools developed in Chap. 1 can be applied. Since it is necessary to restrict the system to constant volume, the functional to be minimized is

$$G = F + \lambda \int_0^W y \, dx \tag{2.4.5}$$

in which λ is a Lagrangian multiplier. The use of Lagrangian multipliers as a method of treating restrictions has been discussed in Sec. 1.5. The first variation in G takes the form

$$\delta G = (\sigma_{AS} - \sigma_{BS}) \, \delta H + g(\rho_A - \rho_B) \int_0^W y \, \delta y \, dx + \lambda \int_0^W \delta y \, dx$$
$$+ \sigma_{AB} \int_0^W \frac{y_x}{(1 + y_x^2)^{1/2}} \frac{d}{dx} \delta y \, dx \tag{2.4.6}$$

Note that the height of the liquid rise along the plate is also subject to variation. In this notation, δH is this change in the height of liquid rise along the plate. After an integration by parts, Eq. (2.4.6) becomes

$$\delta G = \left[(\sigma_{AS} - \sigma_{BS}) - \sigma_{AB} \frac{y_x}{(1 + y_x^2)^{1/2}} \right]_{x=0} \delta H$$
$$+ \int_0^W \left[(\rho_A - \rho_B)gy + \lambda - \frac{d}{dx} \frac{\sigma_{AB} y_x}{(1 + y_x^2)^{1/2}} \right] \delta y \, dx \tag{2.4.7}$$

The intersection of the three-phase boundary is magnified in Fig. 2.4.2. The angle θ is known as the contact angle. This angle is clearly related to

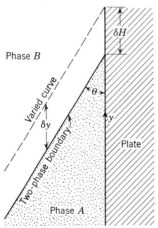

Fig. 2.4.2   A magnified view of a three-phase boundary.

the slope of the interface by the equation

$$\tan \theta = -\frac{dx}{dy} \tag{2.4.8}$$

If δG is to be zero for all possible variations, then

$$g(\rho_A - \rho_B)y + \lambda - \frac{d}{dx} \frac{\sigma_{AB}\, dy/dx}{[1 + (dy/dx)^2]^{\frac{1}{2}}} = 0 \tag{2.4.9}$$

subject to

$$\frac{dy}{dx} \to 0 \quad \text{and} \quad y \to 0 \quad \text{as } x \to W \tag{2.4.10}$$

and the natural boundary condition

$$(\sigma_{AS} - \sigma_{BS}) + \sigma_{AB} \cos \theta = 0 \quad \text{at } x = 0 \tag{2.4.11}$$

Equation (2.4.9) is Laplace's equation[2] applicable to the particular configuration under study. The last boundary condition, Eq. (2.4.11), is the Young's Equation which relates the contact angle to the surface free energies.[3] The analysis given here closely parallels the derivation of Collins and Cook.[4]

The integration of the capillarity equations is not difficult, and the presentation given here is essentially that due to Buff.[2]

Define

$$\tan \psi = -\frac{dy}{dx}$$

and note that

$$\frac{d}{dx} \frac{dy/dx}{[1 + (dy/dx)^2]^{\frac{1}{2}}} = -\frac{d}{dy} \sin \psi \frac{dy}{dx} = -\frac{d}{dy} \cos \psi \tag{2.4.12}$$

Equation (2.4.9) becomes

$$g(\rho_A - \rho_B)y + \lambda + \sigma_{AB} \frac{d}{dy} \cos \psi = 0 \tag{2.4.13}$$

[2] F. P. Buff, "Encyclopedia of Physics," S. Flügge, ed., vol. X, pp. 281–304, Springer-Verlag OHG, Berlin, 1960.

[3] N. K. Adam, "The Physics and Chemistry of Surfaces," p. 179, 3d ed., Oxford University Press, London, 1941.

[4] R. E. Collins and C. E. Cook, "Fundamental Basis for the Contact Angle and Capillary Pressure," *Trans. Faraday Soc.*, vol. 55, p. 1602, 1959.

Boundary condition (2.4.10) requires that

$$\lambda = 0$$

Equation (2.4.13) can be integrated to give

$$y = a\sqrt{1 - \cos \psi} \qquad (2.4.14)$$

where

$$a^2 = \frac{2\sigma_{AB}}{g(\rho_A - \rho_B)}$$

To develop Eq. (2.4.14), one must also impose the condition that as $y \to 0$, $\psi \to 0$. The angle ψ must be equal to $\pi/2 - \theta$ when y is H. Thus the height of liquid along the plate is

$$H = a\sqrt{1 - \sin \theta} \qquad (2.4.15)$$

Using the definition of ψ and Eq. (2.4.14), x can be related to the parametric angle ψ as

$$dx = -\frac{a}{2\sqrt{2}} \left[\frac{1 - 2\cos^2(\psi/2)}{\cos(\psi/2)} \right] d\psi \qquad (2.4.16)$$

The parametric angle ψ can be eliminated from Eq. (2.4.16) by use of Eq. (2.4.14) and the resultant expression integrated to yield:

$$x = \text{const} - \frac{a}{\sqrt{2}} \text{ arc cosh} \frac{\sqrt{2}a}{y} + \sqrt{2a^2 - y^2} \qquad (2.4.17)$$

The constant is determined so that x vanishes at $y = H$.

We have seen how the thermodynamic condition of equilibrium can be used to determine the configuration of an interface. Since the problem was to determine the minimum of free energy, we found that the mathematical statement of the problem was *naturally* one couched in terms of the calculus of variations. In this sense we have cataloged this as a *natural* problem.

PROBLEM 2.4.1   Use the principle of minimum free energy to determine the equilibrium configuration of a droplet resting on a horizontal solid boundary.

If z is measured perpendicular to the plate and $p(z)$ is the profile of the droplet in a plane containing the vertical axis, the differential equation that one should obtain is

$$\sigma_{AB} \left\{ \frac{d^2p/dz^2}{[1 + (dp/dz)^2]^{3/2}} - \frac{1}{p[1 + (dp/dz)^2]^{1/2}} \right\} - g(\rho_A - \rho_B)z = \lambda$$

What are the boundary conditions?

It is of interest to note that we were not forced to give physical significance to the Lagrangian multiplier which was introduced in this first example, since this multiplier vanished. However, in many situations concerning equilibrium at an interface, this multiplier does not vanish, and the preceding analysis must be either modified or extended to provide the physical interpretation of the Lagrangian multiplier. As we shall now show, the Lagrangian multiplier is related to the differential pressure between the phases, and although this difference vanishes across a plane interface, it remains as a factor in considering curved interfaces. For example, in hydrodynamic calculations, it is not uncommon to assume that a condition of local equilibrium exists near the interface and to relate the pressures on either side of an interface by the approximate expression[5]

$$p^{\mathrm{I}} - p^{\mathrm{II}} = \sigma \left(\frac{\partial^2 \zeta}{\partial x_2{}^2} + \frac{\partial^2 \zeta}{\partial x_3{}^2} \right) \tag{2.4.18}$$

where p^{I} and p^{II} are the pressures in phases I and II, respectively, and $\zeta(x_2, x_3)$ is the equation of the interface defined so that

$$x_1 = \zeta(x_2, x_3)$$

gives the x_1 coordinate of the interface as shown in Fig. 2.4.3.

Our task will be to determine the assumptions which are inherent in the writing of Eq. (2.4.18). The development will again rely on finding the conditions which minimize the Helmholtz free energy at constant temperature and volume. Thus the first assumption which we will require is that our system be at *thermodynamic equilibrium*, for it is only under these conditions that the Helmholtz free energy is a minimum.

In this analysis we will visualize the system enclosed in a container of volume $8l_1l_2l_3$ as shown in Fig. 2.4.3. Although we shall maintain the volume of the container as constant, the volumes of each of the two phases will be permitted to vary. This state of affairs should be contrasted with the previous study, in which the volumes of each of the independent phases were fixed. To account for the variation in free energy resulting from the changes in the individual volumes, a more complete definition of the free energy is required. In treating systems enclosing a phase boundary, one splits the free energy as follows.[6]

$$F = F^{\mathrm{I}} + F^{\mathrm{II}} + F^s \tag{2.4.19}$$

---

[5] See, for example, V. G. Levich, "Physicochemical Hydrodynamics," Chap. VII, Prentice-Hall, Inc., Englewood Cliffs, N.J., 1962, for a series of examples showing the applications of such boundary conditions.

[6] S. Ono and S. Kondo, "Encyclopedia of Physics," S. Flügge, ed., vol. X, pp. 136–140, Springer-Verlag OHG, Berlin, 1960.

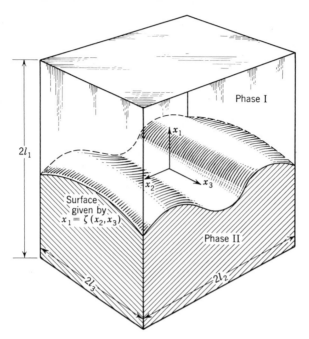

Fig. 2.4.3   Two phases embedded in volume $8l_1l_2l_3$.

where F^s is the free energy associated with the surface and F^{I} and F^{II} are the free energies of the bulk phases I and II, respectively.[7]   These free energies are[8]

$$F^{\mathrm{I}} = U^{\mathrm{I}} - TS^{\mathrm{I}} = -p^{\mathrm{I}}V^{\mathrm{I}} + \mu^{\mathrm{I}}N^{\mathrm{I}} \tag{2.4.20}$$

and

$$F^{\mathrm{II}} = U^{\mathrm{II}} - TS^{\mathrm{II}} = -p^{\mathrm{II}}V^{\mathrm{II}} + \mu^{\mathrm{II}}N^{\mathrm{II}} \tag{2.4.21}$$

where U = internal energy
   T = temperature
   S = entropy
   N = mass
and μ = chemical potential

---

[7] The perceptive reader will detect the ambiguity inherent in these vague definitions. However, the precise definitions are a long story, and it cannot be told here.   The author believes that the most penetrating analysis of the surface is found in the work of Gibbs ("The Collected Works of J. Willard Gibbs," vol. I, pp. 219–331, Longmans, Green & Co., New York, 1928).

These equations are exact provided there are *no external forces* acting on the system. This represents our second assumption. The surface free energy is given by an analogous expression

$$F^s = \sigma A + \mu^s N^s \tag{2.4.22}$$

provided we neglect solid-fluid interactions. Actually, we could easily include such contributions to the free energy, but there is little to be gained in doing so, for as we have seen in the previous example, we would find that Young's equation [Eq. (2.4.11)] is to be satisfied at the three-phase boundary. The total free energy is

$$F = -p^{\mathrm{I}}V^{\mathrm{I}} - p^{\mathrm{II}}V^{\mathrm{II}} + \sigma A + \mu^{\mathrm{I}}N^{\mathrm{I}} + \mu^{\mathrm{II}}N^{\mathrm{II}} + \mu^s N^s \tag{2.4.23}$$

We now assume that the phases are *completely immiscible* so that the mass of each phase remains constant during a variation at constant temperature. This is our third assumption.

Equation (2.4.23) can be written as

$$
\begin{aligned}
F = &-p^{\mathrm{I}} \int_{-l_2}^{l_2} \int_{-l_3}^{l_3} (l_1 - \zeta)\, dx_2\, dx_3 - p^{\mathrm{II}} \int_{-l_2}^{l_2} \int_{-l_3}^{l_3} (l_1 + \zeta)\, dx_2\, dx_3 \\
&+ \sigma \int_{-l_2}^{l_2} \int_{-l_3}^{l_3} \left[1 + \left(\frac{\partial \zeta}{\partial x_2}\right)^2 + \left(\frac{\partial \zeta}{\partial x_3}\right)^2 \right]^{1/2} dx_2\, dx_3 \\
&+ \mu^{\mathrm{I}}N^{\mathrm{I}} + \mu^{\mathrm{II}}N^{\mathrm{II}} + \mu^s N^s
\end{aligned}
\tag{2.4.24}
$$

since an element of surface area is given by[8]

$$dA = \left[1 + \left(\frac{\partial \zeta}{\partial x_2}\right)^2 + \left(\frac{\partial \zeta}{\partial x_3}\right)^2 \right]^{1/2} dx_2\, dx_3$$

The last approximation necessary in the development of Eq. (2.4.18) is to assume that ζ is *small*; that is,

$$\left(\frac{\partial \zeta}{\partial x_2}\right)^2 \ll 1 \tag{2.4.25}$$

$$\left(\frac{\partial \zeta}{\partial x_3}\right)^2 \ll 1 \tag{2.4.26}$$

These assumptions are often invoked to preserve the linearity of the problem. Assuming that Eq. (2.4.25) and Eq. (2.4.26) are valid, we can write the surface area as[†]

$$dA = \left[1 + \frac{1}{2}\left(\frac{\partial \zeta}{\partial x_2}\right)^2 + \frac{1}{2}\left(\frac{\partial \zeta}{\partial x_3}\right)^2 \right] dx_2\, dx_3 \tag{2.4.27}$$

---

[8] I. S. Sokolnikoff, "Advanced Calculus," pp. 161–163, McGraw-Hill Book Company, New York, 1939.

[†] Equation (2.4.27) can be seen immediately if one expands $(1 + x)^{1/2}$ in a Taylor series. This gives

$$(1 + x)^{1/2} = 1 + \tfrac{1}{2}x - \tfrac{1}{8}x^2 + \cdots$$

and for small x, the third term is negligible.

Thus

$$
F = -p^{\mathrm{I}} \int_{-l_2}^{l_2} \int_{-l_3}^{l_3} (l_1 - \zeta) \, dx_2 \, dx_3 - p^{\mathrm{II}} \int_{-l_2}^{l_2} \int_{-l_3}^{l_3} (l_1 + \zeta) \, dx_2 \, dx_3
$$

$$
+ \sigma \int_{-l_2}^{l_2} \int_{-l_3}^{l_3} \left[1 + \frac{1}{2}\left(\frac{\partial \zeta}{\partial x_2}\right)^2 + \frac{1}{2}\left(\frac{\partial \zeta}{\partial x_3}\right)^2 \right] dx_2 \, dx_3
$$

$$
+ \mu^{\mathrm{I}} N^{\mathrm{I}} + \mu^{\mathrm{II}} N^{\mathrm{II}} + \mu^s N^s \tag{2.4.28}
$$

If we vary ζ, clearly the total volume is fixed and the temperature need not change; therefore the resultant change in F must vanish.   We can write

$$
\delta F = \int_{-l_2}^{l_2} \int_{-l_3}^{l_3} \left(p^{\mathrm{I}} - p^{\mathrm{II}} - \sigma \frac{\partial^2 \zeta}{\partial x_2{}^2} - \sigma \frac{\partial^2 \zeta}{\partial x_3{}^2} \right) \delta \zeta \, dx_2 \, dx_3
$$

$$
- V^{\mathrm{I}} \delta p^{\mathrm{I}} - V^{\mathrm{II}} \delta p^{\mathrm{II}} + N^{\mathrm{I}} \delta \mu^{\mathrm{I}} + N^{\mathrm{II}} \delta \mu^{\mathrm{II}} + N^s \delta \mu^s
$$

$$
+ \sigma \int_{-l_3}^{l_3} \left[\frac{\partial \zeta}{\partial x_2} \delta \zeta \bigg|_{x_2 = l_2} - \frac{\partial \zeta}{\partial x_2} \delta \zeta \bigg|_{x_2 = -l_2} \right] dx_3
$$

$$
+ \sigma \int_{-l_2}^{l_2} \left[\frac{\partial \zeta}{\partial x_3} \delta \zeta \bigg|_{x_3 = l_3} - \frac{\partial \zeta}{\partial x_3} \delta \zeta \bigg|_{x_3 = -l_3} \right] dx_2 \tag{2.4.29}
$$

where δp^{I}, δp^{II}, $\delta \mu^{\mathrm{I}}$, $\delta \mu^{\mathrm{II}}$, $\delta \mu^s$ are the changes in the chemical potential and the pressure resulting from the change in the volumes of the individual phases.   These latter terms can be discarded, however, because, according to the Gibbs-Duhem equations,[9]

$$
-V \, dp + N \, d\mu = 0 \qquad \text{at constant temperature}
$$

and

$$
N^s \, d\mu^s = 0 \qquad \text{at constant temperature}
$$

Thus we find

$$
\delta F = \int_{-l_2}^{l_2} \int_{-l_3}^{l_3} \left(p^{\mathrm{I}} - p^{\mathrm{II}} - \sigma \frac{\partial^2 \zeta}{\partial x_2{}^2} - \sigma \frac{\partial^2 \zeta}{\partial x_3{}^2} \right) \delta \zeta \, dx_2 \, dx_3
$$

$$
+ \sigma \int_{-l_3}^{l_3} \left(\frac{\partial \zeta}{\partial x_2} \delta \zeta \bigg|_{x_2 = l_2} - \frac{\partial \zeta}{\partial x_2} \delta \zeta \bigg|_{x_2 = -l_2} \right) dx_3
$$

$$
+ \sigma \int_{-l_2}^{l_2} \left(\frac{\partial \zeta}{\partial x_3} \delta \zeta \bigg|_{x_3 = l_3} - \frac{\partial \zeta}{\partial x_3} \delta \zeta \bigg|_{x_3 = -l_3} \right) dx_2 \tag{2.4.30}
$$

[9] E. A. Guggenheim, "Thermodynamics," 3d ed., p. 33, North-Holland Publishing Company, Amsterdam, 1957.

and Eq. (2.4.18) is a necessary condition for δF to vanish for all variations and our discussion is complete. We summarize our assumptions made during this analysis as

1. Thermodynamic equilibrium
2. No gravitational field
3. Immiscible phases
4. Small deviations from a plane interface

Equation (2.4.18) is often used in connection with hydrodynamic problems even though all of the assumptions stated above are not satisfied. For example, this equation is used in some calculations of wave phenomena. In such studies, one has neither thermodynamic equilibrium nor are the gravitational forces negligible. However, one justifies the use of this equation by assuming that the differential pressure to be substituted into the equation is that which acts immediately across the interface, and thus, very little mass is involved and gravity can have little effect. In addition, one assumes a condition of local equilibrium, so the surface tension appearing in the equation is that found by equilibrium experiments (such as capillary rise).

PROBLEM 2.4.2 Prove that the equation

$$p^{\mathrm{I}} - p^{\mathrm{II}} = \frac{\sigma}{a} - \frac{\sigma}{a^2}\left(\zeta + a^2 \frac{\partial^2 \zeta}{\partial z^2} + \frac{\partial^2 \zeta}{\partial \theta^2} \right)$$

gives the correct expression for the pressure difference across a cylindrical surface of radius a with a superimposed small deformation ζ. The radius of the cylinder is then given by

$$r = a + \zeta(z, \theta)$$

as depicted in Fig. 2.4.4.

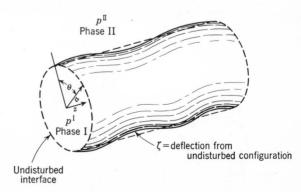

Fig. 2.4.4 Cylindrical column of fluid.

2.5 OPTIMAL DESIGN OF COOLING FINS

We have all seen radiators which have cooling fins attached to increase the rate of heat transfer from the wall to the gas. The design of such fins is a rather complicated task when the designer must account for all of the details such as best material of construction, optimum number of fins per foot, etc. In this section, one of the simpler facets of cooling-fins design will be studied. The problem can be stated as follows: if the mass of a rectangular cooling fin is specified, what is the optimum shape? A sketch of the fin is shown in Fig. 2.5.1. As indicated in the sketch, the temperature scale has been shifted so that the temperature of the wall to which the fin is attached is 1 and the ambient temperature is 0. The length of the fin is b, and x is the coordinate measured along the fin. To solve this problem, let us first write an energy balance as

$$\frac{d}{dx} p(x) \frac{dT}{dx} = \frac{h}{k} \sqrt{1 + \left(\frac{dp}{dx}\right)^2}\, T \tag{2.5.1}$$

in which k is the thermal conductivity and h is the heat-transfer coefficient. If we assume that $(dp/dx)^2$ is small compared with 1, the equation reduces to the following form:

$$\frac{d}{dx} p(x) \frac{dT}{dx} = T \frac{h}{k} \tag{2.5.2}$$

The total amount of heat dissipated from the fin per unit time is given by

$$I' = 2 \int_0^b hT\, dx \tag{2.5.3}$$

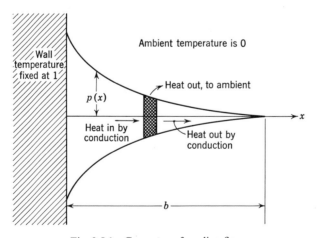

Fig. 2.5.1 Geometry of cooling fin.

and the mass of the fin can be computed as follows:

$$M = 2\rho \int_0^b p(x)\,dx \tag{2.5.4}$$

Now we wish to maximize the dissipation subject to the restriction of fixed mass. Thus, applying the method of Lagrangian multipliers (see Sec. 1.5), we seek to make the following integral stationary:

$$I = \int_0^b [2hT + 2\lambda\rho p(x)]\,dx \tag{2.5.5}$$

Clearly it would be incorrect to assume that $T(x)$ and $p(x)$ are independent, for these two functions are connected by the energy balance. Thus, before a variation is permitted, we must eliminate either $p(x)$ or $T(x)$ from the variational expression.† To accomplish this elimination, integrate the energy balance to obtain

$$-p(x)\frac{dT}{dx} = \frac{h}{k}\int_x^b T\,dy \tag{2.5.6}$$

where it has been assumed that there is no heat flow out the end of the fin. This assumption has also been used in computing the heat flow from the fin as given by Eq. (2.5.3). Solving for $p(x)$ and substituting into the variational integral yields

$$I = 2\int_0^b \left[hT - \frac{\lambda\rho h}{k}\left(\frac{dT}{dx}\right)^{-1}\int_x^b T\,dy \right]dx \tag{2.5.7}$$

The shape $p(x)$ has been eliminated from the variational integral. As a consequence, it is easier to fix b temporarily and to find the optimal temperature distribution for the fixed b. At the end calculation we shall pick the best possible value of the fin length for a given mass. Define the variation as

$$T^*(x) = T(x) + \epsilon\phi(x) \tag{2.5.8}$$

in the usual way. The $\phi(x)$ must again be continuous and continuously differentiable in the interval 0 to b and satisfy the boundary condition

$$\phi(0) = 0 \tag{2.5.9}$$

since the temperature is fixed at the wall. Using Eq. (2.5.8) in Eq. (2.5.7) and expanding to first order in ϵ yields

$$\delta I = 2\int_0^b \epsilon\left[h\phi + \frac{\lambda\rho h}{k}\frac{\phi_x}{(T_x)^2}\int_x^b T\,dy - \frac{\lambda\rho h}{k}\frac{1}{T_x}\int_x^b \phi\,dy \right]dx \tag{2.5.10}$$

---

† An alternate procedure would be to use the technique described in Sec. 2.6. The energy balance would be treated as though it were a kinetic equation.

in which T_x and ϕ_x are T and ϕ differentiated with respect to x. After an integration by parts, Eq. (2.5.10) becomes

$$\delta I = 2\epsilon \int_0^b \left[h + \frac{\lambda \rho h}{k} \frac{2(d^2T/dx^2)}{(dT/dx)^3} \int_x^b T \, dy + \frac{\lambda \rho h T}{k(dT/dx)^2} - \frac{\lambda \rho h}{k} \int_0^x \left(\frac{dT}{dx}\right)^{-1} dy \right] \phi \, dx$$

(2.5.11)

yielding the following Euler-Lagrange equation:

$$h + \frac{\lambda \rho h}{k} \left[\frac{2(d^2T/dx^2)}{(dT/dx)^3} \int_x^b T \, dy + \frac{T}{(dT/dx)^2} - \int_0^x \frac{dy}{dT/dx} \right] = 0$$

(2.5.12)

It is easy to verify that

$$T(x) = 1 - \sqrt{\frac{-\lambda \rho}{k}} \, x$$

(2.5.13)

satisfies the differential equation. The shape of the fin can be computed as follows:

$$p(x) = - \left[\left(\frac{dT}{dx}\right)^{-1} \int_x^b T \, dy \right] \frac{h}{k} = \frac{h}{ka} \left(\frac{ax^2}{2} + x - \frac{ab^2}{2} - b \right)$$

(2.5.14)

in which $a = -\sqrt{-\lambda \rho / k}$.

The Lagrangian multiplier is determined so that the mass of the fin is equivalent to the specified mass. Thus,

$$\frac{M}{2\rho} = \int_0^b p(x) \, dx = -\frac{hb^3}{3k} - \frac{hb^2}{2ka}$$

(2.5.15)

or solving for a, we find

$$a = - \left(\frac{1}{Mk/\rho hb^2 + 2b/3} \right)$$

(2.5.16)

The parameter a is now determined in terms of the physical properties and the dimension b. The task of determining the appropriate value of b still remains. It should be noted that the restriction

$$p(x) > 0 \qquad \text{for } 0 < x < b$$

must be imposed for Eq. (2.5.14) to make physical sense. However, we must now find the value of b which out of all physically admissible values gives the maximum energy dissipation. To find the answer to this question, first compute the energy dissipated as

$$I = 2h \int_0^b T \, dy$$

(2.5.3)

or, using the temperature profile, Eq. (2.5.13), we have upon integration

$$I = 2h \left(b - \frac{3\rho hb^4}{3Mk + 2\rho hb^3} \right)$$

(2.5.17)

The maximum dissipation is found by determining the value of b which satisfies the equation

$$0 = \frac{\partial I}{\partial b} = 2h \left(1 - \frac{6\rho hb^3}{3Mk + 2\rho hb^3} + \frac{18\rho^2 h^2 b^6}{3Mk + 2\rho hb^3} \right) \tag{2.5.18}$$

Solving for b gives

$$b = \sqrt[3]{\frac{3Mk}{\rho h}} \tag{2.5.19}$$

This is the best value of b. The slope becomes

$$a = \frac{1}{b}$$

which is the value recommended by Jakob.[1]

It should be noted that Duffin[2] has given an alternate variational formulation and has reached the same conclusion. Papers considering fin design with radiant transport have been written by Bartas and Sellars[3] and Callinan and Berggren.[4]

2.6 OPTIMAL REACTION TEMPERATURE

The problem to be considered in this section is that of determining the optimal temperature distribution in a reaction system. Specifically, we wish to compute the best operating temperature as a function of axial position along a tubular reactor, assuming that this desired temperature can be produced by some external heating device. No regard will be given to the practical aspects of achieving the desired distribution. This problem is best illustrated by considering the following example.

EXAMPLE 2.6.1   It is desired to maximize the yield of substance B produced by the irreversible reaction

$$A \rightarrow B$$

[1] M. Jakob, "Heat Transfer," vol. I, p. 219, John Wiley & Sons, Inc., 1960.

[2] R. J. Duffin, "A Variational Problem Relating to Cooling Fins," *J. Math. Mech.*, vol. 8, p. 47, 1959.

[3] J. G. Bartas and W. H. Sellars, "Radiation Fin Effectiveness," *J. Heat Transfer*, vol. 82, p. 73, 1960.

[4] J. P. Callinan and W. P. Berggren, "Some Radiator Design Criteria for Space Vehicles," *J. Heat Transfer*, vol. 81, p. 237, 1959.

in a tubular reactor of length L. The kinetic equation is

$$V \frac{dC_A}{dl} = -C_A e^{-E/RT} \qquad (2.6.1)$$

where $V =$ mean velocity in the tube
$\quad\quad C_A =$ concentration of substance A
$\quad\quad l =$ position variable measured along the axis of the tube
$\quad\quad E =$ activation energy
$\quad\quad R =$ gas constant
$\quad\quad T =$ absolute temperature

We want to select $T(l)$ so that $C_A(L)$, the concentration of A leaving the reactor, is minimized. If we let

$$H = e^{-E/RT} \qquad (2.6.2)$$

Eq. (2.6.1) can be integrated to give

$$\ln \frac{C_A(L)}{C_A(0)} = -\int_0^L \frac{H(l)}{V} \, dl \qquad (2.6.3)$$

Since the logarithm is a monotonic function, the minimum of $C_A(L)$ corresponds to the minimum of the term on the left-hand side of Eq. (2.6.3). It is then clear that the problem is trivial, and the solution is to make H as large as possible. This corresponds to choosing the highest possible temperature at every point in the reactor. There is no need to apply variational calculus, for the integral obviously does not possess a stationary value.

This, of course, was a trivial example having an obvious solution. Indeed the reader may well inquire about the reason for including this particular example in the test. The problem has one very desirable feature. It serves to indicate the structure which is necessary to obtain a straightforward solution. An examination of Eq. (2.6.3) shows that a partial integration of the kinetic equations has been effected so that the terms contained in the integration are *dependent only on the temperature and independent of the concentration*. Once this structure has been achieved, the principles of variational calculus can be applied directly. However, as we shall see, it is not always possible in *practice* to make such a partial integration, although in *principle* such a structure can always be formulated. The problem is then more difficult and requires a new treatment.

Before proceeding with the problem of determining the optimal temperature distribution, it is convenient to digress momentarily and consider the use of variable Lagrangian multipliers. Suppose that the following integral is to be maximized.

$$I = \int_0^L f_0(x,T)\, dl \qquad (2.6.4)$$

in which T is the control variable and x is the controlled variable (for example, the concentration of a reactant). Let us further suppose that x is related to T by a kinetic equation

$$\frac{dx}{dl} = f_1(x,T) \qquad (2.6.5)$$

Clearly any change in T gives rise to a corresponding variation in x. The relationship connecting variations in x with respect to changes in T is, of course, Eq. (2.6.5). Our problem is to maximize (or minimize) I subject to the restriction that Eq. (2.6.5) be satisfied everywhere in the interval $0 \le l \le L$. This problem is similar to the type of problem to which we have applied the method of Lagrangian multipliers. The essential idea of the Lagrangian multiplier is to introduce an additional and undetermined parameter into the equations so that all of the variables can be treated as being independent even though a restriction is imposed which could be used to eliminate one of the variables. The value of the undetermined multiplier is selected to insure that the restriction is satisfied. The use of Lagrangian multipliers has been discussed in Sec. 1.5, and the reader is referred to this section for a more detailed discussion. For our discussion here it is important to reiterate that the Lagrangian multiplier is introduced into the equation to permit all variables to be treated as independent.

Let us formulate our problem as

$$I^* = \int_0^L \left\{ f_0(x,T) - \lambda(l)\left[\frac{dx}{dl} - f_1(x,T) \right] \right\} dl \qquad (2.6.6)$$

where $\lambda(l)$ is an undetermined multiplier, which is, in general, a function of position. The undetermined multiplier is a function of position because the kinetic equation must be satisfied locally (at every point $0 \le l \le L$) rather than as a global (integral) restriction. In using the undetermined multiplier, we "uncouple" the variables x and T. In a sense, the kinetic equation is included in the variational principle. If we are to choose x and T such that I^* is stationary, it is necessary that the Euler-Lagrange equations

$$\frac{\partial f_0}{\partial T} + \lambda \frac{\partial f_1}{\partial T} = 0 \qquad (2.6.7)$$

and

$$\frac{\partial f_0}{\partial x} + \frac{d\lambda}{dl} + \lambda \frac{\partial f_1}{\partial x} = 0 \qquad (2.6.8)$$

with boundary conditions

$$x \quad \text{specified at } l = 0 \tag{2.6.9}$$

and

$$\lambda = 0 \quad \text{at } l = L \tag{2.6.10}$$

be satisfied. Equations (2.6.7) to (2.6.10), together with the Pontryagin maximum principle,[1] form the basis of a very important computational scheme. This principle will be discussed shortly. There are several important features to be emphasized. Equation (2.6.8) is used to determine the $\lambda(l)$ as a function of l. Since λ was taken as being independent of variations in T and x, f_0 and f_1 in Eq. (2.6.8) are evaluated for the optimal conditions. The λ defined by Eq. (2.6.8) is sometimes called the adjoint function. We shall investigate the properties of this adjoint function in subsequent paragraphs. Note that the boundary condition on x is defined at the inlet, whereas the boundary condition on λ is at $l = L$. This state of affairs makes the problem more difficult. For to begin integration at $l = 0$ means that the value of λ is unknown; whereas, if we try to integrate backwards (from $l = L$), then the value of x is unknown.

To clarify the meaning of the Euler-Lagrange equations, let us consider an example.

EXAMPLE 2.6.2   Find the minimum of the integral

$$I = \int_0^L (x^2 + T^2)\, dl \tag{2.6.11}$$

given that x and T are related by the differential equation

$$\frac{dx}{dl} = T - x \tag{2.6.12}$$

and the boundary condition

$$x = 1 \quad \text{at } l = 0$$

It is clear that Eq. (2.6.12) can be integrated to give x in terms of T and the resulting expression used to eliminate x from Eq. (2.6.11). Then the appropriate minimizing function, $T(l)$, can be determined using the classical methods of variational calculus. However, let us apply Eqs. (2.6.7) to (2.6.10) to this particular problem. Equation (2.6.7) gives

$$2T + \lambda = 0 \tag{2.6.13}$$

[1] L. S. Pontryagin et al., "The Mathematical Theory of Optimal Processes," translated from the Russian by K. E. Trirogoff, John Wiley & Sons, Inc., New York, 1962.

and Eq. (2.6.8) is

$$2x + \frac{d\lambda}{dl} - \lambda = 0 \qquad\qquad (2.6.14)$$

Eliminating λ, Eq. (2.6.14) and Eq. (2.6.12) reduce to

$$\frac{dT}{dl} - T = x \qquad\qquad (2.6.15)$$

and

$$\frac{dx}{dl} + x = T \qquad\qquad (2.6.16)$$

subject to the boundary conditions

$$x = 1 \qquad \text{at } l = 0 \qquad\qquad (2.6.17)$$
$$T = 0 \qquad \text{at } l = L \qquad\qquad (2.6.18)\dagger$$

This system of equations can be solved to give

$$x = Ce^{-\sqrt{2}l} + De^{+\sqrt{2}l} \qquad\qquad (2.6.19a)$$

and

$$T = C(1 - \sqrt{2})e^{-\sqrt{2}l} + D(1 + \sqrt{2})e^{\sqrt{2}l} \qquad\qquad (2.6.19b)$$

in which C and D are constants to be determined such that Eqs. (2.6.17) and (2.6.18) are satisfied. These constants are

$$C = \frac{(1 + \sqrt{2})e^{\sqrt{2}L}}{2(\sinh \sqrt{2}L + \sqrt{2} \cosh \sqrt{2}L)}$$

and

$$D = \frac{(\sqrt{2} - 1)e^{-\sqrt{2}L}}{2(\sinh \sqrt{2}L + \sqrt{2} \cosh \sqrt{2}L)}$$

which gives the solution to the original problem, since the appropriate $T(l)$ is now defined.

PROBLEM 2.6.1   The differential equation [Eq. (2.6.15)] defining $T(l)$ in Example 2.6.2 can be developed in another way.   Find the variation of the I defined by Eq. (2.6.11) with respect to changes in T.   Remember, however, that a variation of T also gives rise to a variation in x.   Relate the variation of x to the variation of T using Eq. (2.6.12).   Eliminate δT from the integrand of δI using the relationship between δx and δT.   After an integration by parts, one should find Eq. (2.6.15) and Eq. (2.6.18) as the necessary conditions for I to be an extremum.

† This boundary condition follows from Eqs. (2.6.10) and (2.6.13).

It is desirable to generalize the results which have been developed thus far. To make the problem definite, we suppose that the kinetic equations giving the rates of reaction in a tubular reactor are

$$\frac{dx_i}{dl} = f_i(x_1, x_2, \ldots, x_n, T) \qquad i = 1, 2, \ldots, n \tag{2.6.20}$$

in which x_i is the composition of substance i in the n-component reacting mixture. The composition in the reactor, $x_1, \ldots, x_n$, is determined at every point in the interval $0 \leq l \leq L$ by the specification of an initial composition and the temperature as a function of axial position. The problem is to maximize the integral

$$I = \int_0^L f_0(x_1, x_2, \ldots, x_n, T) \, dl \tag{2.6.21}$$

As before, we face the problem of accounting for variations in the compositions resulting from a change in the temperature. The method of variable undetermined multipliers is again applicable.[2,3] However, in order to delve more deeply into the meaning of the adjoint functions, we shall approach the problem from an entirely different point of view. This second approach follows closely the arguments given by Katz.[4]

Begin by defining a "new component" x_0 as

$$\frac{dx_0}{dl} = f_0 \tag{2.6.22}$$

with the inlet condition

$$x_0 = 0 \qquad \text{at } l = 0 \tag{2.6.23}$$

Define

$$J = \int_0^L \frac{d}{dl}\left(\sum_{i=0}^{n} \lambda_i x_i\right) dl \tag{2.6.24}$$

where λ_i are undefined functions of position which are restricted so that

$$\lambda_0(L) = 1 \tag{2.6.25}$$

$$\lambda_i(L) = 0 \qquad i = 1, \ldots, n \tag{2.6.26}$$

[2] F. Horn, "Optimale Temperatur-und Konzentrationsverläufe," *Chem. Eng. Sci.*, vol. 14, p. 77, 1961.

[3] F. Horn, "Über das Problem der Optimalen Rührkesselkaskade für Chemische Reaktion," *Chem. Eng. Sci.*, vol. 15, p. 176, 1961.

[4] S. Katz, "Best Temperature Profiles in a Plug-flow Reactor: Methods of the Calculus of Variations," *Annals New York Acad. Sci.*, vol. 84, p. 441, 1960.

We assert that J differs from I by at most a constant. This assertion can be verified by integrating Eq. (2.6.24) to obtain

$$J = \sum_{i=0}^{n} \lambda_i x_i \bigg|_{l=L} - \sum_{i=0}^{n} \lambda_i x_i \bigg|_{l=0} \tag{2.6.27}$$

which reduces to

$$J = x_0 + \sum_{i=1}^{n} \lambda_i x_i \bigg|_{l=0} \tag{2.6.28}$$

when Eqs. (2.6.23), (2.6.25), and (2.6.26) are invoked. The difference between J and I is

$$J - I = -\sum_{i=0}^{n} \lambda_i(0) x_i(0) \tag{2.6.29}$$

This difference is constant provided the initial compositions are specified, which is assumed in this case. Thus, the temperature distribution giving the maximum of J will also render I a maximum. We then focus our attention on finding the maximum of J, remembering, however, that the functions $\lambda_i(l)$ have only been defined at $l = L$ and are not otherwise restricted.

Define a variation of T as

$$T^* = T + \epsilon\phi(l) \tag{2.6.30}$$

This variation produces a corresponding change in each of the compositions which can be written as

$$x_i^* = x_i + \epsilon\mu_i(l) \qquad i = 0, 1, \ldots, n \tag{2.6.31}$$

where ϵ is a small parameter and the $\epsilon\mu_i(l)$ are related to $\epsilon\phi(l)$ by the kinetic equations. The variation in J is

$$\delta J = \epsilon \int_0^L \left(\frac{d}{dl} \sum_{i=0}^{n} \lambda_i \mu_i \right) dl \tag{2.6.32}$$

since the λ_i are independent of variations in temperature.

We must now investigate the relationship of the variations μ_i to the $\phi(l)$. To the first order in ϵ

$$\frac{dx_i}{dl} + \epsilon \frac{d\mu_i}{dl} = \epsilon \sum_{j=0}^{n} \frac{\partial f_i}{\partial x_j} \mu_j + \epsilon \frac{\partial f_i}{\partial T} \phi + f_i \qquad i = 0, 1, \ldots, n \tag{2.6.33}$$

as can be seen by expanding Eqs. (2.6.20) and (2.6.22) about the optimal path. Thus, we have

$$\frac{d\mu_i}{dl} = \sum_{j=0}^{n} \frac{\partial f_i}{\partial x_j} \mu_j + \frac{\partial f_i}{\partial T} \phi \tag{2.6.34}$$

This expression relates the μ_i to ϕ.   Introducing Eq. (2.6.34) into Eq. (2.6.32) gives

$$\delta J = \int_0^L \left(\sum_{i,j=0}^n \lambda_i \frac{\partial f_i}{\partial x_j} \mu_j + \phi \sum_{i=0}^n \frac{\partial f_i}{\partial T} \lambda_i + \sum_{i=0}^n \mu_i \frac{d\lambda_i}{dl} \right) dl \qquad (2.6.35)$$

We should like to rid ourselves of the variations μ_j, since these functions are not independent of ϕ.   To accomplish this elimination, we use a convenient definition of $\lambda_i(l)$.   These have been undefined previously, except for the boundary conditions expressed by Eqs. (2.6.25) and (2.6.26).   Thus, we are free to define the λ_i as those functions which satisfy the set of coupled differential equations

$$\frac{d\lambda_j}{dl} = -\sum_{i=0}^n \frac{\partial f_i}{\partial x_j} \lambda_i \qquad (2.6.36)$$

and the boundary conditions (2.6.25) and (2.6.26).   It should be remembered that the λ_i are not subject to variations and hence Eq. (2.6.36) must be interpreted as being evaluated with the temperature and compositions corresponding to the optimal path.   With Eq. (2.6.36) serving to define the λ_i, Eq. (2.6.35) becomes

$$\delta J = \epsilon \int_0^L \phi \left(\sum_{i=0}^n \lambda_i \frac{\partial f_i}{\partial T} \right) dl \qquad (2.6.37)$$

Since δJ must vanish for all variations ϕ, it is necessary that

$$\sum_{i=0}^n \lambda_i \frac{\partial f_i}{\partial T} = 0 \qquad \text{for all } 0 \le l \le L \qquad (2.6.38)$$

This is the desired result.   For convenience, let us recapitulate our essential equations.

The temperature distribution which is a necessary (but not sufficient) condition for the integral

$$I = \int_0^L f_0 \, dl \qquad (2.6.21)$$

to be a maximum is that which satisfies

$$\sum_{i=0}^n \lambda_i(l) \frac{\partial f_i}{\partial T} = 0 \qquad \text{for } 0 \le l \le L \qquad (2.6.38)$$

where

$$\frac{d\lambda_i}{dl} = -\sum_{j=0}^n \frac{\partial f_j}{\partial x_i} \lambda_j \qquad i = 0, 1, \ldots, n \qquad (2.6.36)$$

and

$$\frac{dx_i}{dl} = f_i \qquad i = 1, 2, \ldots, n \tag{2.6.20}$$

subject to the boundary conditions

$x_i(0)$ specified at $i = 1, 2, \ldots, n$

$$x_0(0) = 0 \tag{2.6.23}$$

$$\lambda_i(L) = 0 \qquad i = 1, 2, \ldots, n \tag{2.6.26}$$

$$\lambda_0(L) = 1 \tag{2.6.25}$$

It is pertinent to note that these same results would be found by using a Lagrangian formulation of the problem. Let us make these abstract considerations more definite by considering an example.

EXAMPLE 2.6.3   It is desired to maximize the production of substance B in the following reaction scheme.

$$A \rightleftharpoons B \rightarrow C$$

The reactor is a plug-flow tubular reactor in which the local reaction rates are defined by the set of kinetic equations

$$\frac{dx_1}{dl} = H^2 x_2 - H x_1 = f_1 \tag{2.6.39}$$

and

$$\frac{dx_2}{dl} = H x_1 - 3 H^2 x_2 = f_2 \tag{2.6.40}$$

For this case

$$I = \int_0^L f_0 \, dl = \int_0^L f_2 \, dl \tag{2.6.41}$$

since we want to maximize the yield of substance B. Here the parameters can be identified with the usual kinetic equations by noting that H represents a function of the temperature; for example,

$$H = e^{-E_1/RT} \tag{2.6.42}$$

and then

$$H^2 = e^{-E_2/RT} \tag{2.6.43}$$

provided

$$\frac{E_2}{E_1} = 2 \tag{2.6.44}$$

For catalytic reactions H could represent some other function of the temperature. However, for our purposes it is sufficient to recognize that Eqs. (2.6.39) and (2.6.40) have the same structure as the kinetic equations usually applied to describe the reaction scheme considered in this example.

The adjoint functions are defined by Eq. (2.6.36) as

$$\frac{d\lambda_0}{dl} = 0 \tag{2.6.45a}$$

$$\frac{d\lambda_1}{dl} = H\lambda_1 - H(\lambda_2 + \lambda_0) \tag{2.6.45b}$$

$$\frac{d\lambda_2}{dl} = -H^2\lambda_1 + 3H^2(\lambda_2 + \lambda_0) = \frac{d(\lambda_2 + \lambda_0)}{dl} \tag{2.6.45c}$$

Equation (2.6.38) yields

$$\frac{\partial H}{\partial T}[(x_1 - 6Hx_2)(\lambda_2 + \lambda_0) + \lambda_1(2Hx_2 - x_1)] = 0 \tag{2.6.46}$$

Equation (2.6.45a) together with the boundary condition Eq. (2.6.25) can be integrated to give

$$\lambda_0 = 1 \tag{2.6.47}$$

Clearly by defining

$$\bar{\lambda}_2 = \lambda_2 + 1 \tag{2.6.48}$$

The simultaneous equations to be solved become

$$\frac{d\lambda_1}{dl} = H(\lambda_1 - \bar{\lambda}_2) \tag{2.6.49}$$

and

$$\frac{d\bar{\lambda}_2}{dl} = H^2(3.0\bar{\lambda}_2 - \lambda_1) \tag{2.6.50}$$

subject to

$$\lambda_1(L) = 0.0 \tag{2.6.51}$$

$$\bar{\lambda}_2(L) = 1.0 \tag{2.6.52}$$

Also

$$0 = (\bar{\lambda}_2 - \lambda_1)x_1 + 2Hx_2(\lambda_1 - 3\bar{\lambda}_2) \tag{2.6.53}$$

We complete the specification of the problem by defining the inlet feed to the reactor as

$$x_1(0) = 1.0 \qquad\qquad\qquad\qquad\qquad\qquad\qquad (2.6.54)$$

$$x_2(0) = 0.0 \qquad\qquad\qquad\qquad\qquad\qquad\qquad (2.6.55)$$

We must now solve simultaneously Eqs. (2.6.39), (2.6.40), (2.6.49), (2.6.50), and (2.6.53) to determine the optimal temperature function H and the resulting compositions x_1 and x_2. The equations are nonlinear, and an analytic solution does not seem possible. Therefore, we must resort to a numerical calculation.

The numerical analysis of this set of equations is not difficult. A good method of attack has been outlined by Lee.[5] This computational scheme is outlined in the following sequence of steps:

1. Assume values for the temperature function along the reactor length.

2. Once the values of H have been established as a function of l, the compositions can be determined by solving Eqs. (2.6.39) and (2.6.40) numerically. In the present example the Runge-Kutta[6] method was used.

3. After establishing the concentrations, the adjoint functions can be computed again using an approximate numerical integration of Eqs. (2.6.49) and (2.6.50).

4. It is now necessary to determine a better approximation for the optimal temperature. This improved approximation can be found using Eq. (2.6.53). The adjoint functions found in step 3 and the concentrations determined in step 2 can be substituted into this equation [Eq. (2.6.53)] and a better value of the temperature function computed.

5. Steps 2, 3, and 4 should be repeated until the temperature function remains unchanged.

Since a detailed discussion of numerical procedures is beyond the scope of this text, the presentation given here is perhaps somewhat vague. However, it should be instructive to follow steps 1 through 5 as applied to our example.

STEP 1   Assume values for the temperature function. Such a set is shown in Table 2.6.1.

STEP 2   The concentrations can be computed as a function of position. These results are also shown in Table 2.6.1.

[5] E. S. Lee, "Optimization by Pontryagin's Maximum Principle on the Analog Computer," *Am. Inst. Chem. Engrs.*, vol. 10, p. 309, 1964.

[6] J. B. Scarborough, "Numerical Mathematical Analysis," pp. 299–303, 3d ed., The Johns Hopkins Press, Baltimore, 1955.

The values of the temperature function which are given above have been determined from a previous iteration; however, this is not yet the optimal distribution, as will be seen when the improved temperature functions are computed. Also it should be noted that the length of the reactor has been fixed so that L is unity.

The function H has been set equal to 1 at the reactor inlet. Since x_2 is 0 at the inlet, the computed value of H is unbounded and the value of 1 is an upper limit which has been arbitrarily imposed. The Pontryagin maximum principle which is discussed below requires that the largest possible H be selected if its value is bounded. The temperature function takes on a finite value when a small amount of B is produced.

STEP 3 The adjoint functions are given in Table 2.6.2. Note that the integration begins at the outlet of the reactor, since the boundary conditions for the adjoint functions are specified at the outlet. The boundary conditions for the concentrations are, of course, given at the inlet. Thus we have a two-point boundary problem. It is this dual specification of the

TABLE 2.6.1 A FIRST ITERATION

l	x_1	x_2	H
0	1.0	0.0	1.0
0.14	0.918	0.076	0.752
0.26	0.850	0.133	0.634
0.38	0.798	0.172	0.547
0.52	0.747	0.207	0.539
0.64	0.708	0.231	0.542
0.76	0.671	0.250	0.546
0.88	0.638	0.265	0.549
1.0	0.602	0.278	0.553

TABLE 2.6.2 FIRST APPROXIMATION TO ADJOINT FUNCTIONS

l	λ_1	$\bar{\lambda}_2$	H
1.0	0	1.0	0.553
0.88	0.070	0.882	0.549
0.76	0.118	0.795	0.546
0.64	0.159	0.719	0.542
0.52	0.192	0.653	0.539
0.38	0.223	0.586	0.547
0.26	0.245	0.526	0.634
0.14	0.265	0.453	0.752
0.0	0.278	0.390	1.0

boundary which makes the problem difficult. For if both the concentration and the adjoint function were specified at the inlet (or the outlet of the reactor) then the problem would not be of the trial-and-error type, but would be a straightforward numerical calculation.

STEP 4   The new temperature function is computed using Eq. (2.6.53).

$$H = \frac{(\lambda_1 - \bar{\lambda}_2)x_1}{2(\lambda_1 - 3\bar{\lambda}_2)x_2} \qquad (2.6.56)$$

Thus for example, we find at $l = 0.52$ a corrected temperature function of

$$H = \frac{(0.192 - 0.653)0.747}{2[0.192 - 3(0.653)]0.207} = 0.4698$$

which would then replace the 0.539 which was assumed.† A corrected temperature function must be computed at each axial position and the entire process repeated.

The final solution is given in Table 2.6.3. In this table we see that the optimal temperature function is very large near the inlet, since only substance A is present. However, as B is produced, the temperature function decreases such that the rate at which B is degraded to C is reduced. Substance C is a waste material, since the reaction scheme does not provide a path for producing B from C. In studying the results shown in Table 2.6.3, we see that the maximum possible yield of B for the reaction system is quite small. It would seem that such a result, while not actually useful in practice because

† Actually it was found that a better convergence rate was achieved if the new temperature function used in the computation was an average of the previous value and the corrected temperature computed as shown above. Thus the new temperature would be $\frac{1}{2}(0.539 + 0.470)$. Of course, the better convergence using an average of the two may be true only in the special case given here. No other problems have been attempted.

TABLE 2.6.3   OPTIMAL REACTION PATH

l	x_1	x_2	λ_1	$\bar{\lambda}_2$	H
0.0	1.0	0.0	0.287	0.399	1.0
0.12	0.901	0.089	0.268	0.514	0.982
0.24	0.827	0.145	0.238	0.626	0.678
0.36	0.776	0.181	0.205	0.707	0.560
0.50	0.728	0.214	0.164	0.784	0.483
0.62	0.695	0.236	0.127	0.842	0.439
0.74	0.666	0.254	0.089	0.895	0.406
0.86	0.640	0.271	0.049	0.945	0.380
1.0	0.613	0.287	0.0	1.0	0.356

of the difficulty of achieving the optimal temperature profile, has use in giving the designer an ultimate yield.

The previous example serves to point out several interesting features of the computations. In addition we note that a check on the computations can be performed provided the functions $f_i(x_1, \ldots, x_n, T)$ do not depend explicitly on l, the axial position, for in this case one can write[7]

$$\frac{df_i}{dl} = \sum_j \frac{\partial f_i}{\partial x_j} \frac{dx_j}{dl} + \frac{\partial f_i}{\partial T} \frac{dT}{dl} \tag{2.6.57}$$

Using this result together with the definition of the adjoint functions and the stationary conditions expressed by Eq. (2.6.38), we can show that

$$\sum \lambda_i f_i = \text{const} = f_0(L) \tag{2.6.58}$$

To demonstrate this expression, consider

$$\frac{d}{dl} \sum \lambda_i f_i = \sum \lambda_i \frac{df_i}{dl} + \sum f_i \frac{d\lambda_i}{dl}$$

Substituting Eq. (2.6.57) into this result, one finds

$$\frac{d}{dl} \sum \lambda_i f_i = \sum\sum \lambda_i \frac{\partial f_i}{\partial x_j} \frac{dx_j}{dl} + \sum \lambda_i \frac{\partial f_i}{\partial T} \frac{dT}{dl} + \sum \frac{dx_i}{dl} \frac{d\lambda_i}{dl}$$

where the f_i have been replaced by dx_i/dl. The right-hand side of the expression written above can be shown to vanish on using Eqs. (2.6.36) and (2.6.38). Therefore

$$\frac{d}{dl} (\sum f_i \lambda_i) = 0$$

and hence the result given by Eq. (2.6.58) is verified. This summation is approximately 0.11 for all lines in Table 2.6.3, which can easily be verified. Thus we have an independent check on the numerical computations.

We now turn to the task of developing Pontryagin's maximum principle,[8] which is necessary if one is to perform numerical computations or to account for bounds imposed on the temperature. Suppose that there are

---

[7] The derivation given here is convincing only if the temperature choice at any position is such that Eq. (2.6.38) is satisfied. If there are constraints imposed on the temperature, such as limits, then such a choice may not be possible. The method of choosing the temperature in such circumstances is discussed in the next paragraph. However, even if Eq. (2.6.38) does not apply, Eq. (2.6.58) remains valid. An excellent and concise derivation of this is given by L. I. Rozoner, "L. S. Pontryagin's Maximum Principle in Optimal System Theory II," *Automation and Remote Control*, vol. 20, p. 1405, 1959.

[8] L. S. Pontryagin, et al., "The Mathematical Theory of Optimal Processes," translated from the Russian by K. E. Trirogoff, John Wiley & Sons, Inc., New York, 1962.

several values of T which satisfy Eq. (2.6.38). Which is the correct choice? We should now like to develop a stronger principle and, in fact, to prove that the best choice (indeed, a necessary choice) of the local temperature is that which gives

$$\max \left\{ \sum_{i=0}^{n} \lambda_i f_i \right\} \tag{2.6.59}$$

This is known as Pontryagin's maximum principle.

As before, we suppose that the optimal conditions are known as a function of the axial position in the reactor. The temperature is again varied, however, now in the restricted sense of

$$T^* = T + \epsilon\phi \qquad \text{for } l^* - h \le l \le l^* \tag{2.6.60}$$

and

$$T^* = T \qquad \text{everywhere else in the interval } 0 \le l \le L \tag{2.6.61}$$

Here l^* is an arbitrary axial position, h is a positive constant, and T^* is supposed to be an admissible temperature. The problem is to maximize the J defined by Eq. (2.6.24). The change in J resulting from the variation in temperature prescribed by Eqs. (2.6.60) and (2.6.61) is

$$\delta J = \int_0^L \frac{d}{dl} \sum_{i=0}^{n} \epsilon\mu_i \lambda_i \, dl \tag{2.6.62}$$

However, as before

$$\delta J = \int_0^L \left(\sum_{i=0}^{n} \epsilon\mu_i \frac{d\lambda_i}{dl} + \sum_{i=0}^{n} \epsilon\lambda_i \frac{d\mu_i}{dl} \right) dl$$

Using the kinetic equations, Eq. (2.6.20),

$$\delta J = \int_0^L \left\{ \sum_{i=0}^{n} \epsilon\mu_i \frac{d\lambda_i}{dl} + \sum_{i=0}^{n} \lambda_i [f_i(x_1^*, x_2^*, \ldots, x_n^*, T^*) \right. \\ \left. - f_i(x_1, x_2, \ldots, x_n, T)] \right\} dl \tag{2.6.63}$$

Expand

$$f_i(x_1^*, x_2^*, \ldots, x_n^*, T^*) \\ = f_i(x_1, x_2, \ldots, x_n, T^*) + \epsilon \sum_j \frac{\partial f_i(x_1, x_2, \ldots, x_n, T^*)}{\partial x_j} \mu_j \\ + \frac{\epsilon^2}{2} \sum_r \sum_s \frac{\partial^2 f_i(x_1 + \theta_1\mu_1, x_2 + \theta_2\mu_2, \ldots, x_n + \theta_n\mu_n, T^*)}{\partial x_r \, \partial x_s} \mu_r \mu_s \tag{2.6.64}$$

which is a Taylor series with $0 \le \theta_i \le 1$. Note that the expansion has been on the concentrations.

Substituting Eqs. (2.6.64) and (2.6.36) into Eq. (2.6.63), we find

$$\delta J = \int_0^L \left\{ \sum_{i=0}^n \lambda_i [f_i(x_1, x_2, \ldots, T^*) - f_i(x_1, x_2, \ldots, T)] \right.$$

$$+ \epsilon \sum_{i,j=0}^n \lambda_i \mu_j \left[\frac{\partial f_i(x_1, x_2, \ldots, T^*)}{\partial x_j} - \frac{\partial f_i(x_1, x_2, \ldots, T)}{\partial x_j} \right]$$

$$\left. + \epsilon^2 \sum_{i,r,s=0}^n \frac{\partial^2 f_i}{\partial x_r \, \partial x_s} \mu_r \mu_s \right\} dl$$

If the kinetic rate expressions are continuous and have continuous first and second derivatives with respect to x_i, then it is clear the we can choose ϵ sufficiently small that the last two terms are negligible compared with the first.[9] Thus for small ϵ

$$\delta J = \int_0^L \sum_{i=0}^n \lambda_i [f_i(x_1, x_2, \ldots, T^*) - f_i(x_1, x_2, \ldots, T)] \, dl$$

The integrand is zero for all l other than those l in the interval $l^* - h \leq l \leq l^*$, since T^* is identically T in all other regions of the reactor. If we make h small enough, the first mean value theorem of calculus gives

$$\delta J = h \sum_{i=0}^n \lambda_i [f_i(x_1, x_2, \ldots, T^*) - f_i(x_1, x_2, \ldots, T)] \tag{2.6.65}$$

Since J is to be a maximum, then $\delta J \leq 0$ for all changes in the temperature. Moreover, h is a positive constant; therefore

$$\sum_{i=0}^n \lambda_i f_i(x_1, x_2, \ldots, T^*) \leq \sum_{i=0}^n \lambda_i f_i(x_1, x_2, \ldots, T) \tag{2.6.66}$$

The best choice of the temperature is selected such that Eq. (2.6.66) is satisfied. This condition dictates the choice of the temperatures even when the temperatures have physical bounds imposed, for one should always choose the temperature which gives the largest value for the $\Sigma \, \lambda_i f_i$.

At this juncture we should reiterate the important fact that the maximum principle developed in this section represents a set of necessary, but not sufficient, conditions, for we have not attempted to examine the second variation to determine the character of the stationary point. The conditions presented here could in fact be satisfied, but the solution might not represent the optimal solution. One should apply all of the physical intuition and

[9] For a more comprehensive discussion see L. I. Rozoner, *Automation and Remote Control* vol. 20, p. 1288, 1959.

independent checks which are at one's disposal to insure that the solution is a good one. An excellent and readable discussion of the pitfalls associated with the determination of optimal temperature profiles has been published by Coward and Jackson.[10]

PROBLEM 2.6.2   Suppose we have the reaction scheme

$$A \rightleftharpoons B \rightleftharpoons C$$

defined by the kinetic equations applicable to a tubular reactor

$$\frac{dx_i}{dl} = f_i(x_1, x_2, x_3, T) \qquad i = 1, 2, 3 \tag{2.6.67}$$

Develop the system of differential equations which must be satisfied if the amount of B produced is to be a *maximum subject to the restriction that* component A has a fixed composition (x_1 specified) in the outlet stream.   The feed composition is specified.

PROBLEM 2.6.3   The reaction

$$A \rightarrow B \rightarrow C$$

is represented by the two kinetic equations

$$\frac{dx_1}{dl} = -Hx_1$$

and

$$\frac{dx_2}{dl} = Hx_1 - H^2 x_2$$

Prove that the temperature profile must be such that

$$\frac{dH}{dl} = -\frac{H^2 x_1}{2x_2}$$

if the concentration of B is to be maximized in an existing reactor.

2.7   OPTIMAL REACTION SYSTEMS WITH RECYCLE

The use of recycle as a means of increasing plant profits is a technique often applied in the process industries.   The mathematical problem of determining an optimal operating policy for a recycle system is, however, difficult, and

---

[10] I. Coward and R. Jackson, "Optimum Temperature Profiles in Tubular Reactors: An Explanation of Some Difficulties in Use of Pontryagin's Maximum Principle," *Chem. Eng. Sci.*, vol. 20, p. 911, 1965.

has only recently started to receive attention.[1-5] We shall not review critically these contributions here, but we shall demonstrate the solution of the general recycle problem using a modification of Pontryagin's maximum principle[6,7] which has been discussed in the preceding section. The problem is to alter the boundary conditions on the adjoint functions such that the effect of the recycle is included.

The system to be considered consists of a mixer, a tubular reactor, and a separator, arranged as shown in Fig. 2.7.1. Fresh feed is introduced into the reaction system at a constant rate q with a fixed composition $X(I)$. [The symbol $X(j)$ is used here to denote the set of N-weight fractions, $x_1, x_2, \ldots, x_N$, which completely specify the chemical state of an $N + 1$ component stream j]. The separator following the reactor produces a product stream and a recycle stream at the respective flow rates, q and r, with compositions $X(f)$ and $X(r)$. It is assumed that the system already exists, so that the reactor operation can only be varied by manipulating the set of external operating

[1] D. F. Rudd and E. D. Blum, "Optimal Cross-current Extraction with Product Recycle," *Chem. Eng. Sci.*, vol. 17, p. 277, 1962.

[2] R. Jackson, "Comments on the Paper Optimum Cross-current Extraction with Product Recycle," *Chem. Eng. Sci.*, vol. 18, p. 215, 1963.

[3] R. Jackson, "Some Algebraic Properties of Optimization Problems in Complex Chemical Plants," *Chem. Eng. Sci.*, vol. 19, p. 19, 1964.

[4] R. Jackson, "A Generalized Variational Treatment of Optimization Problems in Complex Chemical Plants," *Chem. Eng. Sci.*, vol. 19, p. 253, 1964.

[5] L. Fan and C. Wang, "Optimization of Multistage Processes with Product Recycle," *Chem. Eng. Sci.*, vol. 19, p. 86, 1964.

[6] G. S. G. Beveridge and R. S. Schechter, "Optimal Reaction Systems with Recycle," *Ind. Eng. Chem. Fundamentals*, vol. 4, p. 257, 1965.

[7] M. M. Denn and R. Aris, "Green's Functions and Optimal Systems," *Ind. Eng. Chem. Fundamentals*, vol. 4, p. 248, 1965.

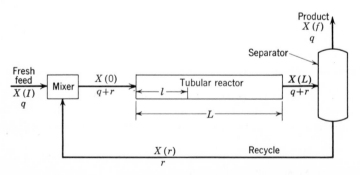

Fig. 2.7.1   Reaction system with recycle.

variables, Y (l).† There are k of these variables which can be altered independently along the length of the reactor. The split in the separator can be characterized by the set of nonnegative separation factors S, where

$$s_j = \frac{x_j(r)}{x_j(f)} \qquad j = 1, 2, \ldots, N \tag{2.7.1}$$

so that from a mass balance over the separator we can write the composition of the jth component in the recycle stream $x_j(r)$ as

$$\frac{r+q}{s_j} x_j(r) = (r+q)x_j(L) \tag{2.7.2}$$

The S denotes the set of separation factors $s_1, s_2, \ldots, s_N$. Since the feed to the reactor $X(0)$ is the sum of the contributions from the fresh feed and the recycle streams, it follows from Eq. (2.7.2) that

$$x_j(0) = \frac{q}{q+r} x_j(I) + \frac{r}{r+q/s_j} x_j(L) \qquad j = 1, 2, \ldots, N \tag{2.7.3}$$

As in the previous section, the composition within the reactor $X(l)$ will vary along its length, the variation being determined by the N kinetic equations

$$\frac{dx_i}{dl} = f_i(X, Y, r) \qquad i = 1, 2, \ldots, N \tag{2.7.4}$$

The reaction rate depends upon the N local compositions $X(l)$, the level of the k control variables $Y(l)$, and the mass flow rate $r+q$. For a given feed rate of a fixed composition, a given set of the operating variables, recycle rate, and separation factors will then uniquely determine the product composition. We may for convenience call such a set an operating policy P, which we shall denote as

$$P[Y(l),S,r] \tag{2.7.5}$$

Having completed a design basis for the problem, it is now necessary to obtain the best design. The objective function generally has the form

$$I(P) = \int_0^L c[X(l),Y(l),r,S] \, dl + C[X(L),S,r] \tag{2.7.6}$$

I is a functional of the policy P.

Again our problem is to choose an operating policy P. The policy making I an extremal (maximum, for definiteness) will be the desired policy.

As before, let us define x_0 as

$$\frac{dx_0}{dl} = c[X(l),Y(l),r,S] = f_0(X, Y, r, S) \tag{2.7.7}$$

---

† In this section we account for the possibility that the temperature is only one member of a set of manipulated variables.

where c is the same function as that in Eq. (2.7.6), $x_0(l)$ being subject to the restriction that

$$x_0(0) = 0 \qquad (2.7.8)$$

Secondly, we will define a new function $J(P)$ given by

$$J(P) = \int_0^L \frac{d}{dl}\left(\sum_{i=0}^{N} x_i \lambda_i\right) dl + g[X(L),S,r] + C[X(L),S,r] \qquad (2.7.9)$$

Upon carrying out the integration in this equation, it will be seen that

$$J(P) \equiv I(P)$$

if

$$\begin{aligned}
g[X(L),S,r] &= -\sum_{j=1}^{N} \lambda_j(L)x_j(L) + \sum_{j=1}^{N} \lambda_j(0)x_j(0) \\
&= \sum_{j=1}^{N} x_j(L)\left[-\lambda_j(L) + \frac{\lambda_j(0)r}{r + q/s_j}\right] + \sum_{j=1}^{N} \frac{q\lambda_j(0)x_j(l)}{q + r}
\end{aligned} \qquad (2.7.10)$$

and if

$$\lambda_0(L) = 1 \qquad (2.7.11)$$

In other words, the maximization of the new functional J will provide the solution to the original problem of maximizing the functional I. Of course, we must remember that g is defined by Eq. (2.7.10).

Suppose now that a small change is imposed upon one of the control variables $y_n(l)$, and all the other variables are held at their optimal values. The variation of the control variables can then be defined in the form

$$y_n^*(l) = y_n(l) + \epsilon_n \omega_n(l) \qquad (2.7.12)$$

This variation from the optimal operating policy will give rise to a variation in the dependent variables, which is given by

$$x_i^*(l) = x_i(l) + \epsilon_n \mu_{in}(l) \qquad (2.7.13)$$

Here ω_n is any arbitrary differentiable function of l, and μ_{in} is the resultant deviation in the ith component, ϵ_n being a small number. The variation μ is related to ω by the system of Eq. (2.7.4) so that

$$\frac{d\mu_{in}}{dl} = \frac{1}{\epsilon_n}\left(\frac{dx_i^*}{dl} - \frac{dx_i}{dl}\right) = \frac{1}{\epsilon_n}(f_i^* - f_i) \qquad (2.7.14)$$

$$= \sum_{j=0}^{N} \frac{\partial f_i}{\partial x_j}\mu_{jn} + \frac{\partial f_i}{\partial y_n}\omega_n \qquad \text{for } i = 0, 1, \ldots, N \qquad (2.7.15)$$

after expanding f_i in a Taylor expansion to first-order terms.

The original variation in the control variable will therefore result in a change δJ in the functional J. Using a Taylor expansion, this change may be written to the first order in ϵ_n as

$$\delta J = \epsilon_n \left[\int_0^L \frac{d}{dl} \left(\sum_{j=0}^N \lambda_j \mu_{jn} \right) dl + \sum_{j=1}^N \left(\frac{\partial g}{\partial x_j} + \frac{\partial C}{\partial x_j} \right) \mu_{jn}(L) \right] \qquad (2.7.16)$$

Upon carrying out the differentiation in the first term of the right-hand side of Eq. (2.7.16) and substituting for $d\mu_{jn}/dl$ from Eq. (2.7.15), the first term on the right-hand side of Eq. (2.7.16) becomes

$$\epsilon_n \int_0^L \left[\sum_{j=0}^n \mu_{jn} \left(\frac{d\lambda_j}{dl} + \sum_{i=0}^N \lambda_i \frac{\partial f_i}{\partial x_j} \right) + \sum_{j=0}^N \lambda_j \frac{\partial f_j}{\partial y_n} \omega_n \right] dl \qquad (2.7.17)$$

The second term, upon substituting for g from Eq. (2.7.10) can be written as

$$\epsilon_n \sum_{j=1}^N \mu_{jn}(L) \left[\frac{r}{r + q/s_j} \lambda_j(0) - \lambda_j(L) + \frac{\partial C}{\partial x_j} \right] \qquad (2.7.18)$$

Again define the adjoint functions by the set of differential equations

$$\frac{d\lambda_j}{dl} = -\sum_{i=0}^N \frac{\partial f_i}{\partial x_j} \lambda_i \qquad (2.7.19)$$

subject to the boundary conditions

$$\frac{r}{r + q/s_j} \lambda_j(0) - \lambda_j(L) + \frac{\partial C}{\partial x_j} = 0 \qquad (2.7.20)$$

Equation (2.7.16) will reduce to

$$\delta J = \epsilon_n \left[\int_0^L \left(\sum_{j=0}^N \lambda_j \frac{\partial f_j}{\partial y_n} \omega_n \right) dl \right] \qquad (2.7.21)$$

At the optimal value of J, when the extremal is not restricted, the value δJ must vanish for all variations $\omega_n(l)$. It is therefore seen from Eq. (2.7.21) that a necessary condition for an optimum is

$$\sum_{j=0}^N \lambda_j \frac{\partial f_j}{\partial y_n} = 0 \qquad \text{for } 0 \le l \le L, n = 1, 2, \ldots, k \qquad (2.7.22)$$

which is the same result found in the preceding section. By a similar argument considering a variation in the recycle rate and in the separation factor, respectively, it can be shown that the other extremal conditions are

$$\int_0^L \sum_{j=0}^N \lambda_j \frac{\partial f_j}{\partial r} dl - \sum_{j=1}^N \frac{q}{(q+r)^2} \lambda_j(0) x_j(I) + \sum_{j=1}^N \frac{q s_j}{(q+s_j r)^2} \lambda_j(0) x_j(L) + \frac{\partial C}{\partial r} = 0$$
$$(2.7.23)$$

and

$$\int_0^L \frac{\partial c}{\partial s_j}\, dl + \frac{qr}{(q + s_j r)^2}\, \lambda_j(0) x_j(L) + \frac{\partial C}{\partial s_j} = 0 \qquad \text{for } j = 1, 2, \ldots, N$$

(2.7.24)

The desired optimal policy is therefore defined by the simultaneous solution of the system of Eqs. (2.7.3), (2.7.4), (2.7.11), (2.7.19), (2.7.20), and (2.7.22) to (2.7.24).

Equation (2.7.22) can be shown to be replaced by a more general Pontryagin principle

$$\frac{\text{max}}{\substack{\text{or} \\ \text{min}}} \left(\sum_{i=0}^N \lambda_i f_i \right)$$

(2.7.25)

and was proved for the nonrecycle case. However, the proof is much the same and will not be given here.

It is clear that many of the results obtained including recycle are identical to those found in the preceding section. The major difference is, in fact, the boundary conditions for the adjoint functions, Eq. (2.7.20). Here we see that the value of the adjoint function at $l = L$ is related to the value at $l = 0$—a coupling owing to the feedback. This difference together with the boundary conditions to be imposed on the concentration [Eq. (2.7.3)] make the problem of computing an answer more difficult, but certainly not impossible. The feasibility of finding the optimal conditions for a recycle system is illustrated in the following two examples.

EXAMPLE 2.7.1   Let us consider the special case of a single irreversible reaction $A \rightarrow B$ being carried out in an existing tubular reactor with a constant fraction of the product being recycled, the separation factor s_1 being unity. Here the vector X has only one component x, the weight fraction of A. The kinetic expression, Eq. (2.7.4), is assumed to be of the form

$$\frac{dx}{dl} = -\frac{K}{r + q} Z x^n \equiv f_A(x, T)$$

(2.7.26)

where K is a constant, and Z a known function of temperature (for example, $Z = T^m$ or $Z = e^{-E/RT}$).

It is desired to optimize the profit from the process, this being defined as the income from the sale of product B less the cost of the raw materials and the cost of operation. It is assumed that the cost of maintaining the level of temperature along the reactor length will be the only important operating cost and that all other costs are negligible or constant, and are thus omitted. The objective function for the process is therefore

$$I = \text{income} - \text{operating cost} - \text{raw material cost}$$

$$= a_1 q x_B(L) - a_2 \int_0^L T\, dl - a_3 q x(I)$$

(2.7.27)

where a_1, a_2, a_3 are, respectively, the value of a unit quantity of B, the cost of providing the temperature per unit length of reactor, and the cost of a unit amount of raw material. Integrating the kinetic equation over the reactor length L we get

$$x(L) - x(0) = \int_0^L f_A \, dl \tag{2.7.28}$$

We can also write the material balance, Eq. (2.7.3), at the inlet to the reactor as

$$rx(L) + qx(I) = (r + q)x(0) \tag{2.7.29}$$

Our objective function may therefore be written, after substituting Eqs. (2.7.28) and (2.7.29) into Eq. (2.7.27), as

$$I = I_0 + \int_0^L f_0 \, dl \tag{2.7.30}$$

where

$$I_0 = [a_1 q - (a_1 + a_3)qx(I)]$$
$$f_0 = -[a_1(r + q)f_A + a_2 T]$$

Since I_0 is a constant for a given feed, our problem is reduced to maximizing the functional $I - I_0$ by the determination of a suitable form of the independent variable T, which is a function of position along the reactor. In other words, we wish to find the function $T(l)$ such that

$$I - I_0 = \int_0^L f_0 \, dl \tag{2.7.31}$$

is maximized. The adjoint functions defined by Eq. (2.7.19) are

$$\frac{d\lambda}{dl} = -\lambda_0 \frac{\partial f_0}{\partial x} - \lambda \frac{\partial f_A}{\partial x} \tag{2.7.32}$$

and

$$\frac{d\lambda_0}{dl} = -\lambda_0 \frac{\partial f_0}{\partial x_0} - \lambda \frac{\partial f_A}{\partial x_0} \tag{2.7.33}$$

for this case. Further, the boundary condition expressed by Eq. (2.7.11), since the f_i do not depend upon x_0, leads to the usual result

$$\lambda_0 = 1 \tag{2.7.34}$$

We will therefore find from Eq. (2.7.32), using Eqs. (2.7.26) and (2.7.34), that

$$\frac{d\lambda}{dl} = \frac{Kn}{r + q} Zx^{n-1}[\lambda - a_1(r + q)] \tag{2.7.35}$$

The adjoint function $\lambda(l)$ may be related to the local composition of the reacting mixture by taking the ratio of Eqs. (2.7.35) and (2.7.26) and then integrating the resultant expression. These steps lead to

$$[\lambda(l) - a_1(r + q)]x^n(l) = [\lambda(0) - a_1(r + q)]x^n(0) \tag{2.7.36}$$

The optimal temperature policy is defined by Eq. (2.7.22). It is clear that this general condition gives

$$[\lambda(l) - a_1(r + q)]\left[-\frac{K}{r + q}Z'x^n(l)\right] = a_2 \tag{2.7.37}$$

where

$$Z' = \frac{\partial Z}{\partial T}$$

for the example under consideration. Rearranging and substituting for $\lambda(l)$ from Eq. (2.7.36), we have

$$Z' = \frac{-a_2(r + q)}{x^n(0)K[\lambda(0) - a_1(r + q)]} \tag{2.7.38}$$

It will be seen that the right-hand side of the equation is independent of the position along the reactor l, being only a function of the inlet and outlet conditions of the reactor. This equation cannot be solved directly for the temperature, but it is obvious that if the temperature is independent of the reactor position, it must be a constant throughout the reactor. The optimal operating policy in this case is therefore to operate the tubular reactor isothermally. This will produce the greatest profit from the system. The cost of achieving the desired temperature level, the rate of recycle, the flow and composition of the fresh feed, and the value of the final product all serve to change the level of the optimal temperature, but in any problem the temperature is independent of the position along the axis of the reaction vessel.

EXAMPLE 2.7.2 Let us consider the consecutive reactions

$$A \rightleftharpoons B \rightarrow C$$

being carried out in an existing tubular reactor with a constant fraction of the product being recycled. Thus the separation factors are all unity. The vector X has two components x_1 and x_2, since the amount reacted to C is "lost." As in Example 2.6.3, our aim is to maximize the production of B. The kinetic equations are assumed to be

$$\frac{dx_1}{dl} = \frac{1}{q + r}(H^2x_2 - Hx_1) = f_1 \tag{2.7.39}$$

and

$$\frac{dx_2}{dl} = \frac{1}{q+r}(Hx_1 - 3H^2x_2) = f_2 \tag{2.7.40}$$

These equations differ from those studied in Example 2.6.3 only in that the flow rate $q + r$ is included. It is necessary to identify the flow, since changing the recycle rate will change the flow.

In Example 2.6.3 the adjoint function λ_0 was shown to be unity. Since the objective function was also the rate of reaction of B, it was convenient to define a new λ_2 which was the original λ_2 plus one [see Eq. (2.6.46)].

The same simplification is again useful. The adjoint functions are defined so that Eq. (2.7.20), which defines the boundary conditions for the adjoint functions, can now be expressed as

$$\lambda_1(L) = \frac{r}{r+q}\lambda_1(0) \tag{2.7.41}$$

and

$$\lambda_2(L) = \frac{r}{r+q}\lambda_2(0) + 1 \tag{2.7.42}$$

Note that the boundary condition on $\lambda_2(l)$ has been changed by the addition of unity to the right-hand side of Eq. (2.7.42). This is precisely the same modification developed in Example 2.6.3, and the boundary conditions imposed on the adjoint functions of Example 2.6.3 can be found from Eqs. (2.7.41) and (2.7.42) by permitting the recycle rate r to vanish. The adjoint equations defined by Eq. (2.7.19) are

$$\frac{d\lambda_1}{dl} = \frac{H}{q+r}(\lambda_1 - \lambda_2) \tag{2.7.43}$$

and

$$\frac{d\lambda_2}{dl} = \frac{H^2}{q+r}(3\lambda_2 - \lambda_1) \tag{2.7.44}$$

The adjoint functions are very similar to those defined by Eqs. (2.6.49) and (2.6.50) of Example 2.6.3. The temperature function is determined by

$$0 = (\lambda_2 - \lambda_1)x_1 + 2Hx_2(\lambda_1 - 3\lambda_2) \tag{2.7.45}$$

To complete the specification of the problem, we define the boundary conditions on the compositions as

$$x_1(0) = \frac{q}{q+r} + \frac{r}{r+q}x_1(L) \tag{2.7.46}$$

and

$$x_2(0) = \frac{r}{r+q}x_2(L) \tag{2.7.47}$$

where Eq. (2.7.3) has been simplified for our example, with the feed to the reaction system being entirely composed of substance A.   (Here $x_1 = 1.0$, $x_2 = 0$ in feed to reactor system).

For a given recycle rate,† the optimal temperature function is defined by Eqs. (2.7.39) to (2.7.44).   The equations are nonlinear and coupled, so that it does not seem possible to achieve an analytical solution.   As in Example 2.6.3, we shall resort to use of numerical techniques.

The computational procedure presented in Example 2.6.3 is still applicable to the reaction system with recycle, and we will not detail the procedure again.   However, it is worth noting that steps 2 and 3 are more difficult if there is recycle.   For even if the temperature function is specified at every point along the reaction path, the determination of the compositions is not a

† If we also wanted the optimal recycle rate, then Eq. (2.7.23) reduced appropriately for the special case under consideration would also be included in the list of equations to be satisfied.   However, in this case the optimal operation is to have no recycle at all.   Thus the results of this analysis would be identical to those given in Example 2.6.3.

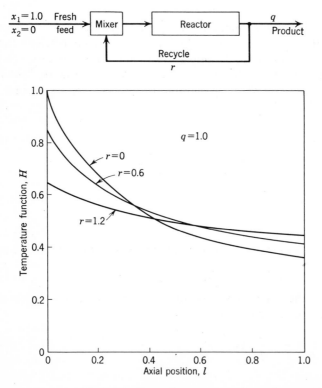

Fig. 2.7.2   Optimal temperatures for various recycle rates.

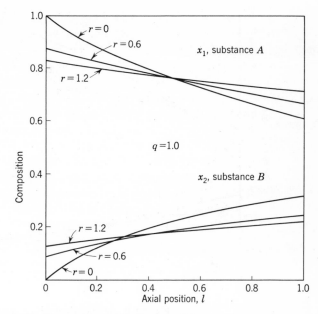

Fig. 2.7.3   Compositions at optimal conditions.

straightforward calculation owing to the nature of the boundary conditions expressed by Eqs. (2.7.46) and (2.7.47). In general, a trial-and-error procedure is required to find the concentrations; however, judging from the experience one develops in performing a few calculations, the determination of the concentrations is not difficult. The same difficulties arise in the computation of the adjoint functions. Apart from the fact that the task of determining the compositions and adjoint functions is more difficult, the computational procedure detailed in Example 2.6.3 applies here. Typical results are shown in Figs. 2.7.2 to 2.7.4. It is interesting to note that the yield of B decreases as the recycle rate is increased. However, the decrease is not significant, going from $x_2 = 0.287$ at $r = 0$ to $x_2 = 0.235$ at $r = 1.2$. But the energy necessary to produce has diminished considerably, since H is a measure of the energy requirement. The values of H for several recycle rates are shown in Fig. 2.7.2. It is clear that the temperature function for $r = 1.2$ is much less on the average than the values for $r = 0$. Therefore we might conclude that a less expensive operation is obtainable at higher recycles. There is, of course, considerable danger in such a brash conclusion, for we have over twice the amount of fluid to be heated for $r = 1.2$ as compared with $r = 0.0$, so that the total heat load could be larger for the system when $r = 1.2$. We will not pursue this line of reasoning further, for clearly cost data are necessary before the computations can be given practical

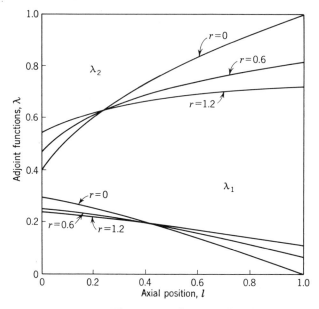

Fig. 2.7.4   Adjoint functions in recycle system.

meaning.   Indeed, in the practical cases one would use a profit function as his objective, not the maximization of a yield.

It should be noted that with recycle the inlet and outlet conditions for both the adjoint functions and the concentrations "float," such that Eqs. (2.7.41), (2.7.42), (2.7.46), and (2.7.47) are satisfied.   The variation of the terminal conditions is clearly shown in Figs. 2.7.3 and 2.7.4.

PROBLEM 2.7.1   Develop the system of differential equations which determines the optimal temperature in a recycle system using the concept of a variable Lagrangian multipliers as applied in Sec. 2.6.   Remember that the kinetic equations, Eq. (2.7.4), must be satisfied locally and that the boundary conditions defined by Eq. (2.7.3) must be natural boundary conditions. These boundary conditions can also be introduced using the method of Lagrangian multipliers.

The Lagrangian formulation of Prob. 2.7.1 is

$$\tilde{I}(p) = \int_0^L \left[c - \sum_{i=1}^{N} \lambda_i \left(\frac{dx_i}{dl} - f_i \right) \right] dl + C[x(L),S,r]$$

$$- \sum_{i=1}^{N} \lambda_i(0) \left[x_i(0) - \frac{q}{q+r} x_i(I) - \frac{r}{r+q/s_i} x_i(L) \right]$$

PROBLEM 2.7.2   The objective function of a chemical-reaction system with recycle is defined by

$$I = \int_0^L (T^2 + x^2)\, dl$$

where x must satisfy the kinetic equation

$$(q + r)\frac{dx}{dl} = T - x$$

where T = control variable—a temperature function

x = concentration

q = fresh feed to reactor

r = recycle rate

If the concentration satisfies the material balance equation

$$x(0) = \frac{q}{q+r} + \frac{q}{r+q}\, x(L)$$

where $x(0)$ is the feed to reactor and $x(L)$ is the effluent concentration, determine the $T(l)$ which minimizes I.

CHAPTER 3
METHODS OF APPROXIMATION

3.1 INTRODUCTION Thus far our primary objective has been the determination of the differential equations which must be satisfied if certain integrals are to be extremals. Indeed, in our study of natural problems (Chap. 2), the integral to be extremalized has played no role in the analysis other than that of providing a means of formulating the differential equations defining the physical system of interest. It was these differential equations which were subsequently solved to yield the pertinent conclusions. Thus the integral to be extremalized has served as an intermediate in the calculation. In this chapter we intend to explore methods of calculation which utilize the variational formulation of the problem directly. These direct calculations are used primarily to develop approximate solutions when the Euler-Lagrange equations are complex and one is forced to settle for something less than an exact solution. We shall attempt to show by example that such direct calculations are both powerful and simple. Thus the variational formulation will assume a new importance, since the integral to be extremalized will not only yield the appropriate differential equations defining the extremalizing functions but will also serve as the basis for developing approximations to these extremalizing functions.

The existence of the direct solutions gives us the incentive to "rephrase" problems not usually thought to be variational problems into such a format. In the following chapter we shall show how many problems can be properly stated as a variational principle rather than in the form of partial differential equations. The methods of analysis discussed in this chapter will then be applicable to a wide variety of engineering problems.

3.2 THE RITZ METHOD

Let us consider the problem of finding the minimum (or maximum) of the functional $I(u)$ with respect to a certain class of admissible functions $u(x,y)$. Admissibility is normally limited only by boundary conditions† and the continuity of the function and its derivatives in a specified region. Let the set of functions $\{\phi_1, \phi_2, \ldots\}$ be continuous and differentiable functions in the region of interest, and, furthermore, assume that any function $u(x,y)$ can be expressed as a linear combination of the ϕ's, valid in the region of interest; that is,

$$u(x,y) = \sum_{i=1}^{\infty} C_i \phi_i \qquad (3.2.1)$$

---

† We shall defer discussion of the problems arising with various types of boundary conditions until the concept of the Ritz method has been introduced. For the moment we focus our attention on those boundary conditions for which the dependent variable is specified.

where the C_i are constants, sometimes called Fourier coefficients. If the expansion expressed by Eq. (3.2.1) is possible for all functions $u(x,y)$, then the ϕ's are termed a complete set in the specified region. Suppose the varied function $u(x,y)$ is approximated by a subset of the complete set ([here the word subset should be taken to mean that Eq. (3.2.1) is truncated to include only a finite number of terms]) and the functional is

$$I(\tilde{u}_n) = I\left(\sum_{i=1}^{n} C_i\phi_i\right) \tag{3.2.2}$$

in which the approximate solution

$$\tilde{u}(x,y) = \sum_{i=1}^{n} C_i\phi_i$$

must still satisfy the boundary conditions.† Choose the constants C_i such that

$$\frac{\partial I}{\partial C_j} = 0 \qquad j = 1, 2, \ldots, n \tag{3.2.3}$$

thus finding the set of constants which makes I as small as possible. Define

$$M_n = I(\tilde{u}_n) \tag{3.2.4}$$

so that M_n is the approximation to the true minimum value M. Since $\tilde{u}$ is an approximation,

$$M_n \geq M \tag{3.2.5}$$

Moreover, as n is increased, it is clear that

$$M_1 \geq M_2 \geq M_3 \tag{3.2.6}$$

since any linear combination of $\phi_1, \phi_2, \ldots, \phi_n$ is included as a linear combination of $\phi_1, \phi_2, \ldots, \phi_n, \phi_{n+1}$. If the set of functions ϕ_i is complete, then convergence of the method has been demonstrated in a limited number of cases.[1] Of course the convergence of this method, known as the Ritz method, obviously depends both on the variational problem and the choice of functions ϕ_i. However, as we shall see, it is often necessary to take only a very small number of terms in the approximating series to obtain a satisfactory approximation to the exact solution.

† We assume that the specified boundary conditions are satisfied for all values of C_i.

[1] L. V. Kantorovich and V. I. Krylov, "Approximate Methods of Higher Analysis," pp. 259–261, Interscience Publishers, Inc., New York, 1958.

EXAMPLE 3.2.1 Consider the problem of finding the extremal of the integral

$$I = \int_0^1 (y_x{}^2 - y^2 - 2x^2 y)\, dx \tag{3.2.7}$$

with the functions y limited to those which satisfy the boundary conditions

$$y(0) = y(1) = 0 \tag{3.2.8}$$

Let us take as our expansion

$$y(x) = x(1 - x)\sum_{i=0}^{\infty} C_i x^i \tag{3.2.9}$$

in the region $0 \leq x \leq 1$. The power series in x is complete in the interval of interest, and, furthermore,

$$\tilde{y}_n(x) = x(1 - x)\sum_{i=0}^{n} C_i x^i \tag{3.2.10}$$

satisfies the boundary conditions expressed by Eq. (3.2.8) for all values of the constants. Taking $\tilde{y}_0(x)$, that is, $\tilde{y}_0(x) = x(1 - x)C_0$, substituting into Eq. (3.2.7), and differentiating with respect to C_0, one finds

$$\frac{\partial \tilde{I}}{\partial C_0} = \int_0^1 [2C_0(1 - 4x + 4x^2) - 2C_0 x^2(1 - 2x + x^2) - 2(x^3 - x^4)]\, dx \tag{3.2.11}$$

On applying Eq. (3.2.3) and integrating Eq. (3.2.11), we obtain

$$C_0 = \tfrac{5}{6}$$

Therefore, the first approximation is

$$\tilde{y}_0 = \tfrac{5}{6}(x)(1 - x) \tag{3.2.12}$$

Let us continue and approximate y as $\tilde{y}_1$. Substituting into the variational integral and differentiating partially,

$$0 = \frac{\partial \tilde{I}}{\partial C_0} = \int_0^1 \{2(1 - 2x)[C_0(1 - 2x) + C_1(2x - 3x^2)]$$
$$- 2[C_0(x)(1 - x) + C_1 x^2(1 - x)]x(1 - x) - 2x^3(1 - x)\}\, dx \tag{3.2.13}$$

and

$$0 = \frac{\partial \tilde{I}}{\partial C_1} = \int_0^1 \{2(2x - 3x^2)[C_0(1 - 2x) + C_1(2x - 3x^2)]$$
$$- 2[C_0(x)(1 - x) + C_1 x^2(1 - x)]x^2(1 - x) - 2x^4(1 - x)\}\, dx \tag{3.2.14}$$

After computing the values of the integrals,

$$\tfrac{3}{10}C_1 + \tfrac{3}{5}C_0 = \tfrac{1}{10} \tag{3.2.15a}$$
$$\tfrac{26}{105}C_1 + \tfrac{3}{10}C_0 = \tfrac{1}{15} \tag{3.2.15b}$$

Solving this set of algebraic equations, we find

$$C_0 = \tfrac{10}{123} \qquad C_1 = \tfrac{7}{41}$$

It is not difficult to show that the Euler-Lagrange equation corresponding to the extremal of Eq. (3.2.7) is

$$y_{xx} + y + x^2 = 0 \tag{3.2.16}$$

The solution of this differential equation subject to the boundary conditions (3.2.8) is

$$y = \left(2\,\frac{\cos 1}{\sin 1} - \frac{1}{\sin 1}\right)\sin x - 2\cos x + 2 - x^2 \tag{3.2.17}$$

Table 3.2.1 compares this exact solution with the approximations which have been developed based on the variational formulation. It is seen that $\tilde{y}_1(x)$ is an acceptable approximation for most engineering purposes.

EXAMPLE 3.2.2   Consider a somewhat more complex differential equation

$$x^2 y_{xx} + x y_x + (x^2 - 1)y = 0 \tag{3.2.18}$$

subject to the boundary conditions

$$\begin{aligned} y(1) &= 2 \\ y(2) &= 4 \end{aligned} \tag{3.2.19}$$

This is a Bessel equation. To simplify the calculations, we can transform to homogeneous boundary conditions by the following change of variable

$$y = z + 2x \tag{3.2.20}$$

The transformed differential equation is

$$x z_{xx} + z_x + \frac{x^2 - 1}{x}\,z + 2x^2 = 0 \tag{3.2.21}$$

TABLE 3.2.1   A COMPARISON OF SOLUTIONS

x	y exact	y_0, first approximation	y_1, second approximation
0.25	0.023	0.031	0.023
0.50	0.041	0.042	0.042
0.75	0.039	0.031	0.039

with the homogeneous boundary condition

$$z(1) = z(2) = 0 \tag{3.2.22}$$

Equation (3.2.21) is the Euler-Lagrange equation for the functional

$$I = \int_1^2 \left(xz_x^2 - \frac{x^2 - 1}{x} z^2 - 4x^2z \right) dx \tag{3.2.23}$$

Let us try the simple approximation

$$\tilde{z}_0 = C_0(x - 1)(2 - x) \tag{3.2.24}$$

Substituting into the variational integral and differentiating with respect to C_0 yields

$$0 = \int_1^2 \left[-C_0 x(3 - 2x)^2 + \frac{x^2 - 1}{x} (x - 1)^2 (2 - x)^2 C_0 \right. $$
$$\left. + 2x^2(x - 1)(2 - x) \right] dx$$

Solving for C_0 gives

$$C_0 = 1.622$$

and the first approximation

$$\tilde{z}_0 = 1.622(x - 1)(2 - x) \tag{3.2.25}$$

The exact solution to the differential equation and its associated boundary conditions is

$$y = 7.2144\, I_1(x) + 1.50390\, Y_1(x) \tag{3.2.26}$$

in which $I_1(x)$ and $Y_1(x)$ are modified Bessel functions of the first and second kind, order one. Table 3.2.2 shows a comparison between the exact solution and the first approximation. Again we see that the results are accurate enough for all practical purposes.

We can summarize the essential features of the Ritz method by noting that the basic idea is to approximate by a function containing a number of unspecified parameters

$$\tilde{y} = \tilde{y}(x, C_1, C_2, \ldots, C_n)$$

TABLE 3.2.2 COMPARISON WITH EXACT SOLUTION

x	z exact	$\tilde{z}_0$ approximate
1.3	2.9412	2.9406
1.5	3.4052	3.4054
1.8	3.8588	3.8594

We shall limit the class of functions to those which satisfy the following restrictions:

1. The approximation must satisfy the boundary conditions for all values of the parameters.

2. The approximating function must be complete in the sense that an arbitrary continuous function can be exactly fitted by the approximation provided the number of undetermined parameters is allowed to become arbitrarily large. The constants in the approximation are then selected so that

$$\frac{\partial I}{\partial C_j} = 0 \quad j = 1, 2, \ldots, n \tag{3.2.3}$$

The convergence of this procedure is discussed by Kantorovich and Krylov.[1] We shall only note that for the problems tested here the convergence is quite rapid and seldom do we need to take a large number of terms in the approximation.

EXAMPLE 3.2.3[2]   In calculating the rates of radiant heat loss, it is frequently necessary to attempt to construct an approximate solution to a complex integral equation. In this example we shall demonstrate the applicability of the Ritz method to such problems.

Before beginning the calculations, let us first acquaint ourselves with a typical radiative problem so that the physical significance of the various quantities entering the calculation will be clear. Consider the geometry depicted in Fig. 3.2.1. Shown is a system of parallel plates of length L and of infinite extent in the direction normal to the plane of the figure. We shall assume the surfaces to be "grey bodies"; that is, the surfaces reflect a proportion of the impinging radiant energy which is independent of the wave

[2] This example is taken from a paper by E. M. Sparrow, "Applications of Variational Methods to Radiative Heat-Transfer Calculations," *J. Heat Transfer*, vol. 82, p. 375, 1960.

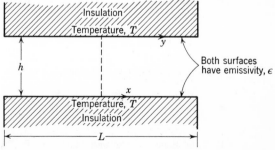

Fig. 3.2.1   Geometry of the parallel plate system.

length of that radiation. The space between the plates is supposedly filled with a transparent gas. Moreover, the plates are assumed to be at the same temperature, so that the net heat flow is attributable solely to the amount of heat which flows out of the gap separating the plates. Our problem is to determine the rate of radiant heat loss from this system.

We begin our analysis by defining the radiant flux arriving at x per unit time per unit of area as $H(x)$ and denoting the amount reflected as $\rho H(x)$. Here ρ is the reflectivity. If $\beta(x)$ is the total energy per unit of time per unit of area leaving an element of area at x, then

$$\beta(x) = \epsilon \sigma T^4 + \rho H(x) \tag{3.2.27}$$

where the emissivity ϵ is equal to $(1 - \rho)$ in accordance with Kirchhoff's law, σ is the Stefan-Boltzmann constant, and T is the absolute temperature. Equation (3.2.27) contains two unknown functions, one of which can be eliminated by finding an expression for $H(x)$ by summing the energy contributions from all elements of area on the upper plate to the element of area at x. To accomplish this calculation, we note that the energy leaving an element of area dA_y at y is

$$\beta(y) \, dA_y \tag{3.2.28}$$

Of this, an amount

$$\beta(y) \, dA_y \, dF_{y \to x} \tag{3.2.29}$$

is intercepted by an element of area at x, where $dF_{y \to x}$ is the angle factor[3] of dA_x as viewed from y. Since

$$dF_{y \to x} \, dA_y = dF_{x \to y} \, dA_x \tag{3.2.30}$$

the expression (3.2.29) can be written as

$$\beta(y) \, dA_x \, dF_{x \to y} \tag{3.2.31}$$

The element of area at x receives radiation from all portions positions y, so that

$$H(x) = \int_{-L/2}^{L/2} \beta(y) \, dF_{x \to y} \tag{3.2.32}$$

From Jakob,[4] the angle factor can be shown to be such that

$$dF_{x \to y} = \frac{h^2}{2} \frac{dy}{[(y - x)^2 + h^2]^{3/2}} \tag{3.2.33}$$

[3] E. R. G. Eckert, "Heat and Mass Transfer," pp. 409–418, McGraw-Hill Book Company, New York, 1959.
[4] M. Jakob, "Heat Transfer," vol. 2, pp. 19–21, John Wiley & Sons, Inc., New York, 1957.

Thus

$$H(x) = \frac{h^2}{2} \int_{-L/2}^{L/2} \frac{\beta(y)\,dy}{[(y-x)^2+h^2]^{3/2}} \tag{3.2.34}$$

Substituting Eq. (3.2.34) into Eq. (3.2.27) gives

$$\beta(x) = \epsilon\sigma T^4 + \frac{\rho h^2}{2} \int_{-L/2}^{L/2} \frac{\beta(y)\,dy}{[(y-x)^2+h^2]^{3/2}} \tag{3.2.35}$$

This integral equation determines $\beta(x)$. It should be noted that β appears both in the integrand as well as on the left-hand side of Eq. (3.2.35). Thus the task of determining $\beta(x)$ is not trivial. To use the Ritz method, the function $\beta(x)$ satisfying the integral equation must also be an extremalizing function for some definite integral; that is, the problem must be posed in variational form. Before writing the variational principle, let us generalize our results by writing Eq. (3.2.35) in dimensionless form

$$B(X) = 1 + \frac{\rho\gamma^2}{2} \int_{-1/2}^{1/2} \frac{B(Y)\,dY}{[(Y-X)^2+\gamma^2]^{3/2}} \tag{3.2.36}$$

where

$$Y = \frac{y}{L}$$

$$X = \frac{x}{L}$$

$$\gamma = \frac{h}{L}$$

$$B = \frac{\beta}{\epsilon\sigma T^4}$$

Referring to Prob. 1.2.2, we see that the necessary condition for the functional I, defined as

$$I = A\int\!\!\int_{X_2}^{X_2} K(Y,X)B(Y)B(X)\,dX\,dY - \int_{X_1}^{X_2} B^2\,dX + 2\int_{X_1}^{X_2} G(X)B(X)\,dX$$

to be an extremal is that Eq. (3.2.36) be satisfied, provided we identify

$$G(X) \equiv 1 \tag{3.2.37}$$

$$K(Y,X) = \frac{1}{[(Y-X)^2+\gamma^2]^{3/2}} \tag{3.2.38}$$

$$A = \frac{\rho\gamma^2}{2} \tag{3.2.39}$$

Thus the function which extremalizes the integral

$$I = \frac{\rho\gamma^2}{2}\int_{-1/2}^{1/2}\!\!\int \frac{B(Y)B(X)\,dY\,dX}{[(Y-X)^2+\gamma^2]^{3/2}} - \int_{-1/2}^{1/2} B^2\,dX + 2\int_{-1/2}^{1/2} B\,dX \tag{3.2.40}$$

is the same function, B, which satisfies Eq. (3.2.36).

We are now in a position to apply the Ritz method. An admissible approximation is

$$B = C_0 + C_2 X^2 \tag{3.2.41}$$

In selecting this trial function, we have noted that $B(X)$ must be a symmetric function, that is, $B(X)$ must equal $B(-X)$ because of the symmetry of the geometry. Moreover, the integrations which must be performed are possible using this particular trial function. No other considerations dictated the choice of the trial function.

Substituting Eq. (3.2.41) into Eq. (3.2.40) gives, after performing the pertinent integrations

$$I = \rho(C_0^2 a_1 + C_0 C_2 a_2 + C_2^2 a_3) - C_0^2 - \frac{1}{6} C_0 C_2 - \frac{1}{80} C_2^2 + 2C_0 + \frac{1}{6} C_2 \tag{3.2.42}$$

where

$$a_1 = (1 + \gamma^2)^{\frac{1}{2}} - \gamma$$

$$a_2 = \left(\frac{1}{6} - \frac{4\gamma^2}{3} \right) (1 + \gamma^2)^{\frac{1}{2}} + \gamma^2 \{ \ln [1 + (1 + \gamma^2)^{\frac{1}{2}}] - \ln \gamma \} + \frac{4\gamma^3}{3} - \frac{\gamma}{2}$$

$$a_3 = \left(\frac{1}{80} - \frac{2\gamma^2}{45} + \frac{4\gamma^4}{45} \right)(1 + \gamma^2)^{\frac{1}{2}} + \frac{\gamma^2}{12} \{ \ln [1 + (1 + \gamma^2)^{\frac{1}{2}}]$$

$$- \ln \gamma \} - \frac{\gamma}{16} - \frac{4\gamma^5}{45}$$

It should be remarked that the constants a_1, a_2, and a_3 depend on γ. Of course, the constants C_0 and C_2 will also depend on γ, and this dependence, while complex, is clearly displayed on solving for C_0 and C_2. Herein lies one of the principal advantages of the Ritz method over numerical methods of approximation. To find the role of a parameter such as γ, one must perform a number of calculations altering the numerical value of the parameter somewhat during each calculation. By this technique the role of the parameter is defined. However, the Ritz method yields an analytical approximation which contains the essential parameters and clearly delineates the role of these parameters.

As in previous examples, we select C_0 and C_2 so that

$$\frac{\partial I}{\partial C_0} = 2C_0(\rho a_1 - 1) + C_2 \left(\rho a_2 - \frac{1}{6} \right) + 2 = 0 \tag{3.2.43}$$

and

$$\frac{\partial I}{\partial C_2} = C_0 \left(\rho a_2 - \frac{1}{6} \right) + C_2 \left(2\rho a_3 - \frac{1}{40} \right) + \frac{1}{6} = 0 \tag{3.2.44}$$

Equations (3.2.43) and (3.2.44) define C_0 and C_2 as a function of the parameters ρ and γ. The approximation to $B(X)$ determined by Eq. (3.2.41) is compared with the exact values for this function in Table 3.2.1. These exact values were generated by solving the integral equation numerically using an iterative method. The values for both the approximate and the exact solution are taken from the paper by Sparrow. An examination of the results presented in Table 3.2.3 will reveal that the approximate solution compares well with the more precise numerical solution, with the agreement becoming poorer as X increases. For $\gamma = 0.1$ the error is 9 percent at the end points $(X = \pm\frac{1}{2})$, with smaller errors at the intermediate points. This agreement seems remarkable in view of the simplicity of the approximation.

Finally we note that the net heat flux at leaving any position on the surface is

$$q = \beta - H \tag{3.2.45}$$

Eliminating H, using Eq. (3.2.27), we find

$$\frac{q}{\epsilon\sigma T^4} = \frac{1 - B\epsilon}{\rho} \tag{3.2.46}$$

so that the local heat flux is easily computed given $B(X)$. The over-all heat transfer (per unit width) is found by integrating Eq. (3.2.46). Thus

$$\frac{Q/L}{\epsilon\sigma T^4} = \frac{1 - \epsilon\int_{-\frac{1}{2}}^{\frac{1}{2}} B\,dx}{\rho} \tag{3.2.47}$$

Or, using our simple trial function, as given by Eq. (3.2.41), we find

$$\frac{Q/L}{\epsilon\sigma T^4} = \frac{1 - \epsilon(C_0 + C_2/12)}{\rho} \tag{3.2.48}$$

The over-all heat loss can now easily be computed.

EXAMPLE 3.2.4   The previous examples showing the applications of the Ritz method have dealt with problems having only one independent variable.

TABLE 3.2.3 COMPARISON OF APPROXI-
MATE WITH EXACT $B(X)$, $\gamma = 0.1$, $\rho = 0.9$

X	$B(X)$ approximate	$B(X)$ exact
0	7.39	7.22
0.1	7.22	7.11
0.2	6.73	6.75
0.3	5.90	6.07
0.4	4.74	4.90
0.5	3.25	2.97

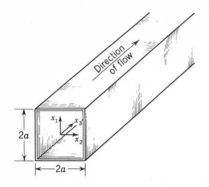

Fig. 3.2.2 Square duct with imposed co-ordinate system.

This example—the determination of the velocity distribution associated with the flow of a Newtonian fluid through a square duct—is intended to illustrate the ease with which the Ritz method can be extended to treat two-dimensional problems. Indeed the method of analysis is not changed at all.

The flow configuration is shown in Fig. 3.2.2. If it is assumed that the velocity components are such that

$$v_1 = v_2 = 0 \tag{3.2.49}$$

$$v_3 = v_3(x_1,x_2) \tag{3.2.50}$$

then $v_3(x_1,x_2)$ will be such that the integral

$$I = \int\!\!\int_{-a}^{a} \left[\left(\frac{\partial v_3}{\partial x_1}\right)^2 + \left(\frac{\partial v_3}{\partial x_2}\right)^2 + \frac{2}{\mu}\frac{\partial p}{\partial x_3} v_3 \right] dx_1\, dx_2 \tag{3.2.51}$$

is a minimum. The reader can easily verify that the Euler-Lagrange equation which stems from requiring I to be stationary is

$$\frac{\partial^2 v_3}{\partial x_1^2} + \frac{\partial^2 v_3}{\partial x_2^2} - \frac{1}{\mu}\frac{\partial p}{\partial x_3} = 0 \tag{3.2.52}$$

with the additional restriction that the velocity vanish on the boundaries of the duct. Of course Eq. (3.2.52) is also the equation of motion in a form applicable to the physical system under study.

Rather than attempt to solve the differential equation, let us assume[5]

$$v_3 = (x_1^2 - a^2)(x_2^2 - a^2)[A_0 + A_1(x_1^2 + x_2^2) + A_2 x_1^2 x_2^2] \tag{3.2.53}$$

where A_0, A_1, and A_2 are undetermined constants. This particular assumed velocity distribution has the merit of satisfying the boundary conditions $v_3 = 0$, $x_1 = \pm a$, and $x_2 = \pm a$ and also exhibiting the necessary symmetries. The undetermined constants are to be determined such that I is made stationary. Substituting Eq. (3.2.53) into Eq. (3.2.51) and integrating yields

---

[5] This calculation has been reported by E. M. Sparrow and R. Siegel, "Variational Method for Fully-Developed Laminar Heat Transfer in Ducts," *J. Heat Transfer*, vol. 81, p. 157, 1959.

$$\frac{I}{4a^6} = 0.71111A_0{}^2a^2 + 0.29799A_1{}^2a^6 + 0.010642A_2{}^2a^{10}$$

$$+ 0.48762A_0A_1a^4 + 0.040635A_0A_2a^6 + 0.077400A_1A_2a^8$$

$$+ C(\tfrac{8}{9}A_0 + {}^{16}\!\!/_{45}A_1a^2 + \tfrac{8}{225}A_2a^4) \quad (3.2.54)$$

where

$$C = \frac{1}{2\mu}\frac{\partial p}{\partial x_3} \quad (3.2.55)$$

which is constant in the present analysis. Setting

$$\frac{\partial I}{\partial A_i} = 0 \quad i = 0, 1, 2 \quad (3.2.56)$$

gives the following set of algebraic equations:

$$1.4222A_0a^2 + 0.48762A_1a^4 + 0.040635A_2a^6 + \tfrac{8}{9}C = 0 \quad (3.2.57)$$
$$0.48762A_0a^2 + 0.59598A_1a^4 + 0.077400A_2a^6 + {}^{16}\!\!/_{45}C = 0 \quad (3.2.58)$$
$$0.040635A_0a^2 + 0.077400A_1a^4 + 0.021284A_2a^6 + \tfrac{8}{225}C = 0 \quad (3.2.59)$$

Solving for the constants, we find

$$A_0 = -\frac{0.58984C}{a^2} \qquad A_1 = -\frac{0.08203C}{a^4} \qquad A_2 = -\frac{0.2461C}{a^6}$$

determining our approximation to the velocity distribution. The final expression can be simplified somewhat if we note that the average velocity is

$$V_{av} = \frac{1}{4a^2}\int\int\limits_{-a}^{a} v_3 \, dx_1 \, dx_2 \quad (3.2.60)$$

Substituting in Eq. (3.2.53) gives

$$V_{av} = \tfrac{4}{9}A_0a^4 + \tfrac{8}{45}A_1a^6 + \tfrac{4}{225}A_2a^8 \quad (3.2.61)$$

and, using the best values of the constants,

$$V_{av} = -0.28111Ca^2 \quad (3.2.62)$$

As a final result

$$\frac{v_3}{V_{av}} = \left[\left(\frac{x_1}{a}\right)^2 - 1\right]\left[\left(\frac{x_2}{a}\right)^2 - 1\right]\left\{2.09825 + 0.29180\left[\left(\frac{x_1}{a}\right)^2\right.\right.$$

$$\left.\left. + \left(\frac{x_2}{a}\right)^2\right] + 0.87545\left(\frac{x_1}{a}\right)^2\left(\frac{x_2}{a}\right)^2\right\} \quad (3.2.63)$$

To assess the accuracy of our approximation, we can make two comparisons. The most obvious check is to compare the approximate values of the velocity with more precise values. Such a comparison is presented in Table 3.2.4.

The "exact" values are the result of a numerical study[6] and are reliable to the reported number of significant figures. A brief study of the table indicates the remarkable accuracy of the approximate solution.

The second check is to compare the product of the Reynolds number and the friction-factor. Let us define

$$N_{\mathrm{Re}} = \frac{2\rho V_{\mathrm{av}} a}{\mu} \tag{3.2.64}$$

and the friction-factor as

$$f = -\frac{\partial p}{\partial x_3} \frac{4a}{\rho V_{\mathrm{av}}^2} \tag{3.2.65}$$

Then Eq. (3.2.62) can be rearranged to give

$$N_{\mathrm{Re}} f = \frac{16}{0.28111} = 56.92 \tag{3.2.66}$$

The exact value[6] is 56.91.   Again we find a remarkable agreement.

TABLE 3.2.4 COMPARISON OF VELOCITIES IN A SQUARE DUCT

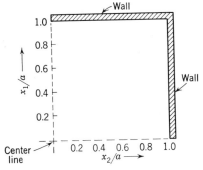

Center line			Diagonal			
v_3/V_{av}	x_1/a	x_2/a	v_3/V_{av}	x_1/a	x_2/a	
2.096	0	0	2.096	0	0	exact
2.098			2.098			approximate
2.025	0.2	0	1.956	0.2	0.2	exact
2.026			1.957			approximate
1.804	0.4	0	1.561	0.4	0.4	exact
1.802			1.562			approximate
1.414	0.6	0	0.986	0.6	0.6	exact
1.410			0.992			approximate
0.826	0.8	0	0.372	0.8	0.8	exact
0.823			0.367			approximate

[6] J. Wheeler and E. H. Wissler, Department of Chemical Engineering, University of Texas, Austin, Tex. (personal communication). An analytical solution can also be found in S. P. Timoshenko and J. N. Goodier, "Theory of Elasticity," 2d ed., McGraw-Hill Book Company, New York, 1951.

Schechter[7] has used a similar method of analysis to determine the velocity distribution resulting from the flow of a power-law fluid through a rectangular duct. We shall not consider more complicated examples here, since our aim is to illustrate the principles of using the Ritz method.

As noted in the introduction to this section, convergence of the Ritz method is assured under certain conditions; however, the quality of a given approximation depends largely on the skill of the computer in selecting "good" functional forms. In most cases one can assess the goodness of fit only by introducing a larger and larger number of free parameters until the answer no longer varies significantly. Although this test is often reliable, it is by no means rigorous. Indeed we can construct certain examples for which this test would fail. Consider the case in which the exact solution includes every fourth member of an orthogonal set of functions. Suppose further that we first use a single member of the orthogonal set as an initial approximation. On adding a second member of the orthogonal set to the approximating function, we would find that this member contributes nothing to the first approximation, since the true solution does not contain this member of the set. Can we then conclude that convergence is complete? Obviously not. Thus there are certain dangers associated with the process of testing convergence by introducing a larger number of free parameters, and the reader should be cautious. However, the test is most often reliable and certainly is the best that can be done in many cases.

In a restricted number of cases, one can place certain bounds on the reliability of an answer. Such a case is the example just completed—that of flow in a square duct. Bounds for this problem can be obtained using the following arguments.

Define a functional of two variables, u and v,

$$M(u,v) = \int\int_{-a}^{a} \left(\frac{\partial v}{\partial x_1} \frac{\partial u}{\partial x_1} + \frac{\partial v}{\partial x_2} \frac{\partial u}{\partial x_2} \right) dx_1\, dx_2 \tag{3.2.67}$$

where the integration is over the square region shown in Fig. 3.2.2.

It is certainly true that

$$M(u,u) \geq 0 \tag{3.2.68}$$

and that

$$M(u - v, u) = M(u,u) - M(u,v) \tag{3.2.69}$$

This latter result is found by substituting into Eq. (3.2.67). In general we shall see that Eq. (3.2.69) is inherent in the definition of a "linear function

[7] R. S. Schechter, "On Steady-Flow of a Non-Newtonian Fluid in Cylinder Ducts," *J. Am. Inst. Chem. Engrs.*, vol. 7, p. 445, 1961.

space," which is basic to the problem of fixing bounds. But this aspect will be discussed after the method of establishing bounds has become clear.

A Schwarz inequality can now be developed. We have

$$M(u - av, u - av) \geq 0 \tag{3.2.70}$$

where a is a constant. Thus

$$M(u,u) - 2aM(u,v) + a^2 M(v,v) \geq 0 \tag{3.2.71}$$

for all real values of a. The left-hand side of this inequality is smallest when a takes on the value

$$a = \frac{M(u,v)}{M(v,v)}$$

Using this value of a, inequality (3.2.71) can be arranged into the following form:

$$M(v,v)M(u,u) \geq [M(u,v)]^2 \tag{3.2.72}$$

which is our Schwarz inequality.

Let us now suppose that we have a class of functions u, which are identifiable by the fact that they satisfy the differential equation.

$$\frac{\partial^2 u}{\partial x_1{}^2} + \frac{\partial^2 u}{\partial x_2{}^2} = 0 \tag{3.2.73}$$

Furthermore, let us define a second class of functions v, which have the property of vanishing on the boundary of the square region under examination, that is,

$$v(x_1,x_2) = 0 \qquad \text{for } x_1 = \pm a \text{ or } x_2 = \pm a \tag{3.2.74}$$

The remainder of our discussion will hinge around these two definitions. Therefore, for all that remains, u will be defined by Eq. (3.2.73) and v by Eq. (3.2.74).

It can be shown that

$$M(u,v) = 0 \tag{3.2.75}$$

The demonstration is straightforward. Write Eq. (3.2.67) as

$$M(u,v) = \int\limits_{-a}^{a}\!\!\int \left(\frac{\partial}{\partial x_1} v \frac{\partial u}{\partial x_1} + \frac{\partial}{\partial x_2} v \frac{\partial u}{\partial x_2} \right) dx_1 \, dx_2 - \int\limits_{-a}^{a}\!\!\int v \left(\frac{\partial^2 u}{\partial x_1{}^2} + \frac{\partial^2 u}{\partial x_2{}^2} \right) dx_1 \, dx_2 \tag{3.2.76}$$

The second term on the right-hand side vanishes because of definition of u (see Eq. 3.2.73). The first term can be integrated to give a line integral which vanishes because of the definition of v. Thus Eq. (3.2.75) is established.

Our problem is to first fix an upper bound for $M(v_3,v_3)$ where $v_3(x_1,x_2)$ is the true velocity distribution in the square duct. It is probably worth noting that v_3 is a member of the set v, since the true velocity vanishes on the boundary. Finding the upper bound is not difficult. Suppose we have a function w which satisfies the differential equation

$$\frac{\partial^2 w}{\partial x_1{}^2} + \frac{\partial^2 w}{\partial x_2{}^2} = \frac{1}{\mu}\frac{\partial p}{\partial x_3} \qquad (3.2.77)$$

but not necessarily the boundary conditions, Eq. (3.2.74). If w also obeyed these boundary conditions, as well as Eq. (3.2.77), then this function would be the solution to the physical problem; that is, w would be the velocity. If w does not satisfy the boundary conditions, it is not a member of the set v. However $v_3 - w$ is a member of the group u. This can be seen by noting that v_3 also satisfies Eq. (3.2.77). Thus the difference $v_3 - w$ must satisfy Eq. (3.2.73) and hence be a member of the set u. Moreover,

$$M(v_3 - w, v_3) = 0 \qquad (3.2.78)$$

or

$$M(v_3,v_3) = M(v_3,w)$$

Squaring both sides,

$$[M(v_3,v_3)]^2 = [M(v_3,w)]^2$$

the Schwarz inequality gives [see Eq. (3.2.72)]

$$M(v_3,v_3) \leq M(w,w) \qquad (3.2.79)$$

which is our upper bound. Thus any function satisfying Eq. (3.2.77) but not necessarily vanishing on the boundary will yield an upper bound for $M(v_3,v_3)$.

Before putting this bound to practical usage, let us find a lower bound. Consider

$$M(v_3 - av, v_3 - av) \geq 0 \qquad (3.2.80)$$

where a is again a real number. Expanding we find

$$M(v_3,v_3) \geq 2aM(v,v_3) - a^2M(v,v) \qquad (3.2.81)$$

Since $v_3 - w$ is in the set of functions u, we can write

$$M(v_3 - w, v) = 0$$

because of Eq. (3.2.75). This can be put into the form

$$M(v_3,v) = M(w,v) \qquad (3.2.82)$$

This is a very interesting result, which is valid for any function w defined by Eq. (3.2.77). Substituting Eq. (3.2.82) into Eq. (3.2.81) yields

$$M(v_3,v_3) \geq 2aM(v,w) - a^2 M(v,v) \tag{3.2.83}$$

Equation (3.2.83) is valid for all real a. However, the best bound can be found by making the right-hand side of this inequality as large as possible. Maximizing the right with respect to a, we find

$$M(v_3,v_3) \geq \frac{[M(v,w)]^2}{M(v,v)} \tag{3.2.84}$$

Thus we can give limits to $M(v_3,v_3)$ by knowing a function w which satisfies a differential equation but no particular boundary conditions and a function v which vanishes on the boundary. The upper bound is defined by inequality (3.2.79), while the lower bound is represented by inequality (3.2.84).

Before proceeding to investigate the quality of the approximation developed in Example 3.2.4, it is interesting to note that $M(v_3,v_3)$ has physical significance. For we can write

$$M(v_3,v_3) = +\int\int_{-a}^{a}\left[\frac{\partial}{\partial x_1}\left(v_3\frac{\partial v_3}{\partial x_1}\right) + \frac{\partial}{\partial x_2}\left(v_3\frac{\partial v_3}{\partial x_2}\right)\right]dx_1\,dx_2$$
$$-\int\int_{-a}^{a}v_3\left(\frac{\partial^2 v_3}{\partial x_1^2} + \frac{\partial^2 v_3}{\partial x_2^2}\right)dx_1\,dx_2$$

Using the equation of motion, Eq. (3.2.52), and noting that v_3 vanishes on the boundary, we find

$$M(v_3,v_3) = -\int\int_{-a}^{a}\frac{1}{\mu}\frac{\partial p}{\partial x_3}v_3\,dx_1\,dx_2$$

Hence

$$M(v_3,v_3) = -\frac{1}{\mu}\frac{\partial p}{\partial x_3}V_{av}4a^2 \tag{3.2.85}$$

Thus, bounds on $M(v_3,v_3)$ in effect measure the precision with which V_{av} is known.

How can we actually apply these bounds? Clearly we must generate a v and w. How is v defined? It is simply a function vanishing on the boundary. However, the more nearly the true velocity v_3 is represented by v, the tighter will be the bounds. We have developed an approximation to the velocity distribution which does vanish on the boundary. This approximation, defined by Eq. (3.2.53), is certainly a member of the set of functions v. What about w? An acceptable choice is

$$w = (x_1^2 + x_2^2)\frac{1}{4\mu}\frac{\partial p}{\partial x_3} \tag{3.2.86}$$

Thus

$$M(w,w) = \int\int_{-a}^{a}(x_1{}^2 + x_2{}^2)\frac{1}{4\mu^2}\left(\frac{\partial p}{\partial x_3}\right)^2 dx_1\,dx_2$$

or

$$M(w,w) = \frac{2a^4}{3\mu^2}\left(\frac{\partial p}{\partial x_3}\right)^2 \tag{3.2.87}$$

Similarly, we find

$$M(v,w) = -\frac{16a^2}{\mu}\frac{\partial p}{\partial x_3}\left(\frac{a^4}{9}A_0 + \frac{2}{45}\frac{a^6}{45}A_1 + \frac{a^8}{225}A_2\right) \tag{3.2.88}$$

where v is the approximation to v_3 defined by Eq. (3.2.53). Moreover, a straightforward calculation gives

$$M(v,v) = 0.5622\,\frac{1}{\mu^2}\left(\frac{\partial p}{\partial x_3}\right)^2 a^4 \tag{3.2.89}$$

Thus we find the true mean velocity† to be bound by the limits

$$-0.1405\,\frac{1}{\mu}\frac{\partial p}{\partial x_3}a^2 \le V_{\mathrm{av}} \le -0.1667\,\frac{1}{\mu}\frac{\partial p}{\partial x_3}a^2 \tag{3.2.90}$$

Of course these limits can be brought closer together by increasing the number of adjustable parameters in both w and v. For example, we could select

$$w = (x_1{}^2 + x_2{}^2)\frac{1}{4\mu}\frac{\partial p}{\partial x_3} + \beta\sinh\frac{x_1}{a}\sin\frac{x_2}{a} \tag{3.2.91}$$

where β is an undetermined constant. Equation (3.2.91) is a valid w for all β, so that we would be free to select β such that $M(w,w)$ is as small as possible, thus giving the smallest upper bound possible based on Eq. (3.2.79).

We can also improve the accuracy of v by introducing a larger number of parameters and making inequality (3.2.84) as strong as is consistent with the choice of the approximating function. Thus new constants could be selected so that

$$\delta\left[\frac{M(v,w)^2}{M(v,v)}\right] = 0$$

This variation vanishes for all admissible v if

$$M(v,v)M(\delta v,w) - M(v,w)M(\delta v,v) = 0 \tag{3.2.92}$$

† The true answer is $-0.14055(1/\mu)(\partial p/\partial x_3)a^2 = V_{\mathrm{av}}$. The lower limit is very accurate, since it is based on the velocity determined in Example 3.2.4.

It is not difficult for the reader to verify that this equation is quadratic in the constants of an assumed v, which is linear in the constants. Thus if

$$v = \Sigma A_i \phi_i(x_1, x_2)$$

then Eq. (3.2.92) is quadratic in the A's, making them relatively difficult to determine. If we are willing to settle for less than the best possible bound, then we can express inequality (3.2.83) as

$$M(v_3 v_3) \geq 2M(v, w) - M(v, v) \tag{3.2.93}$$

by arbitrarily selecting a to be unity. We can now select the values of the parameters such that the right-hand side of this inequality is as large as possible. Thus define the functional I as

$$I(v) = -2M(v, w) + M(v, v)$$

Since

$$M(v, w) = -\frac{1}{\mu} \frac{\partial p}{\partial x_3} \int_{-a}^{a}\!\!\int v \, dx_1 \, dx_2$$

after an integration by parts, then

$$I(v) = \int_{-a}^{a}\!\!\int \left[\frac{2}{\mu} \frac{\partial p}{\partial x_3} v + \left(\frac{\partial v}{\partial x_1} \right)^2 + \left(\frac{\partial v}{\partial x_2} \right)^2 \right] dx_1 \, dx_2 \tag{3.2.94}$$

which is the variational principle used in Example 3.2.4 to establish the approximation to the velocity distribution. Since making the right-hand side of inequality (3.2.93) as large as possible corresponds to reducing $I(v)$ to the smallest possible value, the variational principle is then seen as a means of establishing a lower bound, but not the best possible lower bound. However, the variational principle used in Example 3.2.4 does have the computational advantage of yielding linear equations for the adjustable constants and is the means of improving the approximation which has been adopted here.

We have found both upper and lower bounds for the mean velocity. This is a very satisfying result. It certainly improves our confidence in the validity of the approximation. Unfortunately, the machinery for developing such limits in the general case has not yet been established. For a certain class of linear problems, Synge[8] has devised a very interesting and fruitful geometry applicable in function space. Here geometrical constructions are used to suggest both maxima and minima principles. Although we do not intend to discuss Synge's method in great detail, some of the salient features of his arguments have already been developed. Thus it seems worthwhile to

[8] J. L. Synge, "The Hypercircle in Mathematical Physics," Cambridge University Press, London, 1957.

reformulate our finding in geometric terms. The reader interested in this concept should consult Synge's elegant book for more details.

We must now picture a kind of function space, where functions are imagined to be vectors. Of course, such a space is infinitely dimensional, but many of the vector operations can be translated, so that the comparison is fruitful. We need a measure of length in this function space. To be useful, this metric must have certain properties, such as satisfying the commutative and distributive laws as well as being positive definite. Our definition $M(u,v)$ [see Eq. (3.2.67)] satisfies all of the requirements imposed by Synge and is thus a suitable (there are others) metric for a function space. With a means of measuring the length of vectors in function space suitably defined, Eq. (3.2.72) provides the basis for defining an angle between two vectors u and v. Thus

$$\cos \beta = \frac{M(u,v)}{\sqrt{M(v,v)M(u,u)}} \qquad 0 \le \beta \le \pi \qquad (3.2.95)$$

where β is the angle between two vectors in function space. If $\cos \beta$ vanishes, we can say that the two vectors u and v are at right angles and are orthogonal. Thus Eq. (3.2.75) represents the condition for orthogonality of two vectors u and v. Finally, we can interpret the bounds developed in the preceding paragraphs using notions of geometry. (See also Courant and Hilbert,[9] Sani[10].) Since Eq. (3.2.82) leads us to say that $v_3 - w$ and v are orthogonal, these vectors must be represented as being perpendicular to one another, as shown in Fig. 3.2.3. Here we see two axes—a u axis and a v axis (u and v are orthogonal by Eq. (3.2.75). Since v_3 is in class v, it is shown as being

[9] R. Courant and D. Hilbert, "Methods of Mathematical Physics," p. 276, Interscience Publishers, Inc., New York, 1962.
[10] R. L. Sani, "Dual Variational Statements Viewed from Function Space," J. Am. Inst. Chem. Engrs., vol. 9, p. 277, 1963.

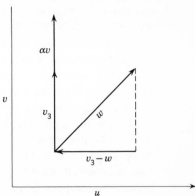

Fig. 3.2.3 Geometry of "vector space."

parallel to v. The vector w is neither u nor v and is shown skew to both axes. However $w - v_3$ is perpendicular to v, as shown in Fig. 3.2.3. Thus we have a geometric picture of the mathematical machinery which was used to develop upper and lower bounds. Indeed it is quite clear that w must be "longer" than v_3 if $v_3 - w$ is orthogonal to v. Thus we have a geometric interpretation of the upper bound given by Eq. (3.2.79). Moreover, the construction shows that the shortest distance from the vector αv, α being a scalar, to the vector w is along $v_3 - w$, since this vector is orthogonal to αv. Stated mathematically,

$$M(w - v_3, w - v_3) \leq M(w - \alpha v, w - \alpha v) \qquad (3.2.96)$$

This inequality suggested by the geometry can be expanded to

$$M(w, v_3) \geq 2\alpha M(w, v) - \alpha^2 M(v, v) \qquad (3.2.97)$$

since $w - v_3$ is orthogonal to v_3. Finally, because of orthogonality

$$M(w - v_3, v_3) = 0$$

giving

$$M(w, v_3) = M(v_3 v_3)$$

Hence we find

$$M(v_3, v_3) \geq 2\alpha M(w, v) - \alpha^2 M(v, v)$$

which is our lower bound.

The process of geometric interpretation in function space has been put to good advantage by Synge. In general this method is characterized by a positive-definite metric (although Synge considers indefinite metrics) and a splitting of a certain class of functions into two orthogonal sets. This latter division into classes is usually brought about by defining one set of functions which satisfy a differential equation and certain boundary conditions and a second set of functions which satisfy certain boundary conditions. Note that the differential equation must be related to the physical problem, and the two classes of functions must be orthogonal if suitable bounds are to be developed. In general, these conditions cannot all be satisfied, and both upper and lower bounds cannot be found. Thus one is forced to rely on the check of increasing the number of parameters and investigating the change in the answer.

Thus far, our study of the Ritz method has been limited to problems having specified dependent variables on the boundary. In selecting trial functions, we have been careful to insure that the boundary conditions are satisfied at every stage of our manipulations. This is a necessary precaution. It should be noted, however, that in treating problems having other types of boundary conditions, one must do more than simply insure that the boundary conditions are satisfied by the approximating functions. The reader will recall the arguments presented in Sec. 1.6, in which it was shown that boundary conditions are an integral part of the variational principle. Indeed the first variation must vanish, and on the boundary, the variation can be made to vanish in one of two ways (see Table 1.7.1).   First of all, the problem may be stated such that the variations vanish on the boundary (these variations could be of the derivatives as well as of the dependent variable itself).   On the other hand, there can exist certain relationships, applicable on the boundary, which will result in the vanishing of the coefficient of the variation.   Thus we often find that variational principles consist of two contributions, one of which stems from the boundary.   The contribution from the boundary is formulated such that the desired natural boundary conditions exist.   It is important to remember that these additional boundary terms must be used in the direct calculations even if the trial function satisfies the boundary conditions!

For example, suppose we seek an approximate solution to the boundary-value problem

$$\frac{\partial^2 T}{\partial x_1^2} + \frac{\partial^2 T}{\partial x_2^2} = f \qquad \text{on } S \tag{3.2.98}$$

with the following condition imposed on the curve Γ enclosing S:

$$\frac{\partial T}{\partial x_1} n_1 + \frac{\partial T}{\partial x_2} n_2 = -\alpha T \qquad \text{on } \Gamma \tag{3.2.99}$$

Here n_1 and n_2 are the components of the outward drawn normal to the curve Γ.   Equation (3.2.99) represents the radiation boundary conditions in a heat-flow problem.

The variational formulation of this boundary-value problem is given as

$$I = \int_S \left[\left(\frac{\partial T}{\partial x_1} \right)^2 + \left(\frac{\partial T}{\partial x_2} \right)^2 + 2fT \right] dS + \int_\Gamma \alpha T^2 \, d\Gamma \tag{3.2.100}$$

where T is to be selected such that I is stationary.   It is a simple matter to verify the correspondence with Eqs. (3.2.98) and (3.2.99).   Suppose we assume a trial function in the form

$$T = \Sigma \, C_i \phi_i(x_1, x_2) \tag{3.2.101}$$

where the ϕ_i are defined such that

$$\frac{\partial \phi_i}{\partial x_1} n_1 + \frac{\partial \phi_i}{\partial x_2} n_2 = -\alpha \phi_i \tag{3.2.102}$$

Then Eq. (3.2.101) satisfies the boundary condition (3.2.99) for all choices of C_i.   However, in selecting values of the constants by the Ritz method, one must still retain the contribution resulting from the line integral of Eq. (3.2.100), or the convergence will not be to the desired solution.   In this case, one can also use trial functions which do not satisfy the boundary conditions. However, in general, more terms are then required in the expansion to adequately approximate the true solution.

It is believed that the examples presented here are sufficient to clearly set forth the technique of calculation and to illustrate the power of the Ritz method. In the next section we shall study still another method of utilizing the variational principle in a direct calculation, but no method has found as much application as the Ritz method.

PROBLEM 3.2.1   Develop an approximation for the solution to the differential equation

$$\frac{d^2y}{dx^2} + 5y = x$$

$$y = 0 \qquad \text{at } x = 0, 1$$

having the form

$$y = x(x - 1)(A + Bx)$$

Compare the approximation with the exact solution at $x = 0.5$.

PROBLEM 3.2.2   Develop an approximate solution to the integral equation

$$\phi(x) = \frac{1}{2} \int_0^1 \sin(\pi x + \pi y)\phi(y) \, dy + 1 - \cos x$$

in the form

$$\phi(x) = \cos \alpha x$$

where α is the undetermined constant. What is the exact solution?

PROBLEM 3.2.3   The product of the Reynolds number and the friction factor for a square duct (see Fig. 3.2.2) is

$$N_{\text{Re}} f = \left(\frac{2\rho V_{\text{av}} a}{\mu}\right)\left(-\frac{\partial p}{\partial x_3} \frac{4a}{\rho V_{\text{av}}^2}\right) = 56.91$$

Assume that the velocity profile is given by

$$v_3 = A \cos\frac{\pi x_1}{2a} \cos\frac{\pi x_2}{2a}$$

and find an approximate value of $N_{\text{Re}} f$ for a square duct. How could you improve this result?

3.3 PARTIAL INTEGRATION

A good approximation to partial differential equations can often be achieved by selecting the functional variation of the unknown dependent function in one dimension but leaving unspecified the relationship to the other independent variables. After fixing, a priori, the form of the solution with respect to one of the variables, the integral to be extremalized can be reduced by performing a partial integration.   After integrating, the integrand will once again be a functional of unknown functions.   These functions can then be selected such that the Euler-Lagrange equations for the reduced variational problem are satisfied.   This procedure amounts to making the best† possible choice selected from the class of functions having the structure of the solution proposed a priori.   This technique is sometimes easier to apply and often leads to a more accurate approximation than the Ritz method.

EXAMPLE 3.3.1   To be more definite, let us find the function $T(x,y)$ which minimizes the integral

$$I = \int_0^\pi \int_0^1 \left[\left(\frac{\partial T}{\partial x} \right)^2 + \left(\frac{\partial T}{\partial y} \right)^2 + \frac{2\beta T}{k} \sin \pi x \sin y \right] dx \, dy \tag{3.3.1}$$

subject to the boundary condition

$$T(1,y) = T(0,y) = T(x,\pi) = T(x,0) = 0 \tag{3.3.1a}$$

This function T corresponds to the temperature of a plate whose edges are maintained at zero temperature and whose surface is losing heat at the rate of $\beta \sin \pi x \sin y$ per unit area.   The parameter k in Eq. (3.3.1) is the thermal conductivity of the plate.   Let us assume

$$T = (x)(1 - x)f(y) \tag{3.3.2}$$

Note that we have selected the structure of the solution and the functional form for the temperature profile in the x direction; however, the temperature change in the y direction has not yet been determined.   Substitute Eq. (3.3.2) into Eq. (3.3.1) to find

$$I = \int_0^\pi \int_0^1 [f^2(1 - 2x)^2 + f_y^2(x - x^2)^2 + 2f \sin y \sin \pi x \, (x - x^2)] \, dx \, dy$$

where β/k has been taken to be one.   Integrating with respect to x yields

$$I = \int_0^\pi \left(\frac{f^2}{3} + \frac{f_y^2}{30} + \frac{8f}{\pi^3} \sin y \right) dy \tag{3.3.3}$$

The function $f(y)$ is to be selected such that I is minimized.   This is the "best" choice of $f(y)$ once the structure proposed in Eq. (3.3.2) has been imposed. What condition must $f(y)$ satisfy if I is to be a possible minimum?   Clearly if δI is to vanish, then

$$\frac{d^2 f}{dy^2} - 10f = \frac{120}{\pi^3} \sin y \tag{3.3.4}$$

---

† There is some question regarding the precise mathematical interpretation of the word "best" as it is used in this context.   The word should not be taken literally, for, as we shall see, the choice is "best" in the sense that the selected function renders a certain integral stationary.

or, integrating this differential equation,

$$f = -\frac{1}{\pi^3}\frac{120}{11}\sin y \tag{3.3.5}$$

The approximate temperature distribution is then

$$T = -\frac{1}{\pi^3}\frac{120}{11}\sin y(x - x^2) \tag{3.3.6}$$

The method of partial integration has provided the correct functional relationship with respect to the y coordinate, which can be seen by comparing the result given in Eq. (3.3.6) with the exact solution. However, before comparing the two solutions, let us consider the following calculation. Define

$$R^2 = \int_0^1 [C(x)(1 - x) - \sin \pi x]^2\, dx \tag{3.3.7}†$$

where C is a constant. The R^2 is a square of a residual which is the difference between the approximate change in temperature along the x coordinate and the exact variation of the temperature. Let us now choose the constant C in the least-square sense; that is, let us select C such that the square of the residual is minimized. Thus, C is selected so that

$$\frac{\partial R^2}{\partial C} = 0 \tag{3.3.8}$$

It is not difficult to show that

$$C = -\frac{120}{\pi^3}$$

and thus the "best" temperature approximation in the least-square sense is

$$T_{\text{least square}} = -\frac{1}{\pi^2 + 1}\frac{120}{\pi^3}(x - x^2)\sin y \tag{3.3.9}$$

Note that Eq. (3.3.9) differs from the best approximation selected in the variational sense by the ratio $(\pi^2 + 1)/11$, a factor which is very nearly, but not exactly, unity. It is seen that our approximation selected in order to minimize the integral given in Eq. (3.3.3) is *not* the "best" in the least-square sense. Indeed we do not intend to establish a precise definition of the word "best." For our purposes, it is sufficient to note that the method of

---

† The exact solution is $T = -1/(\pi^2 + 1)\sin y \sin \pi x$; thus the residual defined here is the deviation of the function $C(x)(1 - x)$ from the true solution.

partial integration reduces the number of independent variables in the Euler-Lagrange equations by one and seems to give excellent approximations.[1]

It may be of considerable importance to develop some estimate of the error in the approximation.   Some estimate of this error may be found in computing a higher-order approximation and then comparing the values of the integrals obtained from the two approximations.† Although one cannot be assured that having a value of I with the higher-order approximation, which is very nearly the same as the previous approximation, implies convergence to the true answer, such a test seems to be representative of the degree of convergence.   This latter remark is based on observations rather than any definitive mathematical analysis.

Let us find the second approximation to our example.   Assume

$$T = x(1 - x)f(y) + x^2(1 - x)^2 g(y) \tag{3.3.10}$$

where both $f(y)$ and $g(y)$ are undetermined functions of y which must vanish at y equal to zero and π to satisfy the boundary conditions.   Substituting Eq. (3.3.10) into Eq. (3.3.1) and integrating with respect to x gives

$$I = \int_0^\pi \left[\frac{f^2}{3} + \frac{2}{15}fg + \frac{2}{105}g^2 + \frac{(f_y)^2}{30} + \frac{g_y f_y}{70} + \frac{(g_y)^2}{630} \right.$$
$$\left. + g\left(\frac{96}{\pi^5} - \frac{8}{\pi^3}\right)\sin y + f\frac{8}{\pi^3}\sin y \right] dy \tag{3.3.11}$$

It is now suggested that both g and y be determined such that I is minimized. This condition requires that $f(y)$ and $g(y)$ satisfy the set of differential equations

$$-\frac{1}{15}\frac{d^2f}{dy^2} - \frac{1}{70}\frac{d^2g}{dy^2} + \frac{2}{15}g + \frac{2}{3}f + \frac{8}{\pi^3}\sin y = 0 \tag{3.3.12}$$

and

$$-\frac{1}{70}\frac{d^2f}{dy^2} - \frac{1}{315}\frac{d^2g}{dy^2} + \frac{4}{105}g + \frac{2}{15}f + \left(\frac{96}{\pi^5} - \frac{8}{\pi^3}\right)\sin y = 0 \tag{3.3.13}$$

subject to the boundary conditions

$$f(y) = 0 \qquad \text{at } y = 0, \pi$$
$$g(y) = 0 \qquad \text{at } y = 0, \pi$$

[1] This method is apparently due to Kantorovich.   See V. L. Kantorovich and V. I. Krylov, "Approximate Methods of Higher Analysis," pp. 304–322, Interscience Publishers, Inc., New York, 1958.

† The upper and lower bounds developed in the preceding section are also applicable to this problem.   The definition of w must be altered so that w satisfies the differential equation governing the temperature (equation of heat conduction); however, all of the remaining conclusions are then applicable.

The solution of this set of equations is

$$f(y) = -\frac{8.87791}{\pi^3} \sin y \qquad (3.3.14)$$

and

$$g(y) = -\frac{10.0912}{\pi^3} \sin y \qquad (3.3.15)$$

The second approximation is then

$$T = -\sin y \left\{ \frac{8.87791}{\pi^3} x(1 - x) + \frac{10.0912}{\pi^3} [x(1 - x)]^2 \right\} \qquad (3.3.16)$$

This is compared with the exact solution and the first approximation in Table 3.3.1. The values of the integral I are shown in Table 3.3.2. We see that the I for the second approximation is about $1\frac{1}{2}$ percent smaller than that of the first. Nothing really definitive can be deduced from viewing these numbers. However, it seems that for linear problems (the ones which can be solved exactly), the difference in I can be used as a *measure* of the difference between the two answers, but not for the deviation from the true answer. One should now make a third approximation and find that I changes very little, since the value must lie between -0.072237 and -0.072258. One then has some confidence that the correct answer has been very nearly approximated.

TABLE 3.3.1 COMPARISON OF APPROXIMATIONS WITH EXACT SOLUTION

x	$-\left(\dfrac{T}{\sin y}\right)^\dagger$ exact	$-\left(\dfrac{T}{\sin y}\right)$ first approximation	$-\left(\dfrac{T}{\sin y}\right)$ second approximation
$\frac{1}{4}$	0.0651	0.066	0.0651
$\frac{1}{2}$	0.09199	0.088	0.09192

$\dagger$ The exact solution is $T(x,y) = -[1/(\pi^2 + 1)] \sin y \sin \pi x$.

TABLE 3.3.2 COMPARISON OF APPROXIMATIONS

	I
First approximation	-0.07129
Second approximation	-0.072237
Exact	-0.072258

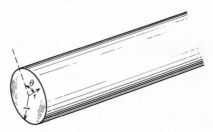

Fig. 3.3.1   Cylindrical rod.

PROBLEM 3.3.1   Heat is generated in an infinite cylindrical rod at the rate of

$$G_1 \sin \theta + G_2 r^3 \sin 2\theta$$

BTU per unit volume per unit time, where G_1 and G_2 are constants. The coordinate system is defined in Fig. 3.3.1.

a. Assuming steady-state and no axial dependence on the temperature, write the differential energy balance.

b. If the temperature vanishes on the boundary $[T(1,\theta) = 0$ for all $\theta]$, develop a variational principle which corresponds to the differential equation obtained in part (a).

c. Assume a function of the form

$$T = f_1(r) \sin \theta + f_2(r) \sin 2\theta$$

and determine f_1 and f_2 by the method of partial integration.

d. Check to see if your answer for part (c) is exact.

EXAMPLE 3.3.2   The equation of motion describing the steady-flow of incompressible Newtonian fluid in an annular segment such as is depicted in Fig. 3.3.2 can be written as

$$0 = -\frac{\partial p}{\partial z} + \mu\left(\frac{1}{r}\frac{\partial}{\partial r}r\frac{\partial v_z}{\partial r} + \frac{1}{r^2}\frac{\partial^2 v_z}{\partial \theta^2}\right) \tag{3.3.17}$$

where $\partial p/\partial z$ = constant pressure gradient applied along the axis of the duct
$\quad\quad v_z$ = axial component of velocity
$\quad\quad \mu$ = viscosity of the Newtonian fluid

To determine the axial velocity as a function of r and θ, one must integrate Eq. (3.3.17) subject to the boundary conditions

$$v_z = 0 \quad\quad \text{at } r = \kappa R \tag{3.3.18}$$

$$v_z = 0 \quad\quad \text{at } r = R \tag{3.3.19}$$

$$v_z = 0 \quad\quad \text{at } \theta = \pm\frac{s}{2} \tag{3.3.20}$$

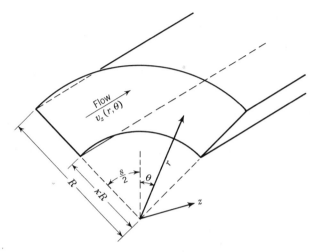

Fig. 3.3.2   Flow in annular segment—sketch of duct showing cylindrical coordinate system.

If we define a Reynolds number as

$$N_{\mathrm{Re}} = \frac{2R\rho V_{\mathrm{av}}}{\mu} \tag{3.3.21}$$

where ρ is the fluid density and V_{av} is the average fluid velocity, and define a friction factor as

$$f = -\frac{\partial p}{\partial z} \frac{2R}{\rho V_{\mathrm{av}}^2} \tag{3.3.22}$$

Eq. (3.3.17) can be expressed as

$$0 = \frac{N_{\mathrm{Re}} f}{4} + \frac{1}{\eta} \frac{\partial}{\partial \eta} \eta \frac{\partial v}{\partial \eta} + \frac{1}{\eta^2} \frac{\partial^2 v}{\partial \theta^2} \tag{3.3.23}$$

in which $\eta = r/R$ and $v = v_z/V_{\mathrm{av}}$.   The solution of this partial differential equation restricted by the pertinent boundary conditions has not been achieved. Therefore, we shall set our goals at gaining an approximate knowledge of the velocity distribution, leaving the exact integration of Eq. (3.3.23) to another.   Let us construct this approximation using the method of partial integration.

Before beginning our calculations, we need to express $v(r,\theta)$ as an extremalizing function.   The reader should verify that a necessary condition for the definite integral I, defined as

$$I = \int_{\kappa}^{1} \int_{-s/2}^{s/2} \left[\left(\frac{\partial v}{\partial \eta} \right)^2 + \frac{1}{\eta^2} \left(\frac{\partial v}{\partial \theta} \right)^2 - \frac{N_{\mathrm{Re}} f v}{2} \right] \eta \, d\eta \, d\theta \tag{3.3.24}$$

to be an extremal is that Eq. (3.3.23) be identically satisfied at every point in the space ($\kappa \leq \eta \leq 1$, $-s/2 \leq \theta \leq s/2$). We restrict the trial functions to those which give a vanishing velocity on the boundaries. A reasonable structure for the velocity is

$$v = \cos \frac{\pi\theta}{s} g(\eta) \tag{3.3.25}$$

where $g(\eta)$ is a function yet to be determined. Substituting this trial function into Eq. (3.3.24), we find, after integrating with respect to θ,

$$I = \int_\kappa^1 \left[\frac{s}{2}\left(\frac{dg}{d\eta}\right)^2 + \frac{\pi^2}{2s}\frac{g^2}{\eta^2} - \frac{sN_{\mathrm{Re}}f}{\pi} g \right] \eta \, d\eta \tag{3.3.26}$$

As before, we shall select $g(\eta)$ such that I is extremalized. Applying the Euler-Lagrange equation, we see that $g(\eta)$ must satisfy the equation

$$-\frac{s}{\eta}\frac{d}{d\eta}\eta\frac{dg}{d\eta} + \frac{\pi^2}{s}\frac{g}{\eta^2} - \frac{sN_{\mathrm{Re}}f}{\pi} = 0 \tag{3.3.27}$$

Integrating this differential equation gives

$$g(\eta) = b\left(\frac{\kappa^2 - \kappa^\alpha}{\kappa^\alpha - \kappa^{-\alpha}}\eta^{-\alpha} - \frac{\kappa^2 - \kappa^{-\alpha}}{\kappa^\alpha - \kappa^{-\alpha}}\eta^\alpha + \eta^2 \right) \tag{3.3.28}$$

where

$$\alpha = \frac{\pi}{s} \tag{3.3.29}$$

and

$$b = \frac{N_{\mathrm{Re}}f}{\pi(\alpha^2 - 4)} \tag{3.3.30}$$

Note that $g(\eta)$ has been determined so that

$$g(\eta) = 0 \qquad \text{at } \eta = \kappa, 1 \tag{3.3.31}$$

The approximate velocity distribution is determined by Eqs. (3.3.25) and (3.3.28). We see again that the method of partial integration is used to reduce the order of the differential equation by taking an assumed structure for the trial function and then manipulating the remaining degrees of freedom such that the variational integral is extremalized. As we have seen in the preceding example, the method is very effective. To develop some feel for the accuracy of this first approximation, we performed a numerical calculation for a particular geometry. The results of this numerical calculation, which amounted to an iterative finite-difference solution of Eq. (3.3.23), will be compared with the results predicted by the first approximation.

Before making this comparison, it is interesting to note that the product of the friction factor and the Reynolds number is fixed for a given geometry.

Indeed we can deduce this product $(N_{\mathrm{Re}}f)$ by noting that the average velocity is defined by

$$V_{\mathrm{av}} = \frac{\int_{-s/2}^{s/2}\int_{\kappa R}^{R} v_z r\, dr\, d\theta}{\int_{-s/2}^{s/2}\int_{\kappa R}^{R} r\, dr\, d\theta} \tag{3.3.32}$$

If we make the change of variable $v = v_z/V_{\mathrm{av}}$ and $\eta = r/R$, then Eq. (3.3.32) becomes

$$\int_{-s/2}^{s/2}\int_{\kappa}^{1}\eta\, d\eta\, d\theta = \int_{-s/2}^{s/2}\int_{\kappa}^{1} v\eta\, d\eta\, d\theta \tag{3.3.33}$$

The left-hand side can be integrated to give

$$\frac{s}{2}(1 - \kappa^2) = \int_{-s/2}^{s/2}\int_{\kappa}^{1} v\eta\, d\eta\, d\theta \tag{3.3.34}$$

The parameter b must be selected so that this equation is satisfied. If we substitute Eq. (3.3.25) into Eq. (3.3.34), we find

$$N_{\mathrm{Re}}f = \frac{\pi^2(\alpha^2 - 4)}{4} \frac{1 - \kappa^2}{\dfrac{\kappa^2 - \kappa^\alpha}{\kappa^\alpha - \kappa^{-\alpha}}\dfrac{1 - \kappa^{2-\alpha}}{2 - \alpha} - \dfrac{\kappa^2 - \kappa^{-\alpha}}{\kappa^\alpha - \kappa^{-\alpha}}\dfrac{2 - \kappa^{2+\alpha}}{2 + \alpha} + \dfrac{1 - \kappa^4}{4}} \tag{3.3.35}$$

for the product of the Reynolds number and the friction factor. Here we see that our approximate velocity profile has yielded an approximation for $N_{\mathrm{Re}}f$ which depends on the geometry through s and κ. Of course this expression is only valid for laminar flow.

The numerical problem which has been solved is for an annular segment subtending an angle of 36° and having a ratio of radii equal to 0.77922. A comparison of Reynolds number times friction-factor constants is shown below.

$$(N_{\mathrm{Re}}f)_{\mathrm{numerical}} = 1,314 \tag{3.3.36}$$

whereas [from Eq. (3.3.35)]

$$(N_{\mathrm{Re}}f)_{\mathrm{approx}} = 1,400 \tag{3.3.37}$$

Here we see that the difference between these two values is of the order of 8 percent. For calculating pressure drops, such an accuracy is normally more than sufficient. However, the velocities predicted by the first approximation do not compare as well as is desirable with those determined numerically. This rather large variation is shown in Fig. 3.3.3. The curves represent the numerical results, and the points are computed from the approximation. We see that at $\theta = 0$, the approximate velocities are larger

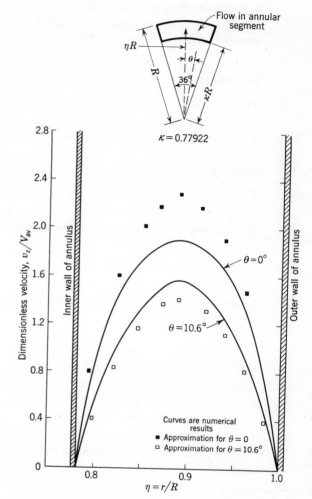

Fig. 3.3.3 First approximation compared with numerical results.

(by 16 percent for maximum velocities) than the numerical values. However, for $\theta = 10.6°$ the computed velocities are less than those obtained by numerical means. Not shown are the results for intermediate angles. Needless to say, however, the comparison is better, and for $\theta = 7.6°$, the agreement is to within 5 percent. Of course, a better approximation could be obtained by making a second approximation. For example, we could assume

$$v = \cos\frac{\theta\pi}{s} g_1(\eta) + \cos\frac{3\pi\theta}{s} g_2(\eta) \qquad (3.3.38)$$

and select both g_1 and g_2 such that I is an extremal. However, we have pushed the calculation far enough to illustrate the essential features of the method and further calculations have not been made.

3.4 EIGENVALUES AND EIGENFUNCTIONS

The integrand

$$I = \int_{r_1}^{r_2} \left[p(r) \left(\frac{dy}{dr} \right)^2 + q(r)y^2 \right] dr + a_1 y^2(r_1) + a_2 y^2(r_2) \tag{3.4.1}$$

subject to the restriction

$$\int_{r_1}^{r_2} W(r)y^2 \, dr = 1 \tag{3.4.2}$$

is stationary if the function $y(r)$ satisfies the Euler-Lagrange equation

$$\frac{d}{dr} \left[p(r) \frac{dy}{dr} \right] - q(r)y + \lambda^2 W(r)y = 0 \tag{3.4.3}$$

in which λ^2 is an undetermined multiplier. In addition we find the natural boundary conditions

$$p \frac{dy}{dr} + a_2 y = 0 \qquad \text{at } r = r_2 \tag{3.4.4}$$

and

$$p \frac{dy}{dr} - a_1 y = 0 \qquad \text{at } r = r_1 \tag{3.4.5}$$

or for a fixed boundary problem we shall consider boundary conditions of the form

$$y = 0 \qquad \text{at } r = r_1, r_2 \tag{3.4.6}$$

Equation (3.4.3) has a structure which frequently arises in physics. The parameter λ^2 is called the eigenvalue, and the function $y(r)$ associated with a given eigenvalue is termed the eigenfunction. If the function $y(r)$ vanishes at both boundaries; the weighting function $W(r)$ is greater than 0 and is continuous in the interval $r_1 \leq r \leq r_2$; $p(r)$ is greater than 0 and is continuous in $r_1 \leq r \leq r_2$; and $q(r)$ is continuous in $r_1 \leq r \leq r_2$, then the eigenvalues can be shown to be discrete.[1] These eigenvalues are very important in the analysis of physical problems, for, in general, they determine the rate of decay

[1] E. L. Ince, "Ordinary Differential Equations," pp. 231–233, Dover Publications, Inc., New York.

of an externally imposed disturbance.   Our attention centers on the possibility of using Eqs. (3.4.1) and (3.4.2) to generate approximate solutions to the very important equations having structure given in Eq. (3.4.3).   We shall begin our exploration by considering an example using a straightforward extension of the Ritz method.

EXAMPLE 3.4.1   The Graetz-Nusselt problem is that of determining the temperature distribution resulting from a fluid in fully developed laminar flow entering a circular tube in which the walls of the tube are maintained at a constant temperature which differs from the temperature of the entering fluid. If the fluid properties are independent of temperature and if axial conduction is small compared with heat flow by convection, then the temperature is given by[2]

$$T - T_s = \sum_{n=1}^{\infty} A_n y_n(r) \exp\left(- \frac{\lambda_n^2}{2} \frac{\alpha}{RV_{av}} \frac{z}{R}\right) \tag{3.4.7}$$

where $T =$ temperature of the fluid

$T_s =$ wall temperature

$\alpha =$ thermal diffusivity

$V_{av} =$ average fluid velocity

$R =$ tube radius

$z, r =$ coordinates as depicted in Fig. 3.4.1

The $y_n(r)$ and λ_n are the eigenfunction and eigenvalue, respectively, satisfying the differential equation

$$\frac{d^2y}{dr^2} + \frac{1}{r}\frac{dy}{dr} + \frac{\lambda^2}{R^2}\left(1 - \frac{r^2}{R^2}\right)y = 0 \tag{3.4.8}$$

and the boundary condition

$$y = 0 \quad \text{at } r = R \tag{3.4.9}$$

Equation (3.4.8) has been solved by expanding y into an infinite power series in $(r/R)^2$; however, the procedure for obtaining numerical results is quite laborious because of the number of terms which must be retained in the power series to achieve sufficient accuracy.   In this example we shall concern ourselves with the estimation of the smallest eigenvalue.   A better estimate of this eigenvalue will be computed in the following example, which will also construct an approximation to the eigenfunction.

To approximate the value of the smallest eigenvalue, we must first establish a variational principle which has Eq. (3.4.8) as its Euler-Lagrange equation.

[2] Max Jakob, "Heat Transfer," vol. I, pp. 451–464, John Wiley & Sons, Inc., New York, 1950.

It is easy to prove that the integral

$$I = \int_0^R \left[r \left(\frac{dy}{dr} \right)^2 \right] dr \tag{3.4.10}$$

subject to the restriction

$$\int_0^R \frac{r}{R^2} \left(1 - \frac{r^2}{R^2} \right) y^2 \, dr = 1 \tag{3.4.11}$$

is stationary if and only if Eq. (3.4.8) is satisfied.   Of course, Eq. (3.4.10) is a special case of the general structure set forth in Eq. (3.4.1).   Thus, finding the y which makes I stationary and satisfying the normalization condition, Eq. (3.4.11), is equivalent to determining the $y(r)$ which satisfies Eq. (3.4.8).

To estimate the first eigenvalue, choose

$$\tilde{y} = A \cos \frac{\pi r}{2R} \tag{3.4.12}$$

Substituting into Eq. (3.4.10) gives

$$\tilde{I} = A^2 \left(\frac{\pi^2}{16} + \frac{1}{4} \right) \tag{3.4.13}$$

Also, from Eq. (3.4.11) we find

$$1 = A^2 \left(\frac{1}{8} + \frac{1}{2\pi^2} - \frac{6}{\pi^4} \right) \tag{3.4.14}$$

The constant A must be determined such that I is rendered stationary subject to the restriction now imposed by Eq. (3.4.14).   Using the method of Lagrangian multipliers gives

$$0 = 2A \left[\left(\frac{\pi^2}{16} + \frac{1}{4} \right) - \lambda^2 \left(\frac{1}{8} + \frac{1}{2\pi^2} - \frac{6}{\pi^4} \right) \right] \tag{3.4.15}$$

If Eq. (3.4.15) is to have a nontrivial solution, then

$$\lambda^2 = \frac{\pi^2/16 + \frac{1}{4}}{\frac{1}{8} + 1/2\pi^2 - 6/\pi^4} \tag{3.4.16}$$

or

$$\lambda \cong 2.76$$

The first eigenvalue is actually 2.704^4, which is 2 percent less than the crude approximation which we find here.

It should be noted that the approximation to the eigenfunction given by Eq. (3.4.12) is in fact specified a priori, and as a consequence, it would only be a matter of good fortune if the $y(r)$ defined by Eq. (3.4.12) resembled the true eigenfunction.

The first example was used to illustrate the application of the variational formulation as an aid in the determination of the smallest eigenvalue. Our next task is to develop a generalized method of finding both the eigenvalues and the associated eigenfunctions. Let us return to Eqs. (3.4.1) and (3.4.2) and attempt to construct an approximate eigenfunction in the form

$$\tilde{y}(r) = \sum_{i=1}^{N} c_i \phi_i(r) \tag{3.4.17}$$

where each ϕ_i is assumed to satisfy the appropriate homogeneous boundary conditions [see Eqs. (3.4.4) through (3.4.6)]. Substituting Eq. (3.4.17) into Eqs. (3.4.1) and (3.4.2), we find, using the Lagrangian formulation,

$$\tilde{I} = \int_{r_1}^{r_2} \left[p(r) \left(\sum_{i=1}^{N} c_i \frac{d\phi_i}{dr} \right)^2 + q(r) \left(\sum_{i=1}^{N} c_i \phi_i \right)^2 \right] dr$$

$$- \lambda^2 \int_{r_1}^{r_2} W(r) \left(\sum_{i=1}^{N} c_i \phi_i \right)^2 dr + a_1 \left(\sum_{i=1}^{N} c_i \phi_i(r_1) \right)^2 \tag{3.4.18}$$

$$+ a_2 \left(\sum_{i=1}^{N} c_i \phi_i(r_2) \right)^2$$

Where λ^2 is an undetermined multiplier, the values of c_k which render $\tilde{I}$ stationary satisfy

$$\frac{\partial \tilde{I}}{\partial c_k} = 0 \tag{3.4.19}$$

giving the set of algebraic equations

$$0 = \sum_{j=1}^{N} (\alpha_{ij} - \lambda^2 \beta_{ij}) c_j \qquad i = 1, 2, \ldots, N \tag{3.4.20}$$

in which

$$\alpha_{ij} = \int_{r_1}^{r_2} \left[p(r) \frac{d\phi_i}{dr} \frac{d\phi_j}{dr} + q(r) \phi_i \phi_j \right] dr + a_1 \phi_i(r_1) \phi_j(r_1)$$

$$+ a_2 \phi_j(r_2) \phi_i(r_2) \tag{3.4.21}$$

and

$$\beta_{ij} = \int_{r_1}^{r_2} W(r) \phi_i \phi_j \, dr \tag{3.4.22}$$

It is clear that

$$\alpha_{ij} = \alpha_{ji} \tag{3.4.23}$$

and

$$\beta_{ij} = \beta_{ji} \tag{3.4.24}$$

The set of equations, Eqs. (3.4.20), are linear and homogeneous in the constants c_j. If the system of algebraic equations is to have a nontrivial solution, then the λ^2 must be chosen so that

$$\det |\alpha_{ij} - \lambda^2 \beta_{ij}| = 0 \tag{3.4.25}$$

where Eq. (3.4.25) means that the determinant of the coefficients of the c_j defined by Eq. (3.4.20) must vanish. Equation (3.4.25) is, in fact, a polynomial in λ^2 of degree N. As a consequence, there are N values of λ^2 which satisfy Eq. (3.4.25). These values are $\lambda_1^2, \lambda_2^2, \ldots, \lambda_N^2$. Although the eigenvalues need not all be distinct, it is convenient to specify them by N distinct symbols. For each eigenvalue, say λ_j^2, a set of c_i can be determined from Eq. (3.4.20) to give

$$\tilde{y}_j(r) = \sum_{i=1}^{N} c_i^{(j)} \phi_i(r) \tag{3.4.26}$$

where $c_i^{(j)}$ is used to denote the values of the coefficients associated with λ_j, and $y_j(r)$ is the approximate eigenfunction given by the linear combination shown above. If λ_i^2 and λ_j^2 are distinct, then an orthogonality relationship exists such that

$$N_{ij} = \int_{r_1}^{r_2} W(r)\tilde{y}_j(r)\tilde{y}_i(r)\, dr = 0 \qquad \lambda_i^2 \neq \lambda_j^2 \tag{3.4.27}$$

The proof of this orthogonality relationship is quite simple. Using Eq. (3.4.26), we can write

$$N_{ij} = \sum_{e,k=1}^{N} c_e^{(i)} c_k^{(j)} \beta_{ek} \tag{3.4.28}$$

Equation (3.4.20) can be written as

$$\frac{1}{\lambda_i^2} \sum_{e=1}^{N} \alpha_{ke} c_e^{(i)} = \sum_{e=1}^{N} \beta_{ke} c_e^{(i)} \tag{3.4.29}$$

Multiply both sides by $c_k^{(j)}$ and sum to obtain

$$N_{ij} = \frac{1}{\lambda_i^2} \sum_{e,k=1}^{N} \alpha_{ke} c_e^{(i)} c_k^{(j)} \tag{3.4.30}$$

It is clear that

$$N_{ij} = \frac{1}{\lambda_j^2} \sum_{e,k=1}^{N} \alpha_{ek} c_e^{(j)} c_k^{(i)} \tag{3.4.31}$$

by the same manipulations. If we subtract Eq. (3.4.31) from Eq. (3.4.30) and recall the symmetry of α_{ek}, then

$$0 = \left(\frac{1}{\lambda_i^2} - \frac{1}{\lambda_j^2} \right) \sum_{e,k=1}^{N} \alpha_{ke} c_e^{(i)} c_k^{(j)} \tag{3.4.32}$$

Since $\lambda_i^2 \neq \lambda_j^2$, we must have

$$0 = \sum_{e,k=1}^{N} \alpha_{ke} c_e^{(i)} c_k^{(j)} \tag{3.4.33}$$

which gives

$$N_{ij} = 0 \qquad \text{for } i \neq j, \lambda_i^2 \neq \lambda_j^2 \tag{3.4.34}$$

proving the orthogonality relationship. This orthogonality among approximate eigenfunctions will prove to be quite useful in subsequent examples.

EXAMPLE 3.4.2 In Example (3.4.1) we found an approximation to the smallest eigenvalue defined by Eq. (3.4.8). Let us determine a better approximation. Let

$$\tilde{y}(r) = c_1 \cos \frac{\pi r}{2R} + c_2 \cos \frac{3\pi r}{2R} \tag{3.4.35}$$

The boundary condition at the wall is automatically satisfied since

$$\cos \frac{2j - 1}{2} \pi = 0 \qquad j = 1, 2, \ldots \tag{3.4.36}$$

Substituting Eq. (3.4.35) into the general expressions developed in the preceding analysis and making the identifications

$$p(r) = r \tag{3.4.37}$$
$$q(r) = 0 \tag{3.4.38}$$
$$W(r) = \frac{r}{R^2}\left(1 - \frac{r^2}{R^2} \right) \tag{3.4.39}$$
$$a_1 = 0 \tag{3.4.40}†$$
$$a_2 = 0 \tag{3.4.41}†$$

---

† The choice of values of a_1 and a_2 given here merits further interpretation. The example being studied does not actually fall into the class of differential equations having $p(r) > 0$ throughout the interval.   For since $p(r) = r$, this term vanishes at the end point ($r = 0$) and the differential equation is said to be singular.   However, if we want the solution to have a bounded first derivative at the origin, then we must have

$$\lim_{r \to 0} r \frac{dy}{dr} = 0$$

which gives $a_1 = 0$ [see Eq. (3.4.4) with $r_1 = 0$], since y does not necessarily vanish at the origin.

we find from Eq. (3.4.20)

$$0 = (\alpha_{11} - \lambda^2 \beta_{11})c_1 + (\alpha_{12} - \lambda^2 \beta_{12})c_2 \tag{3.4.42}$$

$$0 = (\alpha_{12} - \lambda^2 \beta_{12})c_1 + (\alpha_{22} - \lambda^2 \beta_{22})c_2 \tag{3.4.43}$$

where $\alpha_{11} = \dfrac{\pi^2}{4R^2} \displaystyle\int_0^R r \sin \dfrac{\pi r}{2R} \sin \dfrac{\pi r}{2R} \, dr = \dfrac{\pi^2}{16} + \dfrac{1}{4}$

$$\alpha_{12} = \frac{3\pi^2}{4R^2} \int_0^R r \sin \frac{\pi r}{2R} \sin \frac{3\pi r}{2R} \, dr = -\frac{3}{4}$$

$$\alpha_{22} = \frac{9\pi^2}{4R^2} \int_0^R r \sin \frac{3\pi r}{2R} \sin \frac{3\pi r}{2R} \, dr = \frac{9\pi^2}{16} + \frac{1}{4}$$

$$\beta_{11} = \int_0^R \frac{r}{R^2}\left(1 - \frac{r^2}{R^2}\right) \cos \frac{\pi r}{2R} \cos \frac{\pi r}{2R} \, dr = \frac{1}{8} + \frac{1}{2\pi^2} - \frac{6}{\pi^4}$$

$$\beta_{12} = \int_0^R \frac{r}{R^2}\left(1 - \frac{r^2}{R^2}\right) \cos \frac{3\pi r}{2R} \cos \frac{\pi r}{2R} \, dr = \frac{1}{8\pi^2} - \frac{6}{\pi^4}$$

$$\beta_{22} = \int_0^R \frac{r}{R^2}\left(1 - \frac{r^2}{R^2}\right) \cos \frac{3\pi r}{2R} \cos \frac{3\pi r}{2R} \, dr = \frac{1}{8} + \frac{1}{18\pi^2} - \frac{2}{27\pi^4}$$

Substituting the numerical values into Eqs. (3.4.42) and (3.4.43) gives

$$(0.86685 - 0.11407\lambda^2)c_1 + (0.04893\lambda^2 - 0.75)c_2 = 0 \tag{3.4.44}$$

and

$$(0.04893\lambda^2 - 0.75)c_1 + (5.80165 - 0.12987\lambda^2)c_2 = 0 \tag{3.4.45}$$

Thus the eigenvalues must be determined so that the determinate

$$\begin{vmatrix} 0.86685 - 0.11407\lambda^2 & 0.04893\lambda^2 - 0.75 \\ 0.04893\lambda^2 - 0.75 & 5.80165 - 0.12987\lambda^2 \end{vmatrix} = 0$$

We find

$$\lambda_1 = 2.71$$

and

$$\lambda_2 = 7.01$$

These values compare well with the exact values of 2.704 and 6.66 with the second eigenvalue being different by 6 percent. The function $\tilde{y}_n(r)$ can also be compared with the exact values. To compute the approximate eigenfunction associated with each of the eigenvalues, we must solve for $c_1^{(1)}$, $c_2^{(1)}$, $c_1^{(2)}$, and $c_2^{(2)}$. However, it is clear that we can determine these constants only as a ratio of c_1 to c_2. The value of each constant will then be selected so that $y_n(r)$ is equal to one at the origin. This choice was made only because we want to compare our approximate results with those given by Brown.[3]

[3] G. M. Brown, "Heat or Mass Transfer in a Fluid in Laminar Flow in a Circular or Flat Conduit," *J. Am. Inst. Chem. Engrs.*, vol. 6, p. 179, 1960.

With this choice we find

$$\tilde{y}_1(r) = 0.9253 \cos \frac{\pi r}{2R} + 0.0747 \cos \frac{3\pi r}{2R} \qquad (3.4.46)$$

and

$$\tilde{y}_2(r) = 0.259 \cos \frac{\pi r}{2R} + 0.741 \cos \frac{3\pi r}{2R} \qquad (3.4.47)$$

so that

$$c_1^{(1)} = 0.9253$$
$$c_2^{(1)} = 0.0747$$
$$c_1^{(2)} = 0.259$$
$$c_2^{(2)} = 0.741$$

and the approximate values for the eigenfunctions are compared with the numerical values in Table 3.4.1. We see that the eigenfunction associated with the smallest eigenvalue $\tilde{y}_1(r)$ compares quite well with the values as determined numerically by Brown. The largest deviations are approximately 2 percent. The eigenfunction associated with the second eigenvalue $\tilde{y}_2(r)$ does not compare nearly so well and, indeed, is apparently quite inadequate. Of course, the comparison can be improved by including a third term in the approximating series [Eq. (3.4.35)]; however, the work required to achieve the numerical answers is increased considerably.

Fortunately, the information we have found using the simple two-term approximation is sufficient to accurately determine the variation of the mean fluid temperature with axial position. Although the reader may not remember our purpose in making these calculations, he is now reminded that the problem was to determine the temperature distribution resulting

TABLE 3.4.1   COMPARISON OF EIGENFUNCTIONS FOR THE GRAETZ-NUSSELT PROBLEM

	First		Second	
Position r/R	$y_1(r)$ numerical[3]	$\tilde{y}_1(r)$ approximate	$y_2(r)$ numerical[3]	$\tilde{y}_2(r)$ approximate
0	1	1	1	1
0.2	0.929	0.926	0.605	0.702
0.4	0.738	0.725	−0.110	−0.02
0.6	0.483	0.499	−0.432	−0.546
0.8	0.225	0.225	−0.284	−0.520
1.0	0	0	0	0

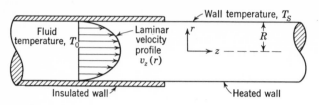

Fig. 3.4.1   Laminar-flow heat transfer.

from a fluid in fully developed laminar flow entering a circular tube in which the walls are maintained at a constant temperature which differs from the temperature of the entering fluid (see Fig. 3.4.1). The difference in the fluid temperature and the wall temperature was expressed as a power series

$$T - T_s = \sum_{n=1}^{\infty} A_n y_n(r) \exp\left(-\frac{\lambda_n^2 \alpha}{2RV_{av}} \frac{z}{R}\right) \tag{3.4.7}$$

Or, using our approximation, we write

$$T - T_s = \sum_{n=1}^{N} \tilde{A}_n \tilde{y}_n(r) \exp\left(-\frac{\lambda_n^2 \alpha}{2RV_{av}} \frac{z}{R}\right) \tag{3.4.48}$$

where the summation now extends to some finite limit N. In the present example N is 2. Thus to determine an approximation for the temperature distribution, we need to find the $\tilde{A}_n$, since we have already established λ_1 and λ_2 together with the associated eigenfunctions $\tilde{y}_1$ and $\tilde{y}_2$. To find the A_n, we note that at the inlet of the heat exchanger ($z = 0$)

$$T_0 - T_s = \sum_{n=1}^{N} \tilde{A}_n \tilde{y}_n(r) \tag{3.4.49}$$

where T_0 is the inlet temperature of the fluid.   If we multiply both sides of this equation by $\tilde{y}_n(r)(r/R^2)(1 - r^2/R^2) \, dr$ and integrate between the limits of 0 to R, we find that

$$\tilde{A}_n = \frac{(T_0 - T_s)\int_0^R (r/R^2)(1 - r^2/R^2)\tilde{y}_n \, dr}{\int_0^R (r/R^2)(1 - r^2/R^2)\tilde{y}_n(r)\tilde{y}_n(r) \, dr} \tag{3.4.50}$$

after imposing the orthogonality relationship expressed by Eq. (3.4.27).   In the present example the $\tilde{y}_n(r)$ are expressed as a series of cosine terms. Substituting such a sum into Eq. (3.4.50) gives

$$\tilde{A}_n = \frac{(T_0 - T_s)\sum_{j=1}^{N} c_j^{(n)} \gamma_j}{\sum_{j,k=1}^{N} c_j^{(n)} c_k^{(n)} \beta_{jk}} \tag{3.4.51}$$

where

$$\gamma_j = \int_0^R \frac{r}{R^2}\left(1 - \frac{r^2}{R^2}\right) \cos \frac{2j-1}{2} \frac{\pi r}{R} \, dr$$

$$= -\frac{4}{\pi^2(2j-1)^2} + \frac{48(-1)^{j+1}}{(2j-1)^3\pi^3} - \frac{96}{\pi^4(2j-1)^4}$$

Using the results of our two-term approximation we find

$$\tilde{A}_1 = (T_0 - T_s)1.44$$

and

$$\tilde{A}_2 = (T_0 - T_s) 0.635$$

Thus an approximation for the temperature distribution is determined. To evaluate this approximation, let us determine the average temperature, which we define to be

$$\langle T \rangle = \frac{\int_0^R T(r,z)(r/R^2)(1 - r^2/R^2) \, dr}{\int_0^R (r/R^2)(1 - r^2/R^2) \, dr} \tag{3.4.52}$$

or

$$\langle T \rangle = 4\int_0^R T(r,z) \frac{r}{R^2}\left(1 - \frac{r^2}{R^2}\right) dr \tag{3.4.53}$$

This average corresponds to the so-called "cup mixing" temperature that would be observed if the fluid at an axial position z was permitted to flow into an insulated cup and come to equilibrium. In terms of our approximation, it is easily shown that

$$\langle T \rangle - T_s \cong 4 \sum_{n,m=1}^N \tilde{A}_n c_m^{(n)} \gamma_m \exp\left(-\frac{\lambda_n^2 \alpha}{2RV_{av}} \frac{z}{R}\right) \tag{3.4.54}$$

or

$$\frac{\langle T \rangle - T_s}{T_0 - T_s} \cong 0.79 \exp\left[-\frac{(2.7)^2\alpha}{2RV_{av}} \frac{z}{R}\right] + 0.11 \exp\left[\frac{(7.0)^2\alpha}{2RV_{av}} \frac{z}{R}\right] \tag{3.4.55}$$

Thus Eq. (3.4.55) relates the mean fluid temperature to the axial position z. We can immediately see that the equation is not accurate for small z. For we know that for $z = 0$, the left-hand side of Eq. (3.4.55) is

$$\frac{\langle T(r,0)\rangle - T_s}{T_0 - T_s} = \frac{\langle T_0 \rangle - T_s}{T_0 - T_s} = 1.0$$

whereas on the right we find a value of 0.9.   Therefore, the approximation is in error by 10 percent at $z = 0$.   However, for larger values of z the approximation improves.   Indeed Brown gives the first two terms as

$$\frac{\langle T \rangle - T_s}{T_0 - T_s} = 0.82 \exp\left[-\frac{(2.7)^2 \alpha}{2RV_{av}} \frac{z}{R}\right] + 0.098 \exp\left[-\frac{(6.66)^2 \alpha}{2RV_{av}} \frac{z}{R}\right] \quad (3.4.56)$$

which differs from the result which would be computed from Eq. (3.4.55) by approximately 2 to 3 percent for sufficiently large z.

Thus our approximation is exceedingly good except very near the inlet where it is in error by 10 percent. This error decreases for larger z to a value of about 2 percent. These error limits are not excessive for most engineering applications, and we have resolved a very difficult computational problem by making an approximation based on the Ritz method.

PROBLEM 3.4.1   Schechter and Wissler[4] have shown that an important eigenvalue problem arises in the determination of a concentration profile in a light-catalyzed reactor.   This problem is defined by the differential equation

$$\frac{d}{dr} r \frac{dy}{dr} + [\lambda^2 r(1 - r^2) - \sigma e^{-N}(e^{+Nr} + e^{-Nr})]y = 0 \quad (3.4.57)$$

subject to the boundary conditions

$$\frac{dy}{dr} = 2\sigma e^{-N} y \quad \text{at } r = 0$$

and

$$\frac{dy}{dr} = 0 \quad \text{at } r = 1$$

Schechter and Wissler reported

$$\lambda_{(1)} = 2.773$$

for $\sigma = 1.0$ and $N = 0.0$.

Approximate this first eigenvalue using the Ritz method.   Take

$$y = c_1\left(\frac{\cos wr}{\sin w} + \frac{\sin wr}{\cos w}\right)$$

where w must be selected so that the boundary condition at $r = 0$ is satisfied.

EXAMPLE 3.4.3   Let us consider the concentration of two components reacting reversibly in a laminar-flow tubular reactor such as that depicted in Fig. 3.4.2. For this case the reaction mechanism is simply

$$c_1 \underset{k_2}{\overset{k_1}{\rightleftharpoons}} c_2 \quad (3.4.58)$$

[4] R. S. Schechter and E. H. Wissler, "Photochemical Reactions in an Isothermal Laminar-flow Chemical Reactor," *Appl. Sci. Res. Sec. A.*, vol. 9, p. 334, 1960.

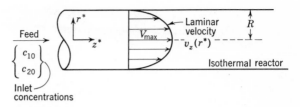

Fig. 3.4.2   Tubular reactor.

where k_1 and k_2 are the reaction-rate constants for the forward and backward reactions, respectively.   The material balance can be written in dimensionless form as

$$v(r)\frac{\partial c_1}{\partial z} = d_1\left(\frac{\partial^2 c_1}{\partial r^2} + \frac{1}{r}\frac{\partial c_1}{\partial r}\right) - c_1 + \xi c_2 \qquad (3.4.59)$$

and

$$v(r)\frac{\partial c_2}{\partial z} = d_2\left(\frac{\partial^2 c_2}{\partial r^2} + \frac{1}{r}\frac{\partial c_2}{\partial r}\right) + c_1 - \xi c_2 \qquad (3.4.60)$$

subject to the boundary conditions

$$\frac{\partial c_1}{\partial r} = \frac{\partial c_2}{\partial r} = 0 \qquad \text{for } r = 0, 1 \qquad (3.4.61)$$

$$c_1 = c_{10} \qquad \text{for } z = 0 \qquad (3.4.62)$$

$$c_2 = c_{20} \qquad \text{for } z = 0 \qquad (3.4.63)$$

where

$$r = \frac{r^*}{R}$$

$$z = \frac{z^* k_1}{V_{\max}}$$

$$v(r) = \frac{v_z(r^*)}{V_{\max}}$$

$$d_i = \frac{D_i}{k_1 R^2}$$

$$\xi = \frac{k_2}{k_1}$$

in which r^* = radial-position vector

z^* = axial-position vector

R = tube radius

$v_z(r^*)$ = laminar velocity distribution

V_{max} = centerline velocity

$\dagger D_i$ = diffusion coefficient of substance I

Let us assume a solution of the form

$$c_i = \sum_{k=0}^{\infty} a_k \phi_{ki}(r) e^{-\lambda_k z} \qquad i = 1, 2 \tag{3.4.64}$$

Substituting into Eqs. (3.4.59) and (3.4.60), we find$\ddagger$

$$-\lambda_k v(r)\phi_{k1} = d_1\left(\frac{d^2\phi_{k1}}{dr^2} + \frac{1}{r}\frac{d\phi_{k1}}{dr}\right) - \phi_{k1} + \xi\phi_{k2} \tag{3.4.65}$$

$$-\lambda_k v(r)\phi_{k2} = d_2\left(\frac{d^2\phi_{k2}}{dr^2} + \frac{1}{r}\frac{d\phi_{k2}}{dr}\right) + \phi_{k1} - \xi\phi_{k2} \tag{3.4.66}$$

We should like to find the integral which has as a necessary condition for the existence of an extremal the two coupled differential equations shown above. It is not difficult to show that the integral

$$I = \int_0^1 \left[d_1\left(\frac{d\phi_1}{dr}\right)^2 + \xi d_2\left(\frac{d\phi_2}{dr}\right)^2 + (\phi_1 - \xi\phi_2)^2 \right] r\, dr \tag{3.4.67}$$

subject to the restriction

$$1 = \int_0^1 (\phi_1{}^2 + \xi\phi_2{}^2) r v(r)\, dr \tag{3.4.68}$$

is stationary if Eqs. (3.4.65) and (3.4.66) are satisfied together with the natural boundary conditions

$$\frac{d\phi_1}{dr} = \frac{d\phi_2}{dr} = 0 \qquad \text{at } r = 0, 1 \tag{3.4.69}$$

To determine an approximate solution, let

$$\tilde{\phi}_{k1} = \sum_{i=0}^{N} A_i^{(k)} J_0(\beta_i r) \tag{3.4.70}$$

$$\tilde{\phi}_{k2} = \sum_{i=0}^{N} B_i^{(k)} J_0(\beta_i r) \tag{3.4.71}$$

$\dagger$ Here we do not take $D_1 = D_2$, since a diluent may be present.

$\ddagger$ Demonstration of the validity of Eqs. (3.4.64) requires a proof of the completeness of the set of functions ϕ_{ki}. To the author's knowledge this proof has not been given.

in which the β_i are selected so that

$$J_1(\beta_i) = 0 \tag{3.4.72}\dagger$$

This condition insures that the natural boundary conditions are satisfied. Here the J_0 are the Bessel functions of order zero and the first kind. J_1 is the Bessel function of order one. Substituting Eqs. (3.4.70) and (3.4.71) into Eq. (3.4.67) [taking into account restriction (3.4.68)] by the method of undetermined multipliers gives

$$\frac{\partial I}{\partial A_j^{(k)}} = 0 = d_1 A_j^{(k)} \beta_j^2 N_j + A_j^{(k)} n_j - \xi B_j^{(k)} n_j - \lambda_k \sum_{i=0}^{N} A_i^{(k)} \psi_{ij} \tag{3.4.73}$$

where[5]

$$N_j = \int_0^1 r J_1^2(\beta_j r)\, dr = \tfrac{1}{2} J_0(\beta_j)^2$$

$$0 = \int_0^1 r J_1(\beta_j r) J_1(\beta_i r)\, dr \qquad i \neq j$$

$$n_j = \int_0^1 r J_0^2(\beta_j r)\, dr = \tfrac{1}{2} J_0(\beta_j)^2$$

$$0 = \int_0^1 r J_0(\beta_j r) J_0(\beta_i r)\, dr \qquad i \neq j$$

$$\psi_{ij} = \int_0^1 r v(r) J_0(\beta_j r) J_0(\beta_i r)\, dr = \begin{cases} \dfrac{-2(\beta_i^2 + \beta_j^2)}{(\beta_i^2 - \beta_j^2)^2} J_0(\beta_j) J_0(\beta_i) & \beta_i \neq \beta_j \\[2mm] \tfrac{1}{3} J_0^2(\beta_i) & \beta_i = \beta_j > 0 \\[2mm] \tfrac{1}{4} & \beta_i = \beta_j = 0 \end{cases}$$

These equations are written for the case in which the β_i satisfy Eq. (3.4.72) and also satisfy $v(r) = 1 - r^2$, the laminar-flow velocity profile. Similarly we find

$$\frac{\partial I}{\partial B_j^{(k)}} = d_2 \beta_j^2 B^{(k)} N_j - A_j^{(k)} n_j + \xi B_j^{(k)} n_j - \lambda_k \sum_{i=0}^{N} B_i^{(k)} \psi_{ij} = 0 \tag{3.4.74}$$

$\dagger\ d/dx\, J_0(x) = -J_1(x)$

[5] Integrals of the type arising in this example can be easily evaluated using the equation

$$\int_0^{z_1} (\alpha^2 - \beta^2) z^p J_\nu(\alpha z) J_{\mu+1}(\beta z)\, dz + (p + \nu + \mu)\beta \int_0^{z_1} z^{p-1} J_\nu(\alpha z) J_\mu(\beta z)\, dz$$

$$+ (p - \nu - \mu - 2)\alpha \int_0^{z_1} z^{p-1} J_{\nu+1}(\alpha z) J_{\mu+1}(\beta z)\, dz$$

$$= z_1^p [\alpha J_{\nu+1}(\alpha z_1) J_{\mu+1}(\beta z_1) + \beta J_\nu(\alpha z_1) J_\mu(\beta z_1)]$$

which has been developed by S. N. Singh, *Appl. Sci. Res. Sec. A*, vol. 7, p. 237, 1958.

Let us truncate Eqs. (3.4.70) and (3.4.71) to include only two terms (that is, $N = 1$) and consider a special example in which

$d_1 = 0.1$

$d_2 = 0.2$

$\xi = 0.5$

The values of the pertinent constants are given in Table 3.4.2. After some calculation, one finds from Eq. (3.4.73)

$$\left(1 - \frac{\lambda_k}{2}\right)A_0^{(k)} - 0.1097A_1^{(k)}\lambda_k - \tfrac{1}{2}B_0^{(k)} = 0 \tag{3.4.75a}$$

and

$$-0.6764\lambda_k A_0^{(k)} + \left(2.468 - \frac{2\lambda_k}{3}\right)A_1^{(k)} - \tfrac{1}{2}B_1^{(k)} = 0 \tag{3.4.75b}$$

From Eq. (3.4.74) we see that

$$-A_0^{(k)} + \left(\frac{1}{2} - \frac{\lambda_k}{2}\right)B_0^{(k)} - 0.1097\lambda_k B_1^{(k)} = 0 \tag{3.4.75c}$$

and

$$-A_1^{(k)} - 0.6764\lambda_k B_0^{(k)} + \left(3.436 - \frac{2\lambda_k}{3}\right)B_1^{(k)} = 0 \tag{3.4.75d}$$

Since these equations are linear and homogeneous in the constants $A_0^{(k)}$, $A_1^{(k)}$, $B_0^{(k)}$, $B_1^{(k)}$, then a nontrivial solution exists only if the determinate of the coefficients vanishes. We find that the following values of λ cause the determinate of the coefficients to vanish:

$\lambda_0 = 0$

$\lambda_1 = 2.41$

TABLE 3.4.2 NUMERICAL VALUES OF PERTI-NENT COEFFICIENTS

j	β_j	$J_0(\beta_j)$	N_j or n_j
0	0	1	$\tfrac{1}{2}$
1	3.832	−0.4028	0.08112
2	7.016	0.3001	0.04503
i	j	ψ_{ij}	
0	0	0.25	
1	0	0.05487	
1	1	0.05408	
2	0	−0.01219	
2	1	0.01297	
2	2	0.0300	

These are the approximations to the true eigenvalues. The first eigenvalue is identically 0, since the concentrations must approach some stationary value (the equilibrium concentration) as z approaches infinity. The eigenfunctions can be determined. Here

$$\tilde{\phi}_{01} = 1.0$$

and

$$\tilde{\phi}_{02} = \frac{1}{\xi} = 2$$

are associated with the $\lambda = 0$. The second eigenfunctions are

$$\tilde{\phi}_{11} = 0.363 + 0.637J_0(3.832r)$$

and

$$\dagger\tilde{\phi}_{12} = -0.485 - 0.0832J_0(3.832r)$$

A higher-order approximation can now be made by assuming that

$$\tilde{\phi}_{k1} = A_0^{(k)} + A_1^{(k)}J_0(\beta_1 r) + A_2^{(k)}J_0(\beta_2 r) \qquad k = 0, 1, 2$$

and

$$\tilde{\phi}_{k2} = B_0^{(k)} + B_1^{(k)}J_0(\beta_1 r) + B_1^{(k)}J_0(\beta_2 r) \qquad k = 0, 1, 2$$

By exactly the same computational scheme shown before we find

$$\lambda_0 = 0$$
$$\lambda_1 = 2.40$$

These compare to the exact eigenvalues of

$$\lambda_0 = 0$$
$$\lambda_1 = 2.400$$

as determined by Sibra.[6] The associated eigenfunctions are

$$\tilde{\phi}_{11} = 0.3284 + 0.6115J_0(3.832r) + 0.0601J_0(7.016r)$$

and

$$\tilde{\phi}_{12} = -0.4462 - 0.05342J_0(3.832r) + 0.0355J_0(7.016r)$$

with $\tilde{\phi}_{01}$ and $\tilde{\phi}_{02}$ being unchanged from the second-order approximation.

† In this system the $\tilde{\phi}_{12}(0)$ can not be normalized independently of $\tilde{\phi}_{11}(0)$. Indeed, in presenting our results, we have forced the value $\tilde{\phi}_1 = 1$ at $r = 0$, but $\tilde{\phi}_2$ at the origin is then fixed by the solution of the algebraic equation (3.4.75).

[6] P. Sibra, "Reversible Reaction and Diffusion in an Isothermal, Tubular Reactor," master's thesis, University of Texas, Austin, Tex., 1959.

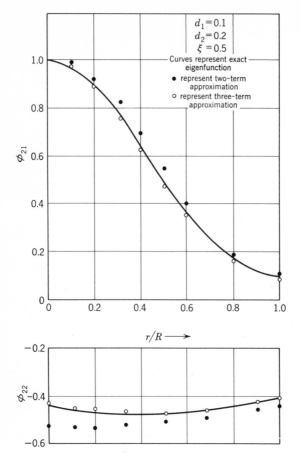

Fig. 3.4.3 Comparison of approximate eigenfunctions.

These approximations are compared with the precise values determined by Sibra in Fig. 3.4.3. It is clear that the three-term approximation is acceptable for most design purposes.

We can complete the problem by finding the variation of the concentration as a function of position. It is of interest to put the solution into its final form. At this point in the example we have developed the functions $\tilde{\phi}_{ki}$ into the form

$$\tilde{\phi}_{k1} = \sum_{i=0}^{N} A_i^{(k)} J_0(\beta_i r) \tag{3.4.76a}$$

and

$$\tilde{\phi}_{k2} = \sum_{i=0}^{N} B_i^{(k)} J_0(\beta_i r) \tag{3.4.76b}$$

From Eq. (3.4.64) we see that

$$c_1(r,z) = \sum_{k=0}^{N} a_k \phi_{k1}(r) e^{-\lambda_k z} \qquad (3.4.77a)$$

and

$$c_2(r,z) = \sum_{k=0}^{N} a_k \phi_{k2}(r) e^{-\lambda_k z} \qquad (3.4.77b)$$

Our remaining task is to determine the constants a_k. To do this we develop an orthogonality property among the approximate eigenfunctions. This orthogonality relationship is unusual in that both eigenfunctions appear in the integrand. We shall prove

$$\int_0^1 r(1 - r^2)(\tilde{\phi}_{k1}\tilde{\phi}_{m1} + \xi\tilde{\phi}_{k2}\tilde{\phi}_{m2})\, dr = 0 \qquad k \neq m \qquad (3.4.78)$$

Note that this is a relationship which exists among the *approximate* eigenfunctions, although by using the defining differential equations, one can prove precisely the same orthogonality property for the exact eigenfunctions.[6]

We begin our proof by substituting Eq. (3.4.76) into Eq. (3.4.78). We find that we wish to demonstrate the following result:

$$\sum_{i,j=0}^{N} [A_i^{(k)}A_j^{(m)} + \xi B_i^{(k)}B_j^{(m)}]\psi_{ij} = 0 \qquad (3.4.79)$$

Equation (3.4.79) is equivalent to Eq. (3.4.78). To prove Eq. (3.4.79), we need the set of algebraic equations which defines the coefficients. Rewriting Eqs. (3.4.73) and (3.4.74),

$$0 = A_j^{(k)}(d_1\beta_j{}^2 N_j + n_j) - \xi B_j^{(k)} n_j - \lambda_k \sum_{i=0}^{N} A_i^{(k)}\psi_{ij} \qquad (3.4.73a)$$

$$0 = -A_j^{(k)} n_j + B_j^{(k)}(d_2\beta_j{}^2 N_j + \xi n_j) - \lambda_k \sum_{i=0}^{N} B_i^{(k)}\psi_{ij} \qquad (3.4.74a)$$

Of course the superscript k is "free," and in fact these two equations are valid for all integers $0 \leq k \leq N$. Thus we can also write Eqs. (3.4.73) and (3.4.74) as

$$0 = A_j^{(m)}(d_1\beta_j{}^2 N_j + n_j) - \xi B_j^{(m)} n_j - \lambda_m \sum_{i=0}^{N} A_j^{(m)}\psi_{ij} \qquad (3.4.73b)$$

and

$$0 = -A_j^{(m)} n_j + B_j^{(m)}(d_2\beta_j{}^2 N_j + \xi n_j) - \lambda_m \sum_{i=0}^{N} A_i^{(m)}\psi_{ij} \qquad (3.4.74b)$$

Now multiply Eq. (3.4.73a) by $A_j^{(m)}$ and sum on j; multiply Eq. (3.4.73b) by $-A_i^{(k)}$ and sum on j; multiply Eq. (3.4.74a) by $\xi B_j^{(m)}$ and sum on j; and multiply Eq. (3.4.74b) by $-\xi B_j^{(k)}$ and sum on j. On adding these four equations, we find

$$(\lambda_k - \lambda_m) \sum_{j,i=0}^{N} [A_j^{(m)} A_i^{(k)} + \xi B_j^{(m)} B_i^{(m)}] \psi_{ij} = 0 \tag{3.4.80}$$

and since $\lambda_k \neq \lambda_m$, Eq. (3.4.79) is proved. It then follows that Eq. (3.4.78) is a valid expression relating the approximate eigenfunctions.

We can now determine the constants a_k appearing in Eq. (3.4.77). These constants must be selected such that the inlet conditions specified by Eqs. (3.4.62) and (3.4.63) are satisfied. Multiply Eq. (3.4.77a) by $rv(r)\tilde{\phi}_{m1}(r)\,dr$ and integrate from $r = 0$ to $r = 1$. We find for the inlet (that is, $z = 0$)

$$\int_0^1 c_{10} rv(r)\tilde{\phi}_{m1}(r)\,dr = \sum_{k=0}^{N} a_k \int_0^1 rv(r)\tilde{\phi}_{m1}\tilde{\phi}_{k1}\,dr \tag{3.4.81}$$

From Eq. (3.4.77b)

$$\int_0^1 \xi c_{20} rv(r)\tilde{\phi}_{m2}(r)\,dr = \sum_{k=0}^{N} a_k \xi \int_0^1 rv(r)\tilde{\phi}_{m2}\tilde{\phi}_{k1}\,dr \tag{3.4.82}$$

Adding these two results and applying the orthogonality condition yields

$$a_m = \frac{\int_0^1 (c_{10}\tilde{\phi}_{m1} + \xi c_{20}\tilde{\phi}_{m2})rv(r)\,dr}{\int_0^1 (\tilde{\phi}_{m1}{}^2 + \xi\tilde{\phi}_{m2}{}^2)rv(r)\,dr} \tag{3.4.83}$$

which determines the Fourier coefficients a_m.

If we specialize our considerations to the situation in which the inlet concentration of substance 2 vanishes ($c_{20} = 0$) and the inlet concentration of substance 1 is fixed at unity ($c_{10} = 1$), then Eq. (3.4.83) becomes

$$a_m = \frac{\displaystyle\sum_{j=0}^{N} \gamma_j A_j^{(m)}}{\displaystyle\sum_{j,i=0}^{N} [A_j^{(m)} A_i^{(m)} + \xi B_j^{(m)} B_i^{(m)}] \psi_{ij}} \tag{3.4.84}$$

where

$$\gamma_j = \int_0^1 rv(r) J_0(\beta_j r)\,dr$$

The values of a_0 and a_1 given in Table 3.4.3 have been computed using both the second and third approximation, and these approximate results are compared with the more precise values of Sibra in the same table. The agreement between the values determined by the third approximation and those of Sibra is indeed remarkable. Of course, the a_0 agree exactly, since the $\tilde{\phi}_{01}$ and $\tilde{\phi}_{02}$ are, in fact, the exact eigenfunctions.

As a final test of the quality of our approximation, let us determine the average concentration of the two substances relative to the axial position z. This average concentration is defined as

$$\langle c_1 \rangle = 4 \int_0^1 rv(r)c_1(r,z)\,dr \tag{3.4.85}$$

which is a volumetric average. Substituting the power-series expansion as given by Eqs. (3.4.76) and (3.4.77) for $c_1(r,z)$, we find

$$\langle c_1 \rangle = 4 \sum_{k=0}^{N} a_k e^{-\lambda_k z} \sum_{i=0}^{N} A_i^{(k)} \gamma_i \tag{3.4.86}$$

or, in terms of our third approximation,

$$\langle c_1 \rangle = \tfrac{1}{3} + 0.55 e^{-2.40z} \tag{3.4.87}$$

Similarly

$$\langle c_2 \rangle = \tfrac{2}{3} - 0.55 e^{-2.40z} \tag{3.4.88}$$

Sibra's expressions are

$$\langle c_1 \rangle = \tfrac{1}{3} + 0.552 e^{-2.40z} + 0.0722 e^{-3.85z} + \cdots \tag{3.4.89a}$$

and

$$\langle c_2 \rangle = \tfrac{2}{3} - 0.552 e^{-2.40z} - 0.0722 e^{-3.85z} - \cdots \tag{3.4.89b}$$

It is clear that the approximate results are very nearly the same as those developed by Sibra. This comparison again indicates the ease and accuracy with which approximations can be made using the Ritz method.

It is interesting to note that the estimates of the eigenvalues found in the foregoing examples have all been larger than the true values. This is not the result of mere chance, for it can be shown that the Ritz method yields an upper bound. To see this, we must have an alternate formulation of the eigenvalue problem.

TABLE 3.4.3 COMPARISON OF FOURIER COEFFICIENTS

	Second approximation	Third approximation	Exact[6]
a_0	$\frac{1}{3}$	$\frac{1}{3}$	$\frac{1}{3}$
a_1	1.10	1.18	1.19

Define E_1^* as the minimum of the functional

$$E = \frac{I(y)}{[Wy,y]} \tag{3.4.90}$$

where $I(y)$ is defined by Eq. (3.4.1) and the brackets are a shorthand notation having the following meaning:

$$[u,v] = \int_{r_1}^{r_2} uv \, dr \tag{3.4.91}$$

Let y_1 be the function which minimizes $E[E(y_1) = E_1^*]$. Then δE must vanish for small variations about y_1. Thus

$$\delta E = 0 = \frac{[Wy,y]\, \delta I - I\delta[Wy,y]}{[Wy,y]^2} \tag{3.4.92}$$

or

$$\delta I - E_1^* \delta[Wy,y] = 0 \tag{3.4.93}$$

If Eq. (3.4.93) is to be satisfied for all variations, then y_1 must satisfy the differential equation

$$L\{y_1\} - E_1^* W y_1 = 0 \tag{3.4.94}$$

and the boundary conditions

$$p(r)\frac{dy_1}{dr} + a_2 y_1 = 0 \qquad \text{at } r = r_2 \tag{3.4.95a}$$

$$-p(r)\frac{dy_1}{dr} + a_1 y_1 = 0 \qquad \text{at } r = r_1 \tag{3.4.95b}$$

where L is the operator

$$L\{ \ \} = \frac{d}{dr} p(r) \frac{d\{ \ \}}{dr} - q(r)\{ \ \}$$

Comparing these Euler-Lagrange equations with Eqs. (3.4.3) to (3.4.5), we can identify E_1^* as the first eigenvalue λ_1^2 and y_1 as the associated eigenfunction. E_1^* is called the first eigenvalue, since this is the minimum possible value that E can assume. We can now begin to see why the Ritz method yields an upper bound. Any approximation to the true minimizing function y_1 will give a value of E which is larger than the minimum. Thus if we can show that the λ_1^2 as determined by the Ritz method is an estimate of E_1^*, then the approximate eigenvalue is clearly an upper bound.

Before investigating this relationship, we will indicate the method required to extract the second, third, and etc. eigenvalues from the variational principle min $\{E\}$.   Let us define E_2^* as the minimum of Eq. (3.4.90) with respect to all functions which are orthogonal to y_1; that is,

$$[Wy, y_1] = 0 \qquad (3.4.96)$$

Here y_1 is the first eigenfunction determined as noted above.   Let y_2 satisfy the orthogonality condition and minimize E.   Then δE must vanish with respect to all admissible variations.   In taking the variation some care is required, since all functions admitted for testing must be orthogonal to y_1.   If we choose

$$\delta y = \epsilon \eta = \epsilon(\phi - [Wy_1, \phi]y_1) \qquad (3.4.97)$$

then

$$[W\eta, y_1] = 0$$

for all ϕ.   Note that y_1 is assumed to be normalized in a way such that Eq. (3.4.2) is satisfied.   The η selected in this way are admissible trial functions.   Thus $\delta E = 0$ requires that

$$[L\{y_2\}, \eta] - E_2^*[Wy_2, \eta] + \left[a_2 y_2 + p(r)\frac{dy_2}{dr} \right]\eta \bigg|_{r=r_2}$$
$$+ \left[a_1 y_2 - p(r)\frac{dy_2}{dr} \right]\eta \bigg|_{r=r_1} = 0 \qquad (3.4.98)$$

Substituting η for Eq. (3.4.97) and applying the orthogonality condition yields

$$[L\{y_2\}, \phi] - [W\phi, y_1][y_2, L\{y_1\}] - E_2^*[Wy_2, \phi] \qquad (3.4.99)$$
$$+ \left(a_2 y_2 + p(r)\frac{dy_2}{dr} \right)\phi \bigg|_{r=r_2} + \left(a_1 y_2 - p(r)\frac{dy_2}{dr} \right)\phi \bigg|_{r=r_1} = 0$$

after using the identity

$$[L\{y_2\}, y_1] = [y_2, L\{y_1\}] + \left(py_1\frac{dy_2}{dr} - py_2\frac{dy_1}{dr} \right)\bigg|_{r=r_2} + \left(py_1\frac{dy_2}{dr} - py_2\frac{dy_1}{dr} \right)\bigg|_{r=r_1}$$

Since y_1 is an eigenfunction, then

$$[L\{y_1\}, y_2] = \lambda_1^2[Wy_1, y_2] = 0$$

We see that

$$[(L\{y_2\} - E_2^* Wy_2), \phi] + \left(a_1 y_2 - p\frac{dy_2}{dr} \right)\phi \bigg|_{r=r_1} + \left(a_2 y_2 + p\frac{dy_2}{dr} \right)\phi \bigg|_{r=r_2}$$

Since ϕ is arbitrary, y_2 must satisfy Eqs. (3.4.94) and (3.4.95) with E_1^* being replaced by E_2^*.   Thus y_2 is the second eigenfunction, and E_2^* can be identified as the second eigenvalue.   The extension of this computational scheme to include the third eigenvalue is evident.   We see that the eigen-functions and eigenvalues are determined by a series of minima of the functional E.   This functional is called the Rayleigh quotient.   It should be noted that a more general class of problem than the one studied here can be expressed in the form of a Rayleigh quotient.   This variational principle plays an important role in the calculations of engineering mechanics.[7]

Let us investigate the relationship of the approximate eigenvalues to the functional E.   We begin by writing Eq. (3.4.20) for the first eigenvalue

$$\sum_{j=1}^{N}(\alpha_{ij} - \lambda_1{}^2\beta_{ij})c_j^{(1)} = 0 \qquad (3.4.100)$$

Multiply both sides of this expression by $c_i^{(1)}$ and sum.   This gives

$$\lambda_1{}^2 = \frac{I(\tilde{y}_1)}{[W\tilde{y}_1,\tilde{y}_1]}$$

Thus the approximation to the first eigenvalue obtained using the Ritz method could just as well have been found by substituting y_1 into Eq. (3.4.90). Here y_1 is an approximation to y_1 as defined by Eq. (3.4.17).   Since this is an estimate of E_1^*, it must be larger than E_1^* and hence greater than the first eigenvalue.   Thus the Ritz method provides an upper bound for the first eigenvalue.   It can be shown that the estimates of the other eigenvalues obtained by the Ritz method are also upper bounds.   Moreover, methods can be developed for obtaining lower bounds for this system of eigenvalues.[8] These calculations are mathematically more complicated than the methods shown here and will be omitted.

We shall conclude this chapter by noting that the direct methods of calculation are simple to understand and to use provided the trial functions are not too complex.   For example, a solution using a trial function containing four free parameters would require considerable calculation. Thus we believe that the direct methods shown here are most useful in obtaining "rough" approximations, whereas other methods, such as the finite-difference methods, should be used if an accuracy of a few tenths of a percent is required.

PROBLEM 3.4.2   Find the appropriate Rayleigh quotient associated with the eigenvalue problem defined by Eqs. (3.4.65), (3.4.66), and (3.4.69). Prove that the Ritz method yields an upper bound for the first eigenvalue.

[7] G. Temple and W. G. Bickley, "Rayleigh's Principle," Dover Publications, Inc., New York, 1956.

[8] S. H. Gould, "Variational Methods for Eigenvalue Problems," pp. 63–67, University of Toronto Press, Toronto, 1957.

CHAPTER 4
VARIATIONAL CALCULUS AND THE MACROSCOPIC BALANCE EQUATIONS

4.1 THE BALANCE EQUATIONS The most important concept basic to the overwhelming number of engineering problems is the continuum theory of matter. The structure of most engineering calculations rests directly on the validity of the balance equations which are the mathematical descriptions of the continuum fluid. The solution of the balance equations is usually quite difficult or impossible for most problems of interest, and some means of approximation must be used. In this chapter we shall be interested in expressing the balance equations as a variational principle, and in Chap. 5 we shall solve selected example problems using the methods developed in Chap. 3. It should be noted that electrical phenomena are not treated in this chapter—the remarks which follow are only intended to apply to the momentum, energy, and mass balances. The inclusion of Maxwell's equations (describing the electrical phenomena) would complicate the analysis beyond our intended scope.

Since the remaining chapters are devoted to a study of approximations to the balance equations, the following list gives a definition of all physically meaningful symbols:

A = cross-sectional area (5)†

A_α = chemical affinity of αth reaction (4,5)

$a_{(\alpha)}$ = physical property associated with time derivative of αth flux (7)

C_v = heat capacity at constant volume (4,5)

C_p = heat capacity at constant pressure (4,5,6,7)

c = concentration (5)

c_I = inlet concentration (5)

c' = fluctuating concentration (5)

D = diffusion coefficient (4,5,7)

D_e = effective diffusion coefficient (5)

$D_{vv}, D_{\beta v}$ = phenomenological coefficients (4)

d_{ij} = component of strain-rate tensor (4,5,6,7)

E = eccentricity (5)

E = entropy production (4,5,6,7)

E^* = local potential (4,5,6,7)

F = magnitude of the drag force (5)

$\bar{F}_i$ = component of the drag force (5)

F_i = component of the body force (4,5,6)

$F_i^{(\alpha)}$ = component of the body force acting on component α (4,5)

h = enthalpy per unit mass (4,5)

h = heat-transfer coefficient (6,7)

h_α = partial specific enthalpy (4,5)

$J_i^{(\alpha)}$ = mass flux of substance α relative to the mass average velocity (4,5)

$J_{(\alpha)}$ = generalized flux (4,7)

† Numerals in parentheses appearing after symbol denote chapter in which this symbol is used.

$\bar{J}_i$ = average mass flux (5)

$j_{(\alpha)}$ = fluctuating component of generalized flux (7)

K_β = rate of progress of the βth chemical reaction (4)

K = restoring force constant (6)

K_M = mass-transfer coefficient (4)

K_H = heat-transfer coefficient (4)

K_{mon} = momentum-transfer coefficient (4)

k = thermal conductivity (4,5,6,7)

k = reaction-rate parameter (5)

k, k_2, k_3 = wave numbers (7)

L = length (5)

l = plate spacing (5)

L_{ij} = phenomenological coefficients (4)

l_1, l_2, l_3 = dimensions of container (7)

$l_{\alpha\beta}$ = phenomenological coefficients (4)

M = mass of dynamic system (6)

M_{vv} = phenomenological coefficient (4)

M_α = molecular weight of substance α (4)

N = number of components (4)

n_i = component of unit outward normal (4,5,6,7)

N_{Nu} = Nusselt number (5,7)

N_{Pr} = Prandtl number (7)

N_{Pe} = Peclet number (5,7)

N_{R} = Rayleigh number (7)

N_{Re} = Reynolds number (3)

p = pressure (4,5,6,7)

Q = volumetric flow rate (6)

q = boundary layer thickness (5,7)

$q_\alpha(t)$ = generalized coordinate (7)

q_i = component of the heat flux (4,5)

R = resistance coefficient (6)

R = number of independent reactions (4)

S = surface (4,5,6,7)

S_i = component of the entropy flux (4)

s = entropy per unit mass (4)

s = reaction-rate parameter (5)

T = temperature (4,5,6,7)

T_i = components of specified force (6)

t = time (4,5,6,7)

U_i = component of specified velocity (6)

U = free-stream velocity (5)

u = internal energy per unit mass (4,5)

$\tilde{V}$ = specific volume (4)

$\tilde{v}_\alpha$ = partial specific volume (4)

V = volume (4,5,6,7)

v_i = component of fluid velocity (4,5,6,7)

v_i = set of functions of x and y (6)

W = width of plate (5)

X_i = generalized forces (4)

Roman Numerals

II = second invariance of the strain-rate tensor (4,6)

III = third invariance of the strain-rate tensor (4,6)

Greek Letters

α_i = mean concentration (5)

β = temperature gradient (7)

Γ = thermal coefficient of viscosity (5)

$\Gamma(d_{mk})$ = scalar function of the strain-rate tensor (6)

Γ = boundary of area A (6)

$\bar{\Gamma}(\tau_{ij})$ = scalar function of the stress (6)

γ = dimensionless thermal coefficient of the viscosity (5)

γ = temperature coefficient of the density (7)

ϵ = porosity (5)

ϵ = small quantity (7)

δ_{ij} = Kroniker delta function; $\delta_{ij} = 0$ if $i \neq j$, $\delta_{ij} = 1$ if $i = j$ (4,5,6,7)

$\Delta_\alpha = (\mu_\alpha - \mu_N)/T$ (4)

$\mathscr{L}$ = Lagrangian density (4,5,6)

ξ = dimensionless decay parameter (7)

η_1, η_2 = scalar function of the second and third invariances of the strain-rate tensor (4,6)

κ = thermal diffusivity (7)

λ = eigenvalue (5)

μ = Newtonian viscosity (4,5,6,7)

μ_α = chemical potential of component α (4,5)

$\nu_{\alpha\beta}$ = stoichiometric coefficient of component α in the βth chemical reaction (4)

ν = kinematic viscosity (6,7)

π_{ij} = component of the pressure tensor (4,5,6)

ρ = fluid density (4,5,6,7)

ρ_α = density of substance α (4)

σ = volumetric rate of entropy production (4,5)

σ = stability parameter (7)

τ_{ij} = reduced-stress tensor (4,5,6,7)

χ = isothermal compressibility (4)

w_α = mass fraction of substance α (4)

The equation of motion[1,2] can be written as

$$\rho \frac{Dv_i}{Dt} = - \frac{\partial \pi_{ij}}{\partial x_j} + \sum_{\alpha=1}^{N} \rho_\alpha F_i^{(\alpha)} \tag{4.1.1}$$

where $v_i(i = 1,2,3)$ = a component of the mass average velocity

ρ_α = density of the αth chemical species

ρ = local density

$F_i^{(\alpha)}$ = force per unit mass acting on component α

π_{ij} = components of the stress tensor

The equation is written for rectangular cartesian coordinates, and the summation and range conventions have been invoked.† Finally it should

[1] R. B. Bird, W. E. Steward, and E. N. Lightfoot, "Transport Phenomena," John Wiley & Sons, Inc., New York, 1960.

[2] R. Aris, "Vectors, Tensors and the Basic Equations of Fluid Mechanics," Chap. 6, Prentice-Hall, Inc., Englewood Cliffs, N.J., 1962.

† In this convention repeated Latin indices are summed; that is,

$$\frac{\partial \pi_{ij}}{\partial x_j} = \frac{\partial \pi_{i1}}{\partial x_1} + \frac{\partial \pi_{i2}}{\partial x_2} + \frac{\partial \pi_{i3}}{\partial x_3}$$

Here we see that a repeated index j in the term on the left implies a summation on that variable with the sum ranging from 1 to 3 as shown on the right-hand side of the above identity. Thus, we also have

$$v_i \frac{\partial}{\partial x_i} = v_1 \frac{\partial}{\partial x_1} + v_2 \frac{\partial}{\partial x_2} + v_3 \frac{\partial}{\partial x_3}$$

Therefore, this convention simply represents a shorthand notation in which several terms can be written as one.

be noted that the time derivative used in Eq. (4.1.1) is the material derivative defined as

$$\frac{D}{Dt} = \frac{\partial}{\partial t} + v_j \frac{\partial}{\partial x_j} \tag{4.1.2}$$

For a discussion of the physical significance of the terms appearing in the equation of motion, the reader is referred to any one of several excellent references.[1,2]   In the discussion to follow it is assumed that the reader is familiar with the meaning of the equation of motion as well as the applications of this equation.

It is also assumed that the reader is familiar with the mass balance equation which can be written as

$$\frac{D\rho_\alpha}{Dt} = -\rho_\alpha \frac{\partial v_i}{\partial x_i} - \frac{\partial J_i^{(\alpha)}}{\partial x_i} + \sum_{\beta=1}^{R} M_\alpha \nu_{\alpha\beta} K_\beta \tag{4.1.3}$$

where $J_i^{(\alpha)}$ = ith component of the diffusional flux of molecular substance α with respect to the mass average velocity

$\quad\quad M_\alpha$ = molecular weight

$\quad\quad \nu_{\alpha\beta}$ = stoichiometric coefficient of compound α in the βth reaction

$\quad\quad R$ = total number of simultaneous chemical reactions

$\quad\quad K_\beta$ = rate of the βth reaction expressed as moles per unit of time per unit of volume

The $\nu_{\alpha\beta}$ are counted as positive if the substance α appears on the right-hand side of the stoichiometric equation defining chemical reaction and is counted as negative when it appears on the left-hand side.   (Thus $\nu_{\alpha\beta}$ is positive if α is *produced*.)   Since mass must be conserved in any chemical reaction,

$$\sum_{\alpha=1}^{N} M_\alpha \nu_{\alpha\beta} = 0 \tag{4.1.4}$$

Thus by summing Eq. (4.1.3) over all N components, we obtain the continuity equation (over-all mass balance)

$$\frac{D\rho}{Dt} = -\rho \frac{\partial v_i}{\partial x_i} \tag{4.1.5}$$

since

$$\sum_{\alpha=1}^{N} J_i^{(\alpha)} = 0 \tag{4.1.6}$$

and

$$\rho = \sum_{\alpha=1}^{N} \rho_\alpha \tag{4.1.7}$$

Equation (4.1.6) is easily verified provided we recall that

$$J_i^{(\alpha)} = \rho_\alpha [v_i^{(\alpha)} - v_i] \tag{4.1.8}$$

where $v_i^{(\alpha)}$ is the ith component of the local average molecular velocity of substance α.

The internal energy balance can be written in many different forms; however, the following expression is most convenient for our purposes.

$$\rho \frac{Du}{Dt} = -\frac{\partial q_i}{\partial x_i} - \pi_{ij} \frac{\partial v_i}{\partial x_j} + \sum_{\alpha=1}^{N} J_i^{(\alpha)} F_i^{(\alpha)} \tag{4.1.9}$$

where u is the internal energy per unit mass and q_i is the heat flux with respect to the mass average velocity.

Equations (4.1.1), (4.1.3), (4.1.5), and (4.1.9) provide the mathematical basis for many engineering calculations. In general the solution of a specific problem requires the integration of these partial differential equations, and the equations of interest are usually coupled and nonlinear. Frequently, the integration is exceedingly difficult, if not impossible. Present-day strategy often entails approximating the differential equation by finite-difference techniques and using a computer to solve the enormous number of resulting algebraic equations. The solution of the finite-difference equations is often difficult, and it is not uncommon to find that some numerical experimentation is required.

An alternate approach to the problem of solving the balance equations is presented in this chapter. We shall consider the reformulation of the differential balance equations into the format of variational calculus. We shall insist that the variational principle have the balance equations as its Euler-Lagrange equations. In this sense no new physical information will be introduced in this chapter. In essence the variational problem is made to "coincide" with the differential form of the balance equations. On the other hand, we shall explore new concepts to guide us in the formulation of the variational principle. These provide an interesting background for this chapter.

Finally, we note that once the balance equations have been written in variational form, the approximate techniques introduced in Chap. 3 are then applicable to momentum, energy, and mass transport. This is an approach to the problem that is basically different from the method of finite differences.

4.2 ENTROPY PRODUCTION

In the introduction we have stated that our goal in this chapter is to replace the balance equations by an equivalent variational problem. The concepts of irreversible thermodynamics will prove quite useful in this endeavor.   Therefore, it is convenient to review these concepts very briefly to focus sharply on the necessary results transcribed into a notation consistent with the previous work.   For the reader not acquainted with the subject of irreversible thermodynamics a number of references are available.[1,2]

The developments of irreversible thermodynamics can be presented most concisely in the form of three postulates.

POSTULATE A

The entropy for a nonequilibrium state is defined by the equation

$$T\frac{Ds}{Dt} = \frac{Du}{Dt} - \frac{p}{\rho^2}\frac{D\rho}{Dt} - \sum_{\alpha=1}^{N}\mu_\alpha\frac{Dw_\alpha}{Dt} \tag{4.2.1}$$

where s = entropy per unit mass

μ_α = chemical potential of substance α

w_α = mass fraction of substance α present in the mixture

This equation is known as the Gibbs equation, and we shall find that the local rate of entropy production will always have the following quadratic structure

$$\sigma = \sum_{i=1}^{r} J_i X_i \tag{4.2.2}$$

when the local entropy is defined by Eq. (4.2.1).   In writing Eq. (4.2.2), we have shown the rate of entropy production σ as a quadratic function of a group of generalized fluxes J_i multiplied by their associated force X_i.

POSTULATE B

The fluxes and forces in Eq. (4.2.2) are related by the linear laws

$$J_i = -\sum_{j=1}^{r} L_{ij} X_j \tag{4.2.3}$$

in which the L_{ij} are known as phenomenological coefficients.

The structure of Eq. (4.2.3) is familiar to us for most of the simple transport situations.   For example, suppose that we were concerned with the transport of heat in an isotropic solid body.   After developing the appropriate form of

[1] I. Prigogine, "Introduction to Thermodynamics of Irreversible Processes," Charles C. Thomas, Publisher, Springfield, Ill., 1955.

[2] S. R. deGroot and P. Mazur, "Non-Equilibrium Thermodynamics," pp. 57–77, North-Holland Publishing Company, Amsterdam, 1962.

the energy balance, we would use Fourier's law to relate the heat flux to the gradient in temperature as follows:

$$q_i = -k \frac{\partial T}{\partial x_i} \qquad (4.2.4)$$

It is clear that Eq. (4.2.4) has the structure shown by Eq. (4.2.3), with the thermal conductivity k interpreted as a phenomenological coefficient and the temperature gradient interpreted as the force associated with the heat flux. Evidently, Fick's and Newton's laws, which provide the basis for simple diffusional and hydrodynamical calculations, are also examples of flux-force equations having the structure indicated by Eq. (4.2.3).

POSTULATE C

The phenomenological coefficients are symmetric; that is,

$$L_{ij} = L_{ji} \qquad (4.2.5)$$

This result is known as the Onsager[3] relationship.

These three postulates form the basis of an internally consistent means of relating the fluxes to the appropriate forces. In this text we confine our attention to the continuum systems. For such systems, the volumetric rate of entropy production can be found by substituting Eqs. (4.1.3), (4.1.5), and (4.1.9) into the defining equation for entropy, Eq. (4.2.1), to obtain

$$\rho T \frac{Ds}{Dt} = -\frac{\partial q_i}{\partial x_i} + \sum_{\alpha=1}^{N} F_i^{(\alpha)} J_i^{(\alpha)} - \tau_{ij} \frac{\partial v_i}{\partial x_j} + \sum_{\alpha=1}^{N} \mu_\alpha \frac{\partial J_i^{(\alpha)}}{\partial x_i} - \sum_{\alpha=1}^{N} \sum_{\beta=1}^{R} M_\alpha \mu_\alpha v_{\alpha\beta} K_\beta$$
$$(4.2.6)$$

after some manipulation and use of the identities

$$w_\alpha = \frac{\rho_\alpha}{\rho}$$

and

$$\pi_{ij} = \tau_{ij} + p\delta_{ij}$$

Here p is the pressure, and the Kroniker delta is defined so that $\delta_{ij} = 1$ if $i = j$ and $\delta_{ij} = 0$ if $i \neq j$. Equation (4.2.6) can also be written in the form

$$\rho \frac{Ds}{Dt} = -\frac{\partial}{\partial x_i} \frac{q_i - \sum_{\alpha=1}^{N} \mu_\alpha J_i^{(\alpha)}}{T} - \frac{1}{T^2} q_i \frac{\partial T}{\partial x_i}$$
$$- \frac{1}{T} \sum_{\alpha=1}^{N} J_i^{(\alpha)} \left[T \frac{\partial}{\partial x_i} \frac{\mu_\alpha}{T} - F_i^{(\alpha)} \right] - \frac{1}{T} \tau_{ij} \frac{\partial v_i}{\partial x_j} - \frac{1}{T} \sum_{\beta=1}^{R} K_\beta A_\beta \qquad (4.2.7)$$

[3] L. Onsager, "Reciprocal Relations in Irreversible Processes I," *Phys. Rev.*, vol. 37, p. 405, 1931; "Reciprocal Relations in Irreversible Processes II," *Phys. Rev.*, vol. 38, p. 2265, 1931.

where the chemical affinity is defined as

$$A_\beta = \sum_{\alpha=1}^{N} \nu_{\alpha\beta} \mu_\alpha M_\alpha$$

Equation (4.2.7) has the structure of a balance equation in which we have the material derivative of a certain property on the left, and on the right-hand side of the equation we have both the diffusional flow of the property into a moving volume element and the generation terms. The entropy flux can be identified as†

$$S_i = \frac{q_i - \sum_{\alpha=1}^{N} \mu_\alpha J_i^{(\alpha)}}{T} \qquad (4.2.8)$$

and the volumetric rate of entropy production as

$$\sigma = q_i \frac{\partial}{\partial x_i} \frac{1}{T} - \sum_{\alpha=1}^{N} J_i^{(\alpha)} \left[\frac{\partial(\partial \mu_\alpha/T)}{\partial x_i} - \frac{F_i^{(\alpha)}}{T} \right] - \frac{1}{T} \tau_{ij} \frac{\partial v_i}{\partial x_j} - \frac{1}{T} \sum_{\beta=1}^{R} A_\beta K_\beta \qquad (4.2.9)$$

where the entropy production must satisfy

$$\sigma \geq 0 \qquad (4.2.10)$$

The mass fluxes are not all independent, since Eq. (4.1.6) must be satisfied. Therefore, Eq. (4.2.9) can be rewritten as

$$\sigma = q_i \frac{\partial}{\partial x_i} \frac{1}{T} - \sum_{\alpha=1}^{N-1} J_i^{(\alpha)} \left[\frac{\partial}{\partial x_i} \frac{\mu_\alpha - \mu_N}{T} - \frac{F_i^{(\alpha)} - F_i^{(N)}}{T} \right]$$

$$- \frac{1}{T} \tau_{ij} \frac{\partial v_i}{\partial x_j} - \frac{1}{T} \sum_{\beta=1}^{R} A_\beta K_\beta \qquad (4.2.11)$$

We now see the quadratic form alluded to in the discussion following postulate A and set forth explicitly by Eq. (4.2.2). For in Eq. (4.2.11) the heat flux q_i is multiplied by its associated force, added to the multiple of the mass flux $J_i^{(\alpha)}$ and its associated force, and so on. The terms representing the entropy production arise from the irreversibilities in the transport processes. For example, the quantity $q_i \, \partial/\partial x_i \, 1/T$ is the entropy produced from the transport of energy in a finite temperature gradient. The other

† A balance equation has the structure

$$\rho \frac{Ds}{Dt} = -\frac{\partial}{\partial x_i} S_i + \sigma$$

where we have the divergence of the flux and the generation term on the right-hand side.

terms on the right-hand side of Eq. (4.2.11) have similar interpretations. If we apply postulate B, the fluxes are

$$K_\beta = -\frac{1}{T}\sum_{\alpha=1}^{R} l_{\beta\alpha}A_\alpha - \frac{D_{\beta v}}{T}\frac{\partial v_i}{\partial x_i} \qquad \beta = 1, 2, \ldots, R \tag{4.2.12}$$

$$J_i^{(\alpha)} = L_{\alpha\theta}\frac{\partial}{\partial x_i}\frac{1}{T} + \sum_{\beta=1}^{N-1} L_{\alpha\beta}\left[\frac{\partial}{\partial x_i}\frac{\mu_\beta - \mu_N}{T} - \frac{F_i^{(\beta)} - F_i^{(N)}}{T}\right]$$
$$\alpha = 1, 2, \ldots, N-1 \tag{4.2.13}$$

$$q_i = L_{\theta\theta}\frac{\partial}{\partial x_i}\frac{1}{T} + \sum_{\beta=1}^{N-1} L_{\theta\beta}\left[\frac{\partial}{\partial x_i}\frac{\mu_\beta - \mu_N}{T} - \frac{F_i^{(\beta)} - F_i^{(N)}}{T}\right] \tag{4.2.14}$$

$$\tau_{ij} = -\frac{1}{T}\Sigma K_\beta D_{\beta v}\delta_{ij} - \frac{D_{vv}}{T}\frac{\partial v_s}{\partial x_s}\delta_{ij} - \frac{M_{vv}}{T}\left(\frac{\partial v_i}{\partial x_j} + \frac{\partial v_j}{\partial x_i}\right) \tag{4.2.15}$$

where the phenomenological coefficients are related by the Onsager relations [Eq. (4.2.5)]

$$l_{\beta\alpha} = l_{\alpha\beta}$$
$$D_{\beta v} = D_{v\beta} \tag{4.2.16}$$
$$L_{\alpha q} = L_{q\alpha}$$
$$L_{\beta\alpha} = L_{\alpha\beta}$$

Notice that we have not indicated any coupling between the scalar reaction rate and the vector quantities. Nor is there any coupling shown between the second-degree tensors and the vectors. This lack of coupling can be rigorously demonstrated for an isotropic fluid by a series of coordinate transformations.[4]

The problems of transport in a continuum are now completely defined. For we now have the fluxes appearing in the balance equations defined in terms of the appropriate forces. A count of equations and unknowns will reveal that they are equal in number, which gives us a closed system of equations which determine the state of a system once the boundary conditions and the initial conditions are specified. However, the set of partial differential equations which results from substituting the flux expressions into the balance equations is quite complex, and in general can not be solved analytically even for the simple systems. It is this difficulty which motivates us to seek a variational formulation of the physical problem so that the direct methods of approximation which were discussed in Chap. 3 can be brought to bear on transport problems.

[4] S. R. deGroot and P. Mazur, "Non-Equilibrium Thermodynamics," pp. 57–77, North-Holland Publishing Company, Amsterdam, 1962.

4.3 THE PRINCIPLE OF MINIMUM ENTROPY PRODUCTION

A stationary state, that is, a time-independent state, is frequently characterized by a condition of minimum entropy production subject to certain
constraints imposed at the boundary.   Unfortunately, all systems do not
gravitate to the configuration giving the minimum of entropy production.
Consequently, the purpose of this section is to establish the limits of
validity so that the principle of minimum entropy production may be
employed where applicable.

Upon some reflection, it would seem intuitively correct that a principle of
minimum entropy production should be valid.   We have seen that the
volumetric rate of entropy production is a measure of the irreversibilities
associated with a process, and we know that in the absence of external
intrusions a system will approach an equilibrium state, that is, a state in
which the entropy production vanishes.   In the presence of certain imposed
constraints, it appears reasonable to assume that the system will come as
closely as possible to equilibrium while satisfying the imposed constraints.
Thus, we feel intuitively that the system in the stationary state will generate
as little entropy as possible by approaching the equilibrium state as closely
as possible.

To define the conditions of validity of the principle of minimum entropy
production, we shall assert that the balance equations written in Sec. 4.1 are
correct and, furthermore, we shall restrict our attention to those states for
which the linear law is valid.   It is the balance equation that will provide the
basis of testing the principle of minimum entropy production, for if we look
for the states giving

$$\min \{E\} = \min \left\{ \int_V \sigma \, dV \right\} \tag{4.3.1}$$

and find that these states are governed by a set of equations differing from the
appropriate balance equation, then we shall conclude that the physically
observable stationary state does not correspond to the one giving the minimum of entropy production.   Hence the principle would fail.   These
considerations will be made somewhat clearer in the paragraphs to follow.

Let us consider a single component system enclosed by walls whose surface
temperatures may vary from point to point on the surface but are time-
independent.   If the walls were at the same temperature, then the system
would come to equilibrium with the wall temperature.   However, if the wall
temperatures depend on position (but not on time), then the heat fluxes will
satisfy the following equation at the stationary state:

$$0 = \frac{\partial}{\partial x_i} q_i \tag{4.3.2}$$

This is the internal energy balance [Eq. (4.1.9)] applied to the simple physical problem described above. For this same problem

$$\sigma = q_i \frac{\partial}{\partial x_i} \frac{1}{T} \qquad (4.3.3)$$

and the linear law gives

$$q_i = L_{\theta\theta} \frac{\partial}{\partial x_i} \frac{1}{T} \qquad (4.3.4)$$

The total entropy production is then given by

$$E = \int_V \sigma \, dV = \int_V \left(L_{\theta\theta} \frac{\partial}{\partial x_i} \frac{1}{T} \frac{\partial}{\partial x_i} \frac{1}{T} \right) dV \qquad (4.3.5)$$

in which V is the volume of the system.

If E is to be an extremal, then $\delta E = 0$ for all variations in temperature, and it is necessary to have

$$T^2 \frac{\partial}{\partial T} L_{\theta\theta} \frac{\partial}{\partial x_i} \frac{1}{T} \frac{\partial}{\partial x_i} \frac{1}{T} + 2 \frac{\partial}{\partial x_i} q_i = 0 \qquad (4.3.6)$$

which is the Euler-Lagrange equation. We see immediately that Eq. (4.3.6) is not the same as Eq. (4.3.2) except under the special conditions

$$\frac{\partial}{\partial T} L_{\theta\theta} = 0 \qquad (4.3.7)$$

Thus, the principle of minimum entropy production can not be valid unless the phenomenological coefficients are constants. Next let us consider a fluid enclosed in a container which has spatially variable, but time-independent, wall temperatures. Let there be certain selected regions of the surface for which the concentrations are fixed and let the remainder of the surface be constructed of material which is impermeable to matter. The entropy production is

$$E = \int_V \left\{ q_i \frac{\partial}{\partial x_i} \frac{1}{T} - \sum_{\alpha=1}^{N-1} J_i^{(\alpha)} \left[\frac{\partial}{\partial x_i} \left(\frac{\mu_\alpha}{T} - \frac{\mu_N}{T} \right) - \frac{F_i^{(\alpha)} - F_i^{(N)}}{T} \right] \right\} dV \qquad (4.3.8)$$

provided there are no chemical reactions and no flow of fluid. To simplify our considerations, we can visualize two new variables, $t = 1/T$ and $\Lambda_\alpha = (\mu_\alpha - \mu_N)/T$, without loss in generality. Our task is to choose t and Λ_α such that E is stationary. The physical problem is governed by the balance equations, which are

$$0 = -\frac{\partial q_i}{\partial x_i} + \sum_{\alpha=1}^{N} J_i^{(\alpha)} F_i^{(\alpha)} \qquad \text{energy balance, Eq. (4.1.9)} \qquad (4.3.9)$$

and

$$0 = -\frac{\partial J_i^{(\alpha)}}{\partial x_i} \qquad \text{mass balance, Eq. (4.1.3)} \qquad (4.3.10)$$

These equations have been written for the steady state under the assumption that the velocity vanishes. Furthermore, the boundary conditions are

$$T(x,y,z) \qquad \text{fixed on } S \qquad (4.3.11)$$

$$\mu_\alpha(x,y,z) \qquad \text{fixed on } S_1 \qquad (4.3.12)$$

$$J_i^{(\alpha)} n_i = 0 \qquad \text{on } S_2 \qquad (4.3.13)$$

where S_1 represents that portion of the surface S enclosing the volume V which is permeable to matter, and S_2 is the part of the surface which is impermeable. Symbolically we can write

$$S_1 + S_2 = S \qquad (4.3.14)$$

The vector n_i is the outward normal at the surface. Using the linear laws, Eq. (4.3.8) becomes

$$E = \int_V \left\{ L_{00} \frac{\partial}{\partial x_i} \frac{1}{T} \frac{\partial}{\partial x_i} \frac{1}{T} + \sum_{\alpha=1}^{N-1} L_{0\alpha} \frac{\partial}{\partial x_i} \frac{1}{T} \left[\frac{\partial}{\partial x_i} \frac{\mu_\alpha - \mu_N}{T} - \frac{F_i^{(\alpha)} - F_i^{(N)}}{T} \right] \right.$$

$$+ \sum_{\alpha=1}^{N-1} L_{\alpha 0} \frac{\partial}{\partial x_i} \frac{1}{T} \left[\frac{\partial}{\partial x_i} \frac{\mu_\alpha - \mu_N}{T} - \frac{F_i^{(\alpha)} - F_i^{(N)}}{T} \right]$$

$$+ \sum_{\beta,\alpha=1}^{N-1} L_{\alpha\beta} \left[\frac{\partial}{\partial x_i} \frac{\mu_\alpha - \mu_N}{T} - \frac{F_i^{(\alpha)} - F_i^{(N)}}{T} \right]$$

$$\left. \times \left[\frac{\partial}{\partial x_i} \frac{\mu_\beta - \mu_N}{T} - \frac{F_i^{(\beta)} - F_i^{(N)}}{T} \right] \right\} dV$$

$$(4.3.15)$$

Let us first vary t holding Λ_α constant. This is permitted, since it is clear that we have two independent variables—the temperature and the composition. Of course, the variables t and Λ_α can be viewed as being the independent variables equally well.

The variation with respect to t gives as a necessary condition for E to be an extremal

$$
-\frac{\partial}{\partial x_i}\left\{2L_{\theta\theta}\frac{\partial}{\partial x_i}\frac{1}{T}+\sum_{\alpha=1}^{N-1}L_{\theta\alpha}\left[\frac{\partial}{\partial x_i}\Lambda_\alpha-\frac{F_i^{(\alpha)}-F_i^{(N)}}{T}\right]\right.
$$

$$
\left.+\sum_{\alpha=1}^{N-1}L_{\alpha\theta}\left[\frac{\partial}{\partial x_i}\Lambda_\alpha-\frac{F_i^{(\alpha)}-F_i^{(N)}}{T}\right]\right\}-\sum_{\alpha=1}^{N-1}L_{\alpha\theta}
$$

$$
\times\frac{\partial}{\partial x_i}\frac{1}{T}[F_i^{(\alpha)}-F_i^{(N)}]-\sum_{\alpha=1}^{N-1}L_{\theta\alpha}\frac{\partial}{\partial x_i}\frac{1}{T}(F_i^{(\alpha)}-F_i^{(N)})
$$

$$
+\sum_{\alpha,\beta=1}^{N-1}\frac{1}{T}L_{\alpha\beta}\left\{2[F_i^{(\alpha)}-F_i^{(N)}][F_i^{(\beta)}-F_i^{(N)}]\right.
$$

$$
\left.-(F_i^{(\alpha)}-F_i^{(N)})\frac{\partial}{\partial x_i}\Lambda_\beta-[F_i^{(\beta)}-F_i^{(N)}]\frac{\partial}{\partial x_i}\Lambda_\alpha\right\}\qquad(4.3.16)
$$

In deriving this equation the phenomenological coefficients have been held constant. It has already been established that the principle of minimum entropy production is not valid unless these coefficients are held fixed. Equation (4.3.16) must correspond to the appropriate form of the energy balance if the principle of minimum entropy production is to be valid. If we invoke the Onsager relations, Eq. (4.2.5), and substitute the flux expressions, Eqs. (4.2.13) and (4.2.14), into Eq. (4.3.16), the resulting expression is the correct form of the energy balance. *It is essential to remember that the correct expressions for the energy balance were found only after assuming that the phenomenological coefficients are constants and that the Onsager relations are valid.* It is necessary for these two conditions to be satisfied if the state of minimum entropy production is to be the observed stationary state.

There is one further condition which must be satisfied for the principle of minimum entropy production to be valid: *the convective terms must be negligible.* This can be seen by considering the flow of a uniform fluid and the simultaneous flow of heat. Let us suppose that both the velocity and the temperature are specified at all points on the boundary and that these values are time-independent so that the system approaches a stationary state. For this case we have

$$
E=\int_V\left(q_i\frac{\partial}{\partial x_i}\frac{1}{T}-\frac{1}{T}\tau_{ij}\frac{\partial v_i}{\partial x_j}\right)dV\qquad(4.3.17)
$$

Substituting the flux expressions, Eqs. (4.2.14) and (4.2.15),

$$
E=\int_V\left[L_{\theta\theta}\frac{\partial}{\partial x_i}\frac{1}{T}\frac{\partial}{\partial x_i}\frac{1}{T}+\frac{1}{T^2}D_{vv}\frac{\partial v_i}{\partial x_i}\frac{\partial v_j}{\partial x_j}+\frac{M_{vv}}{T^2}\frac{\partial v_i}{\partial x_j}\left(\frac{\partial v_j}{\partial x_i}+\frac{\partial v_i}{\partial x_j}\right)\right]
$$

$$
\qquad(4.3.18)
$$

Again, taking the variation with respect to $1/T$, we find the Euler-Lagrange equation

$$-2\frac{\partial}{\partial x_i} L_{\theta\theta} \frac{\partial}{\partial x_i} \frac{1}{T} + \frac{2}{T} D_{vv} \frac{\partial v_i}{\partial x_i} \frac{\partial v_j}{\partial x_j} + 2\frac{M_{vv}}{T} \frac{\partial v_i}{\partial x_j}\left(\frac{\partial v_j}{\partial x_i} + \frac{\partial v_i}{\partial x_j}\right) \tag{4.3.19}$$

Applying the flux expressions gives

$$-2\frac{\partial}{\partial x_i} q_i + 2\tau_{ij} \frac{\partial v_i}{\partial x_j} = 0 \tag{4.3.20}$$

which is the energy balance for a nonuniform fluid except that the convective terms Du/Dt are not present.   There is no way for the principle of minimum entropy production to introduce these terms, and hence we find the third and final restriction: the convective terms must be negligible if the state of minimum entropy production is to be the true state.

We can summarize our findings by stating that *for those systems in which*

1. The phenomenological coefficients are constant
2. The Onsager relations are satisfied
3. The convective terms are negligible

the stationary state of the system is a state of minimum entropy production.

In the next chapter we shall apply this interesting principle to some physical problems.   However, before proceeding to definite examples, we shall devote our attention to the task of developing more general principles which can be used in the determination of the stationary states of systems not satisfying all of the conditions imposed on the principle of minimum entropy production.

PROBLEM 4.3.1   Verify that the Euler-Lagrange equation which results from a variation of E, defined by Eq. (4.3.15), is the material balance, Eq. (4.3.10).   Find the boundary conditions which must be satisfied if E is to be an extremal.

PROBLEM 4.3.2   Show that Eq. (4.3.18) is an extremal if the equation of motion with the inertia and the pressure terms omitted is satisfied.

4.4 THE CONCEPT OF THE LOCAL POTENTIAL

In the last section we have seen that the principle of minimum entropy production is applicable only to a restricted class of systems.   Indeed the restrictions are of such a nature that most problems of engineering interest are excluded.   The task now to be considered is that of developing a general criterion describing the stationary state of a continuous system.   To find such an important and powerful criterion, we must extend our notions of variational calculus.   Otherwise the task is impossible to accomplish.

The analysis to be developed in this section follows closely the paper by Glansdorff and Prigogine.[1] These two authors have been the "fathers" of the theory presented here. For a chronological development the reader should consult the papers noted below.[2–5] The work presented in this section is taken almost completely from this series of articles. The essential ideas of the development to follow can be best illustrated by presenting a simple—almost trivial—example. Let us focus our attention on the problem of determining the temperature distribution in a solid body which is simultaneously heated and cooled on its boundaries. These boundary temperatures do not depend on time. The balance equation describing this system is Eq. (4.1.9) and for the system being studied, Eq. (4.1.9) reduces to

$$\rho \frac{\partial u}{\partial t} = - \frac{\partial q_i}{\partial x_i} \tag{4.4.1}$$

Multiply both sides of this expression by $\partial/\partial t \; 1/T$ and find

$$\rho \frac{\partial}{\partial t} \frac{1}{T} \frac{\partial u}{\partial t} = - \frac{\partial}{\partial x_i} q_i \frac{\partial}{\partial t} \frac{1}{T} + q_i \frac{\partial}{\partial x_i} \frac{\partial}{\partial t} \frac{1}{T} \tag{4.4.2}$$

The change of internal energy per unit mass depends only on the changes in temperature for the system being studied so that

$$\frac{\partial u}{\partial t} = C_v \frac{\partial T}{\partial t} \tag{4.4.3}$$

in which C_v is the specific heat. A function ψ can now be defined so that

$$\psi = \rho C_v \frac{\partial T}{\partial t} \frac{\partial}{\partial t} \frac{1}{T} = - \frac{\rho C_v}{T^2} \left(\frac{\partial T}{\partial t} \right)^2 \leq 0 \tag{4.4.4}$$

The quantity ψ is clearly seminegative definite (less than or equal to zero), since the heat capacity must be positive as a requirement of thermodynamic stability. We can define a function ϕ as

$$\phi = \int_V \psi \, dV = \int_V \left(- \frac{\partial}{\partial x_i} q_i \frac{\partial}{\partial t} \frac{1}{T} + q_i \frac{\partial}{\partial x_i} \frac{\partial}{\partial t} \frac{1}{T} \right) dV \leq 0 \tag{4.4.5}$$

[1] P. Glansdorff and I. Prigogine, "On a General Evolution Criterion in Macroscopic Physics," *Physica*, vol. 30, p. 351, 1964.

[2] P. Glansdorff and I. Prigogine, "Sur les propriétés différentielles de la production d'entropie," *Physica*, vol. 20, p. 773, 1954.

[3] P. Glansdorff, "On a Non-Linear Law of Irreversible Phenomena with Stationary Constraints," *Mol. Phys.*, vol. 3, p. 277, 1960.

[4] P. Glansdorff, I. Prigogine, and D. Hays, "Variational Properties of a Viscous Liquid at a Nonuniform Temperature," *Phys. of Fluids*, vol. 5, p. 144, 1962.

[5] R. S. Schechter, "On a Variational Principle for the Reiner-Rivlin Fluid," *Chem. Eng. Sci.*, vol. 17, p. 803, 1962.

where ϕ is a global property of the system which is seminegative definite. Moreover, ϕ tends to zero as the system tends to the stationary state, although the decay to the stationary state is not necessarily monotonic. Nevertheless, ϕ does "measure" the deviation from the stationary state. The first term of the integrand is equivalent to a certain surface integral in accordance with Gauss' theorem. Thus, Eq. (4.4.5) can be written as

$$\phi = -\int_S q_i \frac{\partial}{\partial t} \frac{1}{T} n_i \, dS + \int_V q_i \frac{\partial}{\partial x_i} \frac{\partial}{\partial t} \frac{1}{T} \, dV \leq 0 \tag{4.4.6}$$

where S is the surface enclosing V and n_i is the normal to the surface. The surface integral vanishes, since the temperature on the surface is time-independent. We then find

$$\phi = +\int_V q_i \frac{\partial}{\partial t} \frac{\partial}{\partial x_i} \frac{1}{T} \, dV \leq 0 \tag{4.4.7}$$

If we introduce the linear law into Eq. (4.4.7), then the nonpositive function is

$$\phi = \int_V L_{\theta\theta} \left(\frac{\partial}{\partial x_i} \frac{\partial}{\partial t} \frac{1}{T} \right) \frac{\partial}{\partial x_i} \frac{1}{T} \, dV \leq 0 \tag{4.4.8}$$

or

$$\phi = \int_V \frac{1}{2} L_{\theta\theta} \frac{\partial}{\partial t} \left(\frac{\partial}{\partial x_i} \frac{1}{T} \right)^2 dV \leq 0 \tag{4.4.9}$$

In general $L_{\theta\theta}$ is a function of the temperature, so that as the system evolves to the steady state, the phenomenological coefficient will take on different numerical values as well. Let us assume that the system is displaced but infinitesimally from the stationary state and define $T^0(x_i)$ as the temperature distribution at that state. We now suppose that for such small displacements from the stationary state $L_{\theta\theta}(T) \cong L_{\theta\theta}(T^0)$ so that

$$\phi = \frac{\partial}{\partial t} \left[\int_V \frac{1}{2} L_{\theta\theta}(T^0) \left(\frac{\partial}{\partial x_i} \frac{1}{T} \right)^2 dV \right] \leq 0 \tag{4.4.10}$$

and the volume integral

$$E^* = \int_V \frac{1}{2} L_{\theta\theta}(T^0) \left(\frac{\partial}{\partial x_i} \frac{1}{T} \right)^2 dV \tag{4.4.11}$$

can only decrease with time. It follows that E^* is a minimum at the stationary state and, moreover, can be identified as the rate of entropy production at the stationary state. We call E^* a local potential or a generalized entropy production. Now we must remark that the minimum of E^* defines the stationary state only if we honor the stipulation that $L_{\theta\theta}(T^0)$ be evaluated at the stationary state and not subject this function to variations about this state. Thus we find a structure not encountered in any of our previous work on variational calculus. The problem is to extremalize E^* by a suitable choice of the temperature. However, during the course of the investigation, one must remember that we have two "classes" of temperature appearing in the integrand of the variational principle. One of these is T, and we are at liberty to manipulate this function as in our previous work on variational calculus. The second class of temperature T^0 is disguised, in the sense that this particular quantity plays the *same* role as a *specified* function of position. In other words, we must assume that T^0 is a known function of position; this dual personality must be maintained until the temperature T is identified as that occurring at the stationary state. Thus, the necessary conditions which must be satisfied if E^* is to be a minimum are found by determining

$$\left(\frac{\delta E^*}{\delta T}\right)_{T^0} = 0 \tag{4.4.12}$$

with the subsidiary condition that

$$T = T^0 \tag{4.4.13}$$

It is essential to distinguish between the stationary temperature T^0 and the local temperature T until the process of variation is complete. Otherwise incorrect results will arise.

Before proceeding to convince ourselves that E^* is in fact a minimum at the stationary state, let us attempt to achieve a better understanding of the structure implied in Eqs. (4.4.11) to (4.4.13). Suppose we seek the minimum of the polynomial

$$E^*(x) = ax^2 + bxx^0 + dx \tag{4.4.14}$$

so that the x must satisfy

$$\left(\frac{\delta E^*}{\delta x}\right)_{x^0} = 0 \tag{4.4.15}$$

In addition, impose the subsidiary condition

$$x = x^0 \tag{4.4.16}$$

We now have a structure quite similar to that developed above. Equation (4.4.15) implies that E^* must vanish for all infinitesimal variations in x. From Eq. (4.4.14) we find

$$\left(\frac{\delta E^*}{\delta x}\right)_{x^0} = (2ax + bx^0 + d) = 0 \tag{4.4.17}$$

At this point (after taking the variation) we invoke the subsidiary condition $x = x^0$ and obtain

$$x^0 = -\left(\frac{d}{2a + b}\right) \tag{4.4.18}$$

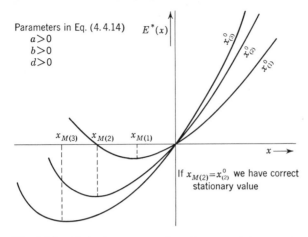

Fig. 4.4.1   Algebraic representation of an unvaried parameter.

To see the process more clearly, note Fig. 4.4.1 illustrates further the type of minimum which is sought. The curves in the figure represent Eq. (4.4.14). It is clear that for each value of x^0 the curve goes through a minimum at some value of x, say x_M. One of these minimum points x_M will be precisely equal to the parameter x^0. This is the curve we seek and this x_M is the point at which E^* is an extremal. It is essential to note that for a given x there exists a minimum of Eq. (4.4.14), and it is clear that the desired curve ($x^0 = x_M$) *does not have the smallest minimum*. There are neighboring curves which exhibit smaller minima. This situation gives rise to some difficulty in computations based on this concept.

We can translate our remarks concerning the polynomial equation (4.4.14) back to the original problem of heat conduction in solids. As was the case for the polynomial, we can show that the local potential does not provide a minimum value except when the precise spatial dependence of the temperature is known and substituted in the place of T^0. This can be seen in the following way. Suppose that we ask the question, What function of T gives the minimum of entropy production? Of course, the question can only be answered for a particular case in which the geometry, boundary conditions, and temperature dependence of the thermal conductivity are specified.

Thus to provide an answer to the question posed above, let us consider a simple one-dimensional process in which heat is transferred through a slab of unit thickness. One face of the slab is maintained at a temperature of $T = 1$, and the other face of the slab is kept at a temperature of $T = 2$. Let x be the position coordinate measured along a perpendicular to the surface of the slab. The entropy production is given by [see Eq. (4.3.5)]

$$E = \int_0^1 L_{\theta\theta} \frac{\partial}{\partial x} \frac{1}{T} \frac{\partial}{\partial x} \frac{1}{T} dx \qquad (4.4.19)$$

and since

$$q_x = -\frac{L_{\theta\theta}}{T^2}\frac{\partial T}{\partial x} \tag{4.4.20}$$

we can identify the thermal conductivity as

$$k = \frac{L_{\theta\theta}}{T^2} \tag{4.4.21}$$

where k is the thermal conductivity.   In terms of the thermal conductivity, the entropy production becomes

$$E = \int_0^1 \frac{\alpha}{T}\left(\frac{d}{dx}\frac{1}{T}\right)^2 dx \tag{4.4.22}$$

where we have arbitrarily selected the thermal conductivity dependence on the temperature as

$$k = \frac{\alpha}{T^3} \tag{4.4.23}$$

We again ask ourselves to determine the temperature giving the minimum of entropy production.   We know that the following Euler-Lagrange equation must be satisfied if a minimum is to exist:

$$\frac{\alpha}{2}\left(\frac{d}{dx}\frac{1}{T}\right)^2 - \frac{d}{dx}\frac{\alpha}{T}\left(\frac{d}{dx}\frac{1}{T}\right) = 0 \tag{4.4.24}$$

where we have taken the variation with respect to $1/T$ rather than T for simplicity.   It is not difficult to show that

$$T^{-3/2} = -\left(1 - \frac{1}{2^{3/2}}\right)x + 1 \tag{4.4.25}$$

is the solution to Eq. (4.4.24) satisfying the boundary conditions

$T = 1$ at $x = 0$

and

$T = 2$ at $x = 1$

Moreover, we can now give a numerical value for the entropy production

$$E = \int_0^1 \frac{\alpha}{T}\left(\frac{d}{dx}\frac{1}{T}\right)^2 dx = \alpha\left(1 - \frac{1}{2^{3/2}}\right)^2 \frac{4}{9} = 0.18573\alpha \tag{4.4.26}$$

Now the temperature distribution given by Eq. (4.4.25) is the one which makes E stationary (we have not shown it to be true, but this is a minimum);

however, this is *not* the temperature distribution which obeys the energy balance equation, and hence it cannot be the observable temperature. The temperature given by the energy balance is defined by

$$\frac{\partial}{\partial x} q_x = 0 = -\frac{\partial}{\partial x} \frac{\alpha}{T^3} \frac{\partial T}{\partial x} \qquad (4.4.27)$$

using the thermal conductivity given by Eq. (4.4.23). This equation can be integrated to yield

$$T = \left(1 - \frac{3x}{4}\right)^{-\frac{1}{2}} \qquad (4.4.28)$$

We can find a value of the entropy production associated with this temperature distribution

$$E = \frac{3\alpha}{16} = 1.875\alpha \qquad (4.4.29)$$

giving a larger entropy production than the temperature distribution expressed by Eq. (4.4.25). Thus, we see first that the configuration giving a minimum of entropy production is not the stationary temperature. Now let us consider the local potential. For this particular example,

$$2E^* = \int_0^1 \frac{\alpha}{T^0} \left(\frac{\partial}{\partial x} \frac{1}{T}\right)^2 dx \qquad (4.4.30)$$

where T^0 denotes the true stationary temperature. Since we know this temperature, having just solved for it, we can write

$$2E^* = \int_0^1 \alpha \left(1 - \frac{3x}{4}\right)^{-\frac{1}{2}} \left(\frac{\partial}{\partial x} \frac{1}{T}\right)^2 dx \qquad (4.4.31)$$

The temperature distribution which minimizes the functional E^* is the observable stationary temperature in the slab. It is not difficult to establish that E^* is truly a minimum at the stationary state. If we substitute any other function of x satisfying the boundary conditions for T other than that given by Eq. (4.4.28), then we shall find a larger value of E^* than the one for the stationary state. In this sense, Eq. (4.4.31) is truly a minimal principle. However, to give it precise analytical expression, we had to know the true temperature distribution in the slab. In the problems that concern us, the determination of the temperature distribution in the stationary state is complex and is, indeed, the desired result. Thus, in general, we will not know the true solution. How can we then expect to utilize the local potential? We shall answer this question in Chap. 5. However, we should note here that if T^0 is unknown, then there exist temperature distributions which make E^* smaller than the observable temperatures. One example of such a temperature distribution is, of course, the temperature distribution giving the minimum of entropy production. In other words, if we are trying to guess the true temperature distribution and are assuming functional relationships which are then substituted in Eq. (4.4.30) for T^0, it is possible to find temperature distributions which give smaller values of E^* than the desired one. This state of affairs gives rise to certain difficulties if one attempts to use direct-search techniques to find the stationary state. However, as already noted, we shall demonstrate a method of utilizing the local potential in making practical calculations in the next chapter.

We now see that the E^* defined by Eq. (4.4.11) is an extremal in a very special sense. In studying small variations around the stationary state, T^0 is constant and it is only *after* the process of variation has been complete that one imposes the auxiliary condition, Eq. (4.4.13).

To develop Eq. (4.4.11), we used an approximation which was not carefully examined. In one of the computational steps [Eq. (4.4.10)] we replaced $L_{\theta\theta}(T)$ by $L_{\theta\theta}(T^0)$, assuming only that the system was very nearly at a time-independent state. This step was not rigorously justified. However, our justification will be, as in the last section, to show that the stationary value of E^* gives the same stationary state as that which is determined by the balance equations. Note

$$\frac{\delta E^*}{2} = \int_V L_{\theta\theta}(T^0) \frac{\partial}{\partial x_i} \frac{1}{T} \frac{\partial}{\partial x_i} \delta \frac{1}{T} dV \qquad (4.4.32)$$

Applying Gauss' theorem and assuming that $\delta(1/T)$ vanishes on the boundary, we find

$$\frac{\delta E^*}{2} = -\int_V \frac{\partial}{\partial x_i} L_{\theta\theta} \frac{\partial}{\partial x_i} \frac{1}{T} dV \, \delta \frac{1}{T} \qquad (4.4.33)$$

or if δE^* is to vanish for all variations

$$\frac{\partial}{\partial x_i} L_{\theta\theta}(T^0) \frac{\partial}{\partial x_i} \frac{1}{T} = 0 \qquad (4.4.34)$$

Now that the process of variation is complete we seek the T which is equal to T^0, so that Eq. (4.4.34) becomes

$$\frac{\partial}{\partial x_i} L_{\theta\theta}(T) \frac{\partial}{\partial x_i} \frac{1}{T} = 0 = \frac{\partial q_i}{\partial x_i} \qquad (4.4.35)$$

which is the correct form of the balance equation describing the simple system now being investigated.

The reader is probably not certain about the applications of the local potential. The applications are discussed in the following chapter, where it will be shown that all of the direct methods developed in Chap. 3 can be applied in conjunction with the local potential. However, before studying the applications, we shall first develop a general evolution criterion.

4.5 GENERAL EVOLUTION CRITERION

The balance Eqs. (4.1.1), (4.1.3), and (4.1.9) can be written in the form

$$\frac{\partial \rho_\alpha}{\partial t} = -\frac{\partial}{\partial x_i}\, \rho_\alpha v_i - \frac{\partial}{\partial x_i}\, J_i^{(\alpha)} + \sum_{\beta=1}^{R} M_\alpha \nu_{\alpha\beta} K_\beta \tag{4.5.1}$$

$$\rho\, \frac{\partial v_i}{\partial t} = -\rho v_j\, \frac{\partial v_i}{\partial x_j} - \frac{\partial}{\partial x_j}\, \pi_{ij} + \sum_{\alpha=1}^{N} \rho_\alpha F_i^{(\alpha)} \tag{4.5.2}$$

$$\frac{\partial \rho u}{\partial t} = -\frac{\partial}{\partial x_i}\, \rho v_i u - \frac{\partial q_i}{\partial x_i} - \pi_{ij}\, \frac{\partial v_i}{\partial x_j} + \sum_{\alpha=1}^{N} J_i^{(\alpha)}\, F_i^{(\alpha)} \tag{4.5.3}$$

The analysis to follow is essentially the same as that demonstrated in the preceding section. Again it will be assumed that the boundary conditions are time-independent. Multiply Eq. (4.5.1) by $-(\partial/\partial t)(\mu_\alpha/T)$, Eq. (4.5.2) by $-(1/T)(\partial v_i/\partial t)$, and Eq. (4.5.3) by $\partial/\partial t\, 1/T$. Then define ψ as

$$\psi = -\left(\frac{\rho}{T}\, \frac{\partial v_i}{\partial t}\, \frac{\partial v_i}{\partial t} + \sum_{\alpha=1}^{N} \frac{\partial}{\partial t}\, \frac{\mu_\alpha}{T}\, \frac{\partial \rho_\alpha}{\partial t} - \frac{\partial T^{-1}}{\partial t}\, \frac{\partial \rho u}{\partial t} \right) \tag{4.5.4}$$

As before, we should like to prove that ψ is never positive. This step requires the use of certain thermodynamic formulas which are applicable only when the system is in local equilibrium. Thus this represents a limitation on the validity of the work to follow. However, it is worth repeating that a variational formulation can be shown to be correct by insuring that the Euler-Lagrange equations are identical (including boundary conditions) with the appropriate forms of the balance equations. If this latter condition is satisfied, one is not required to justify in a rigorous fashion the derivation of the evolution criterion. From thermodynamics the following relationships are well known.

$$\frac{\partial}{\partial t}\, \frac{\mu_\alpha}{T} = \frac{\partial}{\partial T}\, \frac{\mu_\alpha}{T}\, \frac{\partial T}{\partial t} + \frac{1}{T}\, \frac{\partial \mu_\alpha}{\partial p}\, \frac{\partial p}{\partial t} + \frac{1}{T} \sum_{\beta=1}^{N} \frac{\partial \mu_\alpha}{\partial \rho_\beta}\, \frac{\partial \rho_\beta}{\partial t} \tag{4.5.5}$$

with

$$\frac{\partial}{\partial T}\left(\frac{\mu_\alpha}{T} \right)_{p,M} = -\frac{h_\alpha}{T^2} \tag{4.5.6}$$

and

$$\left(\frac{\partial \mu_\alpha}{\partial p} \right)_{T,M} = \bar{v}_\alpha \tag{4.5.7}$$

in which h_α is the partial specific enthalpy $(\partial H/\partial M_\alpha)_{p,T,M_\beta}$, $\tilde{v}_\alpha$ is the partial specific volume $(\partial V/\partial M_\alpha)_{p,T,M_\beta}$, and the subscript M is intended to denote that the concentrations are held constant.   The subscript M_β implies that the masses of all substances except M_α are held fixed.   Therefore Eq. (4.5.5) can be written as

$$\frac{\partial}{\partial t}\frac{\mu_\alpha}{T} = -\frac{h_\alpha}{T^2}\frac{\partial T}{\partial t} + \frac{1}{T}\tilde{v}_\alpha\frac{\partial p}{\partial t} + \frac{1}{T}\sum_{\beta=1}^{N}\frac{\partial \mu_\alpha}{\partial \rho_\beta}\frac{\partial \rho_\beta}{\partial t} \tag{4.5.8}$$

The last term in Eq. (4.5.4) can also be expanded.   Thus

$$\frac{\partial \rho u}{\partial t} = \frac{\partial}{\partial t}(-p + \rho h) = -\frac{\partial p}{\partial t} + \rho\frac{\partial h}{\partial t} + h\frac{\partial \rho}{\partial t} \tag{4.5.9}$$

by definition of the enthalpy h.   The derivative of the enthalpy is

$$\frac{\partial h}{\partial t} = \frac{\partial h}{\partial T}\frac{\partial T}{\partial t} + \frac{\partial h}{\partial p}\frac{\partial p}{\partial t} + \sum_{\alpha=1}^{N}h_\alpha\frac{\partial w_\alpha}{\partial t} \tag{4.5.10}$$

We again apply well-known definitions and equations such as

$$\frac{\partial h}{\partial T} = C_p \tag{4.5.11}$$

and

$$\frac{\partial h}{\partial p} = \frac{1}{\rho} + \frac{T}{\rho^2}\frac{\partial \rho}{\partial T} \tag{4.5.12}$$

Thus

$$\rho\frac{\partial h}{\partial t} = \rho C_p\frac{\partial T}{\partial t} + \frac{\partial p}{\partial t} + \frac{T}{\rho}\frac{\partial \rho}{\partial T}\frac{\partial p}{\partial t} + \rho\sum_{\alpha=1}^{N}h_\alpha\frac{\partial w_\alpha}{\partial t} \tag{4.5.13}$$

Substituting Eq. (4.5.13) into (4.5.9) gives

$$\frac{\partial \rho u}{\partial t} = \rho C_p\frac{\partial T}{\partial t} + \frac{T}{\rho}\frac{\partial \rho}{\partial T}\frac{\partial p}{\partial t} + \rho\sum_{\alpha=1}^{N}h_\alpha\frac{\partial w_\alpha}{\partial t} + h\frac{\partial \rho}{\partial t} \tag{4.5.14}$$

Utilizing Eqs. (4.5.8) and (4.5.14), the expression for ψ becomes

$$\psi = \left[-\frac{\rho}{T}\frac{\partial v_i}{\partial t}\frac{\partial v_i}{\partial t} + \frac{1}{T^2}\sum_{\alpha=1}^{N}h_\alpha\frac{\partial \rho_\alpha}{\partial t}\frac{\partial T}{\partial t} - \frac{1}{T}\sum_{\alpha=1}^{N}\tilde{v}_\alpha\frac{\partial \rho_\alpha}{\partial t}\frac{\partial p}{\partial t} \right.$$
$$- \frac{1}{T}\sum_{\alpha,\beta=1}^{N}\frac{\partial \mu_\alpha}{\partial \rho_\beta}\frac{\partial \rho_\beta}{\partial t}\frac{\partial \rho_\alpha}{\partial t} - \frac{1}{T^2}\rho C_p\left(\frac{\partial T}{\partial t}\right)^2 - \frac{1}{\rho T}\frac{\partial \rho}{\partial T}\frac{\partial p}{\partial t}\frac{\partial T}{\partial t}$$
$$\left. - \frac{\rho}{T^2}\sum_{\alpha=1}^{N}h_\alpha\frac{\partial w_\alpha}{\partial t}\frac{\partial T}{\partial t} - \frac{h}{T^2}\frac{\partial \rho}{\partial t}\frac{\partial T}{\partial t} \right] \tag{4.5.15}$$

We note that

$$\frac{1}{T^2}\sum_{\alpha=1}^{N}h_\alpha\frac{\partial\rho_\alpha}{\partial t} = \frac{1}{T^2}\sum_{\alpha=1}^{N}h_\alpha\frac{\partial}{\partial t}w_\alpha\rho = \frac{1}{T^2}\frac{\partial\rho}{\partial t}h + \frac{\rho}{T^2}\sum_{\alpha=1}^{N}h_\alpha\frac{\partial w_\alpha}{\partial t}$$

Hence

$$\psi = \left[-\frac{\rho}{T}\frac{\partial v_i}{\partial t}\frac{\partial v_i}{\partial t} - \frac{1}{T}\sum_{\alpha=1}^{N}\tilde{v}_\alpha\frac{\partial\rho_\alpha}{\partial t}\frac{\partial p}{\partial t} - \frac{1}{T}\sum_{\alpha,\beta=1}^{N}\frac{\partial\mu_\alpha}{\partial\rho_\beta}\frac{\partial\rho_\beta}{\partial t}\frac{\partial\rho_\alpha}{\partial t} \right.$$
$$\left. - \frac{1}{T^2}\rho C_p\left(\frac{\partial T}{\partial t}\right)^2 - \frac{1}{\rho T}\frac{\partial\rho}{\partial T}\frac{\partial p}{\partial t}\frac{\partial T}{\partial t} \right] \tag{4.5.16}$$

The final expression for ψ can be found by first computing

$$\sum_{\alpha=1}^{N}\tilde{v}_\alpha\frac{\partial\rho_\alpha}{\partial t} = \tilde{V}\frac{\partial\rho}{\partial t} + \rho\sum_{\alpha=1}^{N}\tilde{v}_\alpha\frac{\partial w_\alpha}{\partial t} \tag{4.5.17}$$

where $\tilde{V} = 1/\rho$ (specific volume).   Reducing Eq. (4.5.17) further, we find

$$\tilde{V}\frac{\partial\rho}{\partial t} + \rho\sum_{\alpha=1}^{N}\tilde{v}_\alpha\frac{\partial w_\alpha}{\partial t} = -\rho\left[\left(\frac{\partial\tilde{V}}{\partial T}\right)_{p,M}\frac{\partial T}{\partial t} + \left(\frac{\partial\tilde{V}}{\partial p}\right)_{T,M}\frac{\partial p}{\partial t}\right] \tag{4.5.18}$$

where we have used

$$\frac{\partial\rho}{\partial t} = -\frac{1}{\tilde{V}^2}\frac{\partial\tilde{V}}{\partial t} = -\frac{1}{\tilde{V}^2}\left[\left(\frac{\partial\tilde{V}}{\partial T}\right)_{p,M}\frac{\partial T}{\partial t} + \left(\frac{\partial\tilde{V}}{\partial p}\right)_{T,M}\frac{\partial p}{\partial t} + \sum_{\alpha=1}^{N}\tilde{v}_\alpha\frac{\partial w_\alpha}{\partial t}\right]$$

to derive Eq. (4.5.18).   Substituting into Eq. (4.5.16) gives

$$\psi = \left\{ -\frac{\rho}{T}\frac{\partial v_i}{\partial t}\frac{\partial v_i}{\partial t} + \frac{\rho}{T}\left[\left(\frac{\partial\tilde{V}}{\partial T}\right)_{p,M}\frac{\partial T}{\partial t} + \left(\frac{\partial\tilde{V}}{\partial p}\right)_{T,M}\frac{\partial p}{\partial t}\right]\frac{\partial p}{\partial t} \right.$$
$$\left. -\frac{1}{T}\sum_{\alpha,\beta=1}^{N}\frac{\partial\mu_\alpha}{\partial\rho_\beta}\frac{\partial\rho_\beta}{\partial t}\frac{\partial\rho_\alpha}{\partial t} - \frac{1}{T^2}\rho C_p\left(\frac{\partial T}{\partial t}\right)^2 - \frac{1}{\rho T}\frac{\partial\rho}{\partial T}\frac{\partial p}{\partial t}\frac{\partial T}{\partial t} \right\} \tag{4.5.19}$$

If the thermodynamic equation

$$C_v - C_p = T\frac{(\partial\tilde{V}/\partial T)^2_{p,M}}{(\partial\tilde{V}/\partial p)_{T,M}} \tag{4.5.20}$$

and the definition of the isothermal compressibility

$$\chi = -\frac{1}{\tilde{V}}\left(\frac{\partial\tilde{V}}{\partial p}\right)_{T,M} = -\rho\left(\frac{\partial\tilde{V}}{\partial p}\right)_{T,M} \tag{4.5.21}$$

are substituted into Eq. (4.5.19), one obtains

$$
\psi = \left[-\frac{\rho}{T} \frac{\partial v_i}{\partial t} \frac{\partial v_i}{\partial t} - \frac{\rho^2}{\chi T} \left(\frac{\chi}{\rho} \frac{\partial p}{\partial t} - \frac{\partial \tilde{V}}{\partial T} \frac{\partial T}{\partial t} \right)^2 \right.
$$

$$
\left. - \frac{1}{T} \sum_{\alpha,\beta=1}^{N} \frac{\partial \mu_\alpha}{\partial \rho_\beta} \frac{\partial \rho_\beta}{\partial t} \frac{\partial \rho_\alpha}{\partial t} - \frac{1}{T^2} \rho C_v \left(\frac{\partial T}{\partial t} \right)^2 \right]
\tag{4.5.22}
$$

It can be stated that ψ is never positive as a consequence of the conditions for thermodynamic stability around the state of local equilibrium

$$
C_v > 0, \qquad \chi > 0, \qquad \sum_{\beta,\alpha=1}^{N} \frac{\partial \mu_\alpha}{\partial \rho_\beta} \frac{\partial \rho_\beta}{\partial t} \frac{\partial \rho_\alpha}{\partial t} > 0
$$

Thus

$$
\psi \leq 0 \tag{4.5.23}
$$

which is the result we have sought in our first computation.   The quantity ψ can also be evaluated from the balance Equations (4.5.1) to (4.5.3) as

$$
\psi = \left[+\sum_{\alpha=1}^{N} \frac{\partial}{\partial t} \frac{\mu_\alpha}{T} \frac{\partial}{\partial x_i} \rho_\alpha v_i + \sum_{\alpha=1}^{N} \frac{\partial}{\partial t} \frac{\mu_\alpha}{T} \frac{\partial}{\partial x_i} J_i^{(\alpha)} - \sum_{\beta=1}^{R} \sum_{\alpha=1}^{N} \frac{\partial}{\partial t} \frac{\mu_\alpha}{T} M_\alpha \nu_{\alpha\beta} K_\beta \right.
$$

$$
+ \frac{\rho}{T} \frac{\partial v_i}{\partial t} v_j \frac{\partial v_i}{\partial x_j} + \frac{1}{T} \frac{\partial v_i}{\partial t} \frac{\partial \pi_{ij}}{\partial x_j} - \frac{1}{T} \frac{\partial v_i}{\partial t} \sum_{\alpha=1}^{N} \rho_\alpha F_i^{(\alpha)}
$$

$$
\left. - \frac{\partial T^{-1}}{\partial t} \frac{\partial}{\partial x_i} \rho v_i u - \frac{\partial T^{-1}}{\partial t} \frac{\partial q_i}{\partial x_i} - \frac{\partial T^{-1}}{\partial t} \pi_{ij} \frac{\partial v_i}{\partial x_j} + \frac{\partial T^{-1}}{\partial t} \sum_{\alpha=1}^{N} J_i^{(\alpha)} F_i^{(\alpha)} \right]
\tag{4.5.24}
$$

After some rearrangement, Eq. (4.5.24) can be written in the form

$$
\psi = \frac{\partial}{\partial x_i} \left[\sum_{\alpha=1}^{N} (\rho_\alpha v_i + J_i^{(\alpha)}) \frac{\partial}{\partial t} \frac{\mu_\alpha}{T} + \frac{\pi_{ij}}{T} \frac{\partial v_j}{\partial t} - \frac{\partial T^{-1}}{\partial t} \rho u v_i - q_i \frac{\partial T^{-1}}{\partial t} \right]
$$

$$
- \sum_{\alpha=1}^{N} (\rho_\alpha v_i + J_i^{(\alpha)}) \frac{\partial}{\partial t} \frac{\partial}{\partial x_i} \frac{\mu_\alpha}{T} - \sum_{\beta=1}^{R} \frac{\partial}{\partial t} \frac{A_\beta}{T} K_\beta
$$

$$
+ \left(\rho u v_i + q_i + \pi_{ij} v_j + \frac{1}{2} \rho v_i \frac{v^2}{2} \right) \frac{\partial}{\partial t} \frac{\partial}{\partial x_i} \frac{1}{T}
$$

$$
+ \left(v_i \sum_{\alpha=1}^{N} \rho_\alpha F_i^{(\alpha)} + \sum_{\alpha=1}^{N} J_i^{(\alpha)} F_i^{(\alpha)} \right) \frac{\partial}{\partial t} \frac{1}{T} - (\rho v_i v_j + \pi_{ij}) \frac{\partial}{\partial t} \frac{\partial}{\partial x_j} \frac{v_i}{T}
$$

$$
+ \rho v_j \frac{\partial}{\partial x_j} \frac{\partial}{\partial t} \frac{v^2}{2T} - \frac{\partial}{\partial t} \frac{v_i}{T} \sum_{\alpha=1}^{N} \rho_\alpha F_i^{(\alpha)} \leq 0
\tag{4.5.25}
$$

No new equations or concepts were necessary to develop Eq. (4.5.25) starting from Eq. (4.5.24). Several rearrangements of this equation are possible; however, for our purposes, Eq. (4.5.25) will suffice. First of all, it is interesting to note that the equation has the structure

$$\psi = \Sigma J_{(K)} \frac{\partial X_{(K)}}{\partial t} \leq 0 \qquad (4.5.26)$$

in which the $X_{(K)}$'s are a generalized force and the $J_{(K)}$'s an associated flow. By using the procedure outlined in the preceding section, we can develop various variational formulations for each transport problem, starting with Eq. (4.5.25). Special cases will be considered in the following sections. Thus ψ, as defined by Eq. (4.5.25), is a powerful tool in the study of transport systems.

4.6 THE POTENTIAL FOR SPECIAL CASES

The evolution criterion, Eq. (4.5.25), is quite complex owing to its generality. It is desirable to reduce this equation to simpler terms for various special cases. Also, it will be convenient to have these special results in hand when we begin to apply the method to particular problems.

EXAMPLE 4.6.1   For a single chemical substance in isothermal motion, Eq. (4.5.24) reduces to

$$\psi = \frac{\partial}{\partial x_i}\left(\rho v_i \frac{\partial}{\partial t}\frac{\mu}{T} + \frac{\pi_{ij}}{T}\frac{\partial v_j}{\partial t}\right) - \rho v_i \frac{\partial}{\partial t}\frac{\partial}{\partial x_i}\frac{\mu}{T} - \frac{\rho v_i v_j + \pi_{ij}}{T}\frac{\partial}{\partial t}\frac{\partial v_i}{\partial x_j}$$

$$+ \frac{\rho v_j}{2T}\frac{\partial}{\partial t}\frac{\partial v^2}{\partial x_j} - \frac{1}{T}\frac{\partial v_i}{\partial t}\rho F_i \leq 0 \qquad (4.6.1)$$

The following thermodynamic relationship is applicable:

$$\left[d\left(\frac{\mu}{T}\right)\right]_{T,M} = \frac{1}{\rho T}dp \qquad (4.6.2)$$

and we also define

$$\pi_{ij} = \tau_{ij} + \delta_{ij}p \qquad (4.6.3)$$

Equation (4.6.1) can then be written in the form

$$\psi = \frac{\partial}{\partial x_i}\left(\frac{1}{T}\frac{\partial}{\partial t}v_i p + \frac{\tau_{ij}}{T}\frac{\partial v_j}{\partial t}\right) - \frac{\rho v_i}{T}\frac{\partial}{\partial t}\frac{1}{\rho}\frac{\partial p}{\partial x_i} - \frac{\rho v_i v_j}{T}\frac{\partial}{\partial t}\frac{\partial v_j}{\partial x_i}$$

$$- \frac{\pi_{ij}}{T}\frac{\partial}{\partial t}\frac{\partial v_i}{\partial x_j} + \frac{\rho v_j}{2T}\frac{\partial}{\partial t}\frac{\partial v^2}{\partial x_j} - \frac{1}{T}\frac{\partial v_i}{\partial t}\rho F_i \leq 0 \qquad (4.6.4)$$

This expression serves as the basis for developing the appropriate local potential for a special hydrodynamic situation. The method follows the example shown in Sec. 4.4. As a special example, let us try to find a variational formulation for an incompressible, non-Newtonian fluid. Consider a fluid defined by the constitutive equation

$$\tau_{ij} = -2\eta_1(\text{II},\text{III})d_{ij} - 3\eta_2(\text{II},\text{III})d_{ik}d_{kj} \tag{4.6.5}$$

where II and III are the second and third invariances of the strain-rate tensor defined as

$$\text{II} = d_{ij}d_{ji} \qquad \text{III} = \det d_{ij}$$

and the components of the strain-rate tensor are

$$d_{ij} = \frac{1}{2}\left(\frac{\partial v_i}{\partial x_j} + \frac{\partial v_j}{\partial x_i}\right)$$

To simplify the analysis somewhat, we again impose the condition of time-independent boundary conditions so that

$$\int_V \frac{\partial}{\partial x_i}\left(\frac{1}{T}\frac{\partial}{\partial t}v_i p + \frac{\tau_{ij}}{T}\frac{\partial v_j}{\partial t}\right)dV$$
$$= \int_S \left(\frac{1}{T}\frac{\partial}{\partial t}v_i p + \frac{\tau_{ij}}{T}\frac{\partial v_j}{\partial t}\right)n_i\,dS$$
$$= 0$$

since the time derivatives vanish on the surface. Therefore for the incompressible, non-Newtonian fluid

$$\phi = \int_V \psi\,dV = \int_V\left(-\frac{v_i}{T}\frac{\partial}{\partial t}\frac{\partial p}{\partial x_i} - \frac{\rho v_i v_j}{T}\frac{\partial}{\partial t}\frac{\partial v_i}{\partial x_j}\right.$$
$$-\frac{p}{T}\frac{\partial}{\partial t}\frac{\partial}{\partial x_i}v_i + \frac{\eta_1}{T}\frac{\partial}{\partial t}d_{ij}d_{ij} + \frac{\eta_2}{T}\frac{\partial}{\partial t}d_{ik}d_{kj}d_{ij}$$
$$\left.+\frac{\rho v_j}{2T}\frac{\partial}{\partial t}\frac{\partial}{\partial x_j}v^2 - \frac{1}{T}\frac{\partial}{\partial t}v_i\rho F_i\right)dV \leq 0 \tag{4.6.6}$$

For a system very close to the stationary state, Eq. (4.6.6) can be written approximately as

$$T\phi = \frac{\partial}{\partial t}E^* \tag{4.6.7}$$

in which

$$E^* = \int_V\left(-v_i^0\frac{\partial p}{\partial x_i} - \rho^0 v_i^0 v_j^0\frac{\partial v_i}{\partial x_j} - p^0\frac{\partial v_i}{\partial x_j} + \eta_1^0 d_{ij}d_{ij}\right.$$
$$\left.+\eta_2^0 d_{ik}d_{ij}d_{kj} + \frac{\rho^0}{2}v_j^0\frac{\partial}{\partial x_j}v^2 - \rho^0 F_i^0 v_i\right)dV \tag{4.6.8}$$

where again the superscript zero refers to quantities evaluated at the stationary state and these quantities are not subject to variation. Thus, the velocity and pressure associated with a fluid motion in a volume V will be such that E^* is stationary provided the velocity and the pressure satisfy the specified conditions on the surface and provided that the auxiliary conditions

$$v_i^0 = v_i \qquad (4.6.9)$$

$$p^0 = p \qquad (4.6.10)$$

are satisfied. Here p^0 is a constant, since we restricted our analysis to an incompressible fluid.

PROBLEM 4.6.1   Show that for the E^* of Eq. (4.6.8)

(a) $\dfrac{\delta E^*(v_i,p;v_i^0,p^0)}{\delta p} = 0 \qquad (4.6.11)$

gives

$$\frac{\partial}{\partial x_i} v_i = 0 \qquad (4.6.12)$$

(b) $\dfrac{\delta E^*}{\delta v_i} = 0 \qquad (4.6.13)$

gives

$$\rho v_j \frac{\partial v_i}{\partial x_j} + \frac{\partial p}{\partial x_i} - 2\frac{\partial}{\partial x_j}\eta_1 d_{ij} - 3\frac{\partial}{\partial x_j}\eta_2 d_{kj}d_{ik} - \rho F_i = 0 \qquad (4.6.14)$$

when the auxiliary equations (4.6.9) and (4.6.10) are used. Compare Eqs. (4.6.12) and (4.6.14) with the appropriate form of the balance equations for mass and momentum to insure that they are in agreement.

PROBLEM 4.6.2   If the inertia terms may be neglected and the velocity components satisfy the continuity equation, show that the motion of a Newtonian fluid with constant velocity will be such that the dissipation within a region will be less than that of any other motion having the same velocity components on the boundary. This is the classic Helmholtz theorem of hydrodynamics[1] and, in fact, is a principle of minimum entropy production.

EXAMPLE 4.6.2   Let us now consider a fluid consisting of a single chemical substance in which there exists both the transport of heat and momentum.

---

[1] Horace Lamb, "Hydrodynamics," pp. 617–619, 6th ed., Dover Publications, Inc., New York, 1945.

The evolution criterion reduces to

$$\psi = \frac{\partial}{\partial x_i}\left(\rho v_i \frac{\partial}{\partial t}\frac{\mu}{T} + \frac{\pi_{ij}}{T}\frac{\partial v_j}{\partial t} - \rho u v_i \frac{\partial}{\partial t}\frac{1}{T} - q_i \frac{\partial}{\partial t}\frac{1}{T}\right)$$

$$+ \left(\rho u v_i + q_i + \pi_{ij} v_j + \rho v_i \frac{v^2}{2}\right)\frac{\partial}{\partial t}\frac{\partial}{\partial x_i}\frac{1}{T} - \rho v_i \frac{\partial}{\partial t}\frac{\partial}{\partial x_i}\frac{\mu}{T}$$

$$+ v_i \rho F_i \frac{\partial}{\partial t}\frac{1}{T} - (\rho v_i v_j + \pi_{ij})\frac{\partial}{\partial t}\frac{\partial}{\partial x_i}\frac{v_j}{T} + \rho v_j \frac{\partial}{\partial x_j}\frac{\partial}{\partial t}\frac{v^2}{2T}$$

$$- \frac{\partial}{\partial t}\frac{v_i}{T}\rho F_i \le 0 \tag{4.6.15}$$

The change in chemical potential is determined by [see Eq. (4.5.8)]

$$\frac{\partial}{\partial t}\frac{\mu}{T} = h\frac{\partial}{\partial t}\frac{1}{T} + \frac{1}{T\rho}\frac{\partial p}{\partial t} \tag{4.6.16}$$

so that after some reduction, we find

$$\psi = \frac{\partial}{\partial x_i}\left(\frac{\partial}{\partial t}\frac{v_i p}{T} + \tau_{ij}\frac{\partial v_j}{\partial t} - q_i \frac{\partial}{\partial t}\frac{1}{T}\right) + \left(q_i + \tau_{ij}v_j + \rho v_i \frac{v^2}{2}\right)\frac{\partial}{\partial t}\frac{\partial}{\partial x_i}\frac{1}{T}$$

$$- \rho C_p v_i \frac{\partial T}{\partial t}\frac{\partial}{\partial x_i}\frac{1}{T} - v_i \frac{\partial p}{\partial t}\frac{\partial}{\partial x_i}\frac{1}{T} - v_i \frac{T}{\rho}\frac{\partial \rho}{\partial T}\frac{\partial p}{\partial t}\frac{\partial}{\partial x_i}\frac{1}{T}$$

$$- \rho v_i \frac{\partial}{\partial t}\frac{1}{T\rho}\frac{\partial p}{\partial x_i} + v_i \rho F_i \frac{\partial}{\partial t}\frac{1}{T} - (\rho v_i v_j + p\delta_{ij} + \tau_{ij})\frac{\partial}{\partial t}\frac{\partial}{\partial x_i}\frac{v_j}{T}$$

$$+ \rho v_j \frac{\partial}{\partial t}\frac{\partial}{\partial x_j}\frac{v^2}{2T} - \frac{\partial}{\partial t}\frac{v_i}{T}\rho F_i \le 0 \tag{4.6.17}$$

with the use of Eqs. (4.5.11) to (4.5.13). We now use the linear laws, Eqs. (4.2.14) and (4.2.15), specialized to suit the problem at hand. Thus,

$$q_i = L_{\theta\theta}\frac{\partial}{\partial x_i}\frac{1}{T} \tag{4.6.18}$$

$$\tau_{ij} = -\frac{D_{vv}}{T}\frac{\partial v_r}{\partial x_r}\delta_{ij} - 2\frac{M_{vv}}{T}d_{ij} \tag{4.6.19}$$

We ignore the contribution of bulk viscosity and assert that

$$\delta_{ij}\tau_{ij} = 0$$

giving

$$-D_{vv} = \frac{2}{3}M_{vv} \tag{4.6.20}$$

(Note that M_{vv}/T is the usual fluid viscosity of Newtonian fluids.)

Equation (4.6.17) can be further reduced by grouping some of the terms in a somewhat different fashion. We note that

$$- v_i \frac{\partial p}{\partial t} \frac{\partial}{\partial x_i} \frac{1}{T} - p \frac{\partial}{\partial t} \frac{\partial}{\partial x_i} \frac{v_i}{T} = - \frac{\partial}{\partial t} p \frac{\partial}{\partial x_i} \frac{v_i}{T} + \frac{1}{T} \frac{\partial p}{\partial t} \frac{\partial v_i}{\partial x_i} \tag{4.6.21}$$

and

$$\tau_{ij} v_j \frac{\partial}{\partial t} \frac{\partial}{\partial x_i} \frac{1}{T} - \tau_{ij} \frac{\partial}{\partial t} \frac{\partial}{\partial x_i} \frac{v_i}{T} = - \tau_{ij} \frac{\partial}{\partial x_j} \frac{1}{T} \frac{\partial v_i}{\partial t} - \tau_{ij} \frac{\partial}{\partial t} \frac{1}{T} \frac{\partial v_i}{\partial x_j} \tag{4.6.22}$$

Using linear law

$$- \tau_{ij} \frac{\partial}{\partial t} \frac{1}{T} \frac{\partial v_i}{\partial x_j} = - \frac{M_{vv}}{3} \frac{\partial}{\partial t} \left(\frac{1}{T} \frac{\partial v_s}{\partial x_s} \right)^2 + M_{vv} \frac{\partial}{\partial t} \frac{d_{ij}}{T} \frac{d_{ij}}{T} \tag{4.6.23}$$

If these identities are substituted into Eq. (4.6.17), then

$$\psi = \frac{\partial}{\partial x_i} \left(\frac{\partial}{\partial t} \frac{v_i p}{T} + \frac{\tau_{ij}}{T} \frac{\partial v_j}{\partial t} - q_i \frac{\partial}{\partial t} \frac{1}{T} \right)$$

$$+ \frac{1}{2} L_{\theta\theta} \frac{\partial}{\partial t} \left(\frac{\partial}{\partial x_i} \frac{1}{T} \frac{\partial}{\partial x_i} \frac{1}{T} \right) - \rho c_p v_i \frac{\partial T}{\partial t} \frac{\partial}{\partial x_i} \frac{1}{T}$$

$$+ \rho v_i \frac{v^2}{2} \frac{\partial}{\partial t} \frac{\partial}{\partial x_i} \frac{1}{T} - \frac{v_i T}{\rho} \frac{\partial \rho}{\partial T} \left(\frac{\partial}{\partial x_i} \frac{1}{T} \right) \frac{\partial p}{\partial t} - \rho v_i \frac{\partial}{\partial t} \left(\frac{1}{T\rho} \frac{\partial p}{\partial x_i} \right)$$

$$+ \rho v_i F_i \frac{\partial}{\partial t} \frac{1}{T} - \rho v_i v_j \frac{\partial}{\partial t} \frac{\partial}{\partial x_i} \frac{v_j}{T} - \frac{\partial}{\partial t} \left(p \frac{\partial}{\partial x_i} \frac{v_i}{T} \right) + \frac{1}{T} \frac{\partial p}{\partial t} \frac{\partial v_i}{\partial x_i}$$

$$- \tau_{ij} \left(\frac{\partial}{\partial x_j} \frac{1}{T} \right) \frac{\partial v_i}{\partial t} - \frac{M_{vv}}{3} \frac{\partial}{\partial t} \frac{(\partial v_s / \partial x_s)^2}{T^2} + M_{vv} \frac{\partial}{\partial t} \frac{d_{ij}}{T} \frac{d_{ij}}{T}$$

$$+ \rho v_j \frac{\partial}{\partial t} \frac{\partial}{\partial x_j} \frac{v^2}{2T} - \frac{\partial}{\partial t} \frac{v_i}{T} \rho F_i \leq 0 \tag{4.6.24}$$

It should be clear that other arrangements of the terms are possible. No claim of uniqueness or superiority can be laid for Eq. (4.6.24). This expression simply represents a convenient stopping point in the analysis. The simultaneous transport of energy and momentum in a stationary state can now be represented by a variational theorem which is mathematically equivalent to the differential representation offered by the balance equations. To find this representation, we first construct the generalized potential

$$\phi = \int_V \psi \, dV \leq 0 \tag{4.6.25}$$

and about the stationary state determine an E^* such that

$$\phi = \frac{\partial E^*}{\partial t} \leq 0 \tag{4.6.26}$$

The stationary state is determined by the minimum of E^*. For the particular physical system under consideration, it is clear that

$$
E^* = \int_V \left[\frac{1}{2} L_{\theta\theta}{}^0 \frac{\partial}{\partial x_i} \frac{1}{T} \frac{\partial}{\partial x_i} \frac{1}{T} - \rho^0 C_p{}^0 v_i{}^0 \ T \frac{\partial}{\partial x_i} \frac{1}{T^0} \right.
$$

$$
+ \frac{\rho^0 v_i{}^0}{2} (v^0)^2 \frac{\partial}{\partial x_i} \frac{1}{T} - \frac{T^0 v_i{}^0}{\rho^0} \frac{\partial \rho^0}{\partial T^0} P \frac{\partial}{\partial x_i} \frac{1}{T^0} - \frac{\rho^0 v_i{}^0}{T\rho} \frac{\partial p}{\partial x_i} + \frac{\rho^0 v_i{}^0 F_i}{T}
$$

$$
- \rho^0 v_i{}^0 v_j{}^0 \frac{\partial}{\partial x_i} \frac{v_j}{T} - p \frac{\partial}{\partial x_i} \frac{v_i}{T} + \frac{1}{T^0} \frac{\partial v_i{}^0}{\partial x_i} p - \tau_{ij}{}^0 v_i \frac{\partial}{\partial x_j} \frac{1}{T^0}
$$

$$
- \frac{M_{vv}{}^0}{3} \left(\frac{\partial v_s}{\partial x_s} \right)^2 \left(\frac{1}{T} \right)^2 + M_{vv}{}^0 \frac{d_{ij} d_{ij}}{T} \frac{}{T} + \rho^0 v_j{}^0 \frac{\partial}{\partial x_j} \frac{v^2}{2T} - \frac{v_i}{T} \rho^0 F_i \right] dV
$$

$$
\text{(4.6.27)}
$$

for time-independent boundary conditions. The pressure, temperature, and velocity which cause E^* to be stationary, which satisfy the specified boundary conditions, and which satisfy the auxiliary conditions

$$
p = p^0
$$

$$
v_i = v_i{}^0 \tag{4.6.28}
$$

$$
T = T^0
$$

are the observable values of the temperature, pressure, and velocity.

To prove this assertion, one need only demonstrate that the balance equations are satisfied by the same temperature, pressure, and velocity functions as those which satisfy the conditions set forth above. We note that

$$
\frac{\delta E^*}{\delta \, 1/T} = 0 \tag{4.6.29}
$$

gives

$$
\rho C_p v_i \frac{\partial T}{\partial x_i} = - \frac{\partial}{\partial x_i} \left(L_{\theta\theta} \frac{\partial}{\partial x_i} \frac{1}{T} \right) - \frac{\partial \ln \rho}{\partial \ln T} \frac{\partial p}{\partial x_i} v_i
$$

$$
- \frac{2}{3} \frac{M_{vv}}{T} \left(\frac{\partial v_s}{\partial x_s} \right)^2 + \frac{2 M_{vv}}{T} d_{ij} d_{ij} \tag{4.6.30}
$$

after some manipulation and also after use of Eq. (4.6.28). This expression is the valid internal energy balance for the fluid which obeys the linear laws. It is not difficult to demonstrate Eq. (4.6.30). The variation of the E^*

defined by Eq. (4.6.27) with respect to the reciprocal of the temperature is

$$
\delta E^* = \int_V \left[L_{\theta\theta}{}^0 \frac{\partial}{\partial x_i} \frac{1}{T} \frac{\partial}{\partial x_i} \delta \frac{1}{T} + \rho^0 C_p{}^0 v_i{}^0 \frac{\partial}{\partial x_i} \frac{1}{T^0} T^2 \delta \frac{1}{T} \right.
$$

$$
+ \rho^0 v_i{}^0 \frac{(v^0)^2}{2} \frac{\partial}{\partial x_i} \delta \frac{1}{T} - \frac{\rho^0 v_i{}^0}{\rho} \frac{\partial p}{\partial x_i} \delta \frac{1}{T} + \frac{T \rho^0 v_i{}^0}{\rho^2} \frac{\partial \rho}{\partial T} \delta \frac{1}{T} \frac{\partial p}{\partial x_i}
$$

$$
+ \rho^0 v_i{}^0 F_i \, \delta \frac{1}{T} - \rho^0 v_i{}^0 v_j{}^0 \frac{\partial}{\partial x_i} \left(v_j \, \delta \frac{1}{T} \right) - p \frac{\partial}{\partial x_i} \left(v_i \, \delta \frac{1}{T} \right)
$$

$$
- \frac{2 M_{vv}{}^0}{3} \left(\frac{\partial v_s}{\partial x_s} \right)^2 \frac{1}{T} \delta \frac{1}{T} + \frac{2 M_{vv}{}^0}{T} d_{ij} d_{ij} \, \delta \frac{1}{T} + \rho^0 v_j{}^0 \frac{\partial}{\partial x_j} \left(\frac{v^2}{2} \delta \frac{1}{T} \right)
$$

$$
\left. - v_i \rho^0 F_i \, \delta \frac{1}{T} \right] dV \tag{4.6.31}
$$

Note that the quantities with the superscript zero have been held fixed during the process of variation as required by the distinction between two types of functions. Also, it should be noted that the pressure p and velocity v_i have been held fixed during the process of variation with respect to temperature since these are visualized as independent functions. However, the density ρ is a function of the pressure and the temperature and hence is changed as the temperature is varied. If we recall that the variation of the temperature must vanish on the surface enclosing the volume V, then Eq. (4.6.31) can be written as

$$
\delta E^* = \int_V \left[-\frac{\partial}{\partial x_i} \left(L_{\theta\theta}{}^0 \frac{\partial}{\partial x_i} \frac{1}{T} \right) + \rho^0 C_p{}^0 v_i{}^0 \frac{\partial}{\partial x_i} \frac{1}{T^0} T^2 - \frac{\partial}{\partial x_i} \frac{\rho^0 v_i{}^0 (v^0)^2}{2} \right.
$$

$$
- \frac{\rho^0 v_i{}^0}{\rho} \frac{\partial p}{\partial x_i} + \frac{T \rho^0 v_i{}^0}{\rho^2} \frac{\partial \rho}{\partial T} \frac{\partial p}{\partial x_i} + \rho^0 v_i{}^0 F_i + v_j \frac{\partial}{\partial x_j} \rho^0 v_i{}^0 v_j{}^0
$$

$$
+ v_i \frac{\partial p}{\partial x_i} - \frac{2}{3} \frac{M_{vv}{}^0}{T} \left(\frac{\partial v_s}{\partial x_s} \right)^2 + \frac{2 M_{vv}{}^0}{T} d_{ij} d_{ij} - \frac{v^2}{2} \frac{\partial}{\partial x_j} \rho^0 v_j{}^0
$$

$$
\left. - v_i \rho^0 F_i \right] \delta \frac{1}{T} \, dV \tag{4.6.32}
$$

Since we require δE^* to vanish for all δT and because Eq. (4.6.28) can now be applied, then Eq. (4.6.30) is shown to be the correct Euler-Lagrange equation, which must be satisfied if E^* is to be stationary with respect to variations in temperature. It should be noted that the continuity equation

$$
\frac{\partial}{\partial x_i} \rho v_i = 0 \tag{4.6.33}
$$

must also be used to develop Eq. (4.6.28).

PROBLEM 4.6.3   Show that the continuity equation (4.6.33) results from requiring the E^* of Eq. (4.6.27) to be stationary with respect to variations in pressure.

PROBLEM 4.6.4   Show that the equation of motion is the Euler-Lagrange equation found upon requiring the E^* of Eq. (4.6.27) to be stationary with respect to variations in the components of velocity.

4.7 BOUNDARY CONDITIONS

In all of the considerations presented in this chapter we have assumed that the state variables μ_α/T, $1/T$, and v_i have specified values on the boundary.   Of course, these boundary conditions must be time-independent if the system is to reach a stationary state.   However, many other types of boundary conditions are used in engineering computations, and the aim of the following discussion is to classify the kinds of boundary conditions usually encountered in engineering analysis and to show that these boundary conditions can be incorporated (indeed, *must* be included) in the integral to be made stationary. We have already seen that the boundary conditions are an integral part of the variational principle.   (See Sec. 1.6 for a formal discussion.)

We begin our discussion by attempting to classify the various types of boundary conditions usually imposed in engineering calculations.

TYPE A: SPECIFIED STATE   In many instances, the state variables μ_α/T, $1/T$, and v_i are, being fixed by physical considerations, specified at the boundary. For example, the velocity on a solid boundary is usually assumed to be that of the boundary (no slip condition), or the temperature at a wall where steam is condensing is fixed by the temperature of the saturated steam.   In both of these cases one would impose specific values on one or more of the state variables.   Thus far, all our work in this chapter has been confined to this type of boundary condition.

TYPE B: SPECIFIED FLUX   It is often desirable, and even necessary, to specify the fluxes at the boundary rather than at the state variables.   By fluxes we refer to

(a) Mass flux $[v_i\rho_\alpha + J_i^{(\alpha)}]n_i$ $\qquad\qquad\qquad\qquad\qquad$ (4.7.1)

(b) Heat flux $(\rho u v_i + q_i)n_i$ $\qquad\qquad\qquad\qquad\qquad$ (4.7.2)

(c) Momentum flux $(\rho v_i v_j + \pi_{ij})n_i$ $\qquad\qquad\qquad\qquad$ (4.7.3)

where n_i is the normal to the surface.   Note the fluxes are "total" flows including both the convective and the diffusive part, and thus represent fluxes relative to a fixed coordinate system.   Also it is clear that only the projection along the normal is to be specified, since it is this component which defines the flow across the boundary.   There are a number of examples of this type of boundary condition which are familiar to the reader. An insulated surface, a surface on which the stress is specified, or a surface through which a fixed amount of substance flows are all examples of this type of boundary condition.

TYPE C: SEMIDETAILED Both types of boundary conditions discussed above are imposed without regard for the problem of achieving the particular specified flux or state variable. The type C boundary condition, in a gross way, accounts for the transport mechanism by which the system communicates with the environment. This type of boundary condition is normally applied when the hydrodynamic flows in the environment are complex. Such boundary conditions are stated in the following form:

(a) Mass flux $$J_i^{(\alpha)} n_i = K_M\left[\frac{\mu_\alpha}{T} - \left(\frac{\mu_\alpha}{T}\right)_e\right] \qquad (4.7.4)$$

(b) Heat flux $$q_i n_i = K_H\left[\frac{1}{T} - \left(\frac{1}{T}\right)_e\right] \qquad (4.7.5)$$

(c) Momentum flux $$\tau_{ij} n_i = K_{\text{Mom}}[v_j - (v_j)_e] \qquad (4.7.6)$$

where K_M and K_H are called the mass and the heat transfer coefficients, respectively. We shall call the coefficient K_{Mom} a momentum flux coefficient. The quantities subscripted by an e refer to state variables evaluated in the environment. These quantities are specified, and the transport rates are determined by the value of the system state variables at the boundary.

There are a number of books and research papers in the literature[1-3] which deal with the heat and mass transfer coefficients similar to those defined here. One can find values of K_M and K_H for a large variety of geometrical and dynamical conditions. For our purposes we need only note that there exists a copious literature examining flux equations having a structure very similar to Eqs. (4.7.4) and (4.7.5). However, there does not appear to have been much consideration given the momentum flux coefficient which is defined by Eq. (4.7.6). It is worth noting that Basset has defined a coefficient of friction which is identical to our momentum flux coefficient. He has applied this coefficient to the determination of the terminal velocity of a sphere being slowly translated through a viscous medium.[4]

[1] T. K. Sherwood and R. L. Pigford, "Absorption and Extraction," pp. 51–94, 2d ed., McGraw-Hill Book Company, New York, 1950.

[2] Max Jakob, "Heat Transfer," vol. I, pp. 421–577, John Wiley & Sons, Inc., New York, 1950.

[3] R. B. Bird, W. E. Stewart, and E. N. Lightfoot, "Transport Phenomena," pp. 389–428; pp. 636–736, John Wiley & Sons, Inc., New York, 1960.

[4] Horace Lamb, "Hydrodynamics," p. 604, 6th ed., Dover Publications, Inc., New York 1945.

The boundary conditions expressed by Eqs. (4.7.4) to (4.7.6) have been termed semidetailed because the structure is designed to account for the transport mechanism from the environment to the system in a gross sense.

TYPE D: DETAILED CONDITIONS   To utilize the detailed boundary conditions, one must consider two subsystems of a grand system.   The detailed boundary conditions are those which are applicable at the common boundary of the two subsystems.   Such a grand system is depicted in Fig. 4.7.1, where we see that two subsystems are in communication via a common boundary. This boundary could be, for example, an interface between two phases.   The applicable boundary conditions are given by equality of fluxes at the boundary

$$[\rho_\alpha v_i + J_i^{(\alpha)}]^\mathrm{I} n_i = [\rho_\alpha v_i + J_i^{(\alpha)}]^\mathrm{II} n_i \tag{4.7.7}$$

$$(\rho u v_i + q_i)^\mathrm{I} n_i = (\rho u v_i + q_i)^\mathrm{II} n_i \tag{4.7.8}$$

$$(\rho v_i v_j + \pi_{ij})^\mathrm{I} n_i = (\rho v_i v_j + \pi_{ij})^\mathrm{II} n_i \tag{4.7.9}\dagger$$

and by the equality of states at the surface

$$\left(\frac{\mu_\alpha}{T}\right)^\mathrm{I} = \left(\frac{\mu_\alpha}{T}\right)^\mathrm{II} \tag{4.7.10}$$

$$\left(\frac{1}{T}\right)^\mathrm{I} = \left(\frac{1}{T}\right)^\mathrm{II} \tag{4.7.11}$$

$$v_i{}^\mathrm{I} = v_i{}^\mathrm{II} \tag{4.7.12}$$

These detailed conditions are useful only if the states of both subsystems are to be studied simultaneously and the solutions adjusted so that the detailed boundary conditions are satisfied.   This is a difficult task and in most cases, the calculator attempts to make some approximations which will "uncouple"

† We neglect surface tension.

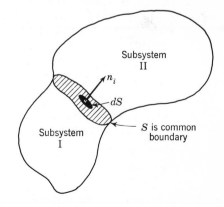

Fig. 4.7.1 Subsystems with common boundary.

the subsystems. However, in some cases the only means of obtaining the desired information is to find the simultaneous solution of the balance equations and to satisfy the detailed conditions at the common surface.

We have classified the boundary conditions commonly encountered in engineering into four distinct groups. Our aim is to demonstrate the modifications which are necessary if the appropriate boundary conditions are to be included as a part of the variational formulation. It should be stressed that boundary conditions other than those of type A must be included as *natural boundary conditions*. In other words, the correct boundary conditions must appear in the list of conditions to be satisfied if the appropriate potential is to be stationary. We shall see that this requirement usually gives rise to a surface integral, which should be added to the volume integrals already encountered in our previous work.

In order that we may see clearly the principles involved in constructing the correct potential which corresponds to the boundary conditions, let us consider a series of examples which are simple enough that long and complicated manipulations do not arise and yet of sufficient scope that there is no doubt about the means of approaching any problem.

EXAMPLE 4.7.1 The conduction of heat in an isotropic solid body is characterized by the potential

$$\psi = -\frac{\partial}{\partial x_i}\left(q_i \frac{\partial}{\partial t}\frac{1}{T}\right) + q_i \frac{\partial}{\partial t}\frac{\partial}{\partial x_i}\frac{1}{T} \leq 0 \tag{4.7.13}$$

We note that the ψ consists of two parts in the most general case—the divergence of a vector and the sum of terms consisting of generalized fluxes multiplied by an associated force. In forming ϕ, defined as

$$\phi = \int_V \psi \, dV \tag{4.7.14}$$

the volume integral splits into a surface and a volume contribution. In all previous examples, we have discarded the surface terms on the grounds that the boundary conditions were of type A. However, if the boundary conditions fit into some other category, then this surface term will not vanish and its structure will determine the form of the natural boundary conditions. Let us assume that the solid body is enclosed by a surface which is divided into two distinct types of surfaces.

Assume that on S_1 the temperature is specified and on S_2 the heat flux is specified. Moreover,

$$S = S_1 + S_2 \tag{4.7.15}$$

where S is the complete surface enclosing V. For this case

$$\phi = \int_V \left[-\frac{\partial}{\partial x_i}\left(q_i \frac{\partial}{\partial t}\frac{1}{T}\right) + q_i \frac{\partial}{\partial t}\frac{\partial}{\partial x_i}\frac{1}{T}\right] dV \leq 0 \tag{4.7.16}$$

Using Gauss' theorem

$$\phi = -\int_S q_i \frac{\partial}{\partial t} \frac{1}{T} n_i \, dS + \int_V q_i \frac{\partial}{\partial t} \frac{\partial}{\partial x_i} \frac{1}{T} \, dV \leq 0 \tag{4.7.17}$$

The surface integral vanishes on S_1, since the temperature is time-independent on this surface. Thus

$$\phi = -\int_{S_2} \tilde{q}_i n_i \frac{\partial}{\partial t} \frac{1}{T} \, dS + \int_V q_i \frac{\partial}{\partial t} \frac{\partial}{\partial x_i} \frac{1}{T} \, dV \leq 0 \tag{4.7.18}$$

where $\tilde{q}_i$ is the specified heat flux on S_2. This function is known a priori and is fixed (time-independent) if the system is to approach a stationary state. Following the procedure adopted previously, we can approximate ϕ in the form

$$\phi = \frac{\partial}{\partial t} E^* \leq 0 \tag{4.7.19}$$

where the local potential is

$$E^* = -\int_{S_2} \tilde{q}_i n_i \frac{1}{T} \, dS + \int_V \frac{1}{2} L_{\theta\theta}(T^0) \frac{\partial T^{-1}}{\partial x_i} \frac{\partial T^{-1}}{\partial x_i} \, dV \tag{4.7.20}$$

Note that the E^* for this case differs from that previously derived in that we now have a surface contribution. Let us find the natural boundary conditions and the Euler-Lagrange equations. After performing the usual manipulations, we find

$$\delta E^* = \int_{S_2} \left(-q_i n_i + L_{\theta\theta}^0 \frac{\partial T^{-1}}{\partial x_i} n_i \right) \delta \frac{1}{T} \, dS - \int_V \frac{\partial}{\partial x_i} \left(L_{\theta\theta}^0 \frac{\partial T^{-1}}{\partial x_i} \right) \delta \frac{1}{T} \, dV \tag{4.7.21}$$

or if δE^* is to vanish for all variations, then

$$\tilde{q}_i n_i = L_{\theta\theta} \frac{\partial T^{-1}}{\partial x_i} n_i \qquad \text{on } S_2 \tag{4.7.22}$$

and

$$\frac{\partial q_i}{\partial x_i} = 0 \tag{4.7.23}$$

Equation (4.7.23) is the proper balance equation and Eq. (4.7.22) shows that stationary heat flux must equal the specified heat flux on S_2. Thus the requirement that the heat flux be equal to the specified value appears as a *natural boundary condition*. This must be true for all boundary conditions other than those of type A, which in essence require that the variations vanish on the surface. The requirement that the physical boundary conditions appear as natural boundary conditions has given rise to an additional term in the local potential—a surface integral. We shall see that, in general, E^* will be the sum of a volume integral and a surface integral.

EXAMPLE 4.7.2   Let us consider the isothermal, incompressible flow of a fluid in a region which is bounded by a surface S. Let S_1 be the portion of S on which the velocities are specified. On the remainder of S, S_2, let the momentum flux through the surface be specified. Then from Eq. (4.6.4) we find

$$\psi = \frac{\partial}{\partial x_i}\left(\frac{\partial}{\partial t}\frac{v_i p}{T} + \frac{\tau_{ij}}{T}\frac{\partial v_j}{\partial t}\right) - \frac{v_i}{T}\frac{\partial}{\partial t}\frac{\partial p}{\partial x_i}$$

$$- \frac{\rho v_i v_j}{T}\frac{\partial}{\partial t}\frac{\partial v_j}{\partial x_i} - \frac{\pi_{ij}}{T}\frac{\partial}{\partial t}\frac{\partial v_j}{\partial x_i} + \frac{\rho v_j}{T}\frac{\partial}{\partial t}\frac{\partial}{\partial x_j}\frac{v^2}{2}$$

$$- \frac{\partial v_i}{\partial t}\frac{\rho F_i}{T} \leq 0 \tag{4.7.24}$$

Thus

$$\phi = \frac{\partial}{\partial t}E^*$$

where, for the flow of an incompressible Newtonian fluid,

$$E^* = \int_{S_2}\frac{v_j}{T}(\tilde{p}\delta_{ij} + \tilde{\tau}_{ij})n_i\,dS + \int_V\left(-\frac{v_i{}^0}{T}\frac{\partial p}{\partial x_i} - \frac{\rho v_i{}^0 v_j{}^0}{T}\frac{\partial v_j}{\partial x_i}\right.$$

$$\left.+ \frac{\mu}{T}d_{ij}d_{ij} + \frac{\rho v_j{}^0}{T}\frac{\partial}{\partial x_j}\frac{v^2}{2} - \frac{v_i\rho F_i}{T}\right)dV \tag{4.7.25}$$

Here $(\tilde{p}\delta_{ij} + \tilde{\tau}_{ij})n_i$ is the specified momentum flux. It is worth noting that one need not specify all nine components of the stress tensor. Indeed the only terms that arise are those appearing in the contracted expression $\tilde{\pi}_{ij}n_i v_j$. This will be an important consideration in the example to follow.

PROBLEM 4.7.1   Show that if the E^* defined by Eq. (4.7.25) is to be stationary, then it is necessary that

$$\tilde{\pi}_{ij}n_j\,\delta v_i = \pi_{ij}n_j\,\delta v_i \quad \text{on } S_2 \tag{4.7.26}$$

EXAMPLE 4.7.3   To make the considerations of the preceding section more definite, let us consider a specific example. Shown in Fig. 4.7.2 is a rectangular duct through which we have the laminar of an incompressible Newtonian fluid. As is usual we assume

$$v_1 = v_2 = 0 \tag{4.7.27}$$

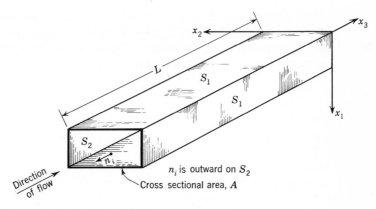

Fig. 4.7.2   Laminar flow in a rectangular duct.

and

$$v_3 = v_3(x_1, x_2) \tag{4.7.28}$$

If the fluid is Newtonian then

$$\tau_{11} = 0 \qquad \tau_{12} = 0 \qquad \tau_{13} = -\mu \frac{\partial v_3}{\partial x_1}$$

$$\tau_{21} = 0 \qquad \tau_{22} = 0 \qquad \tau_{23} = -\mu \frac{\partial v_3}{\partial x_2}$$

$$\tau_{31} = -\mu \frac{\partial v_3}{\partial x_1} \qquad \tau_{32} = -\mu \frac{\partial v_3}{\partial x_2} \qquad \tau_{33} = 0 \tag{4.7.29}$$

It is clear from a consideration of Fig. 4.7.2 that there are two types of boundaries and hence two boundary conditions. On S_1 the velocity must vanish, since we assume that there is no slip at the solid-liquid interface. The surface S_2 (the areas perpendicular to flow) must be treated differently. On this surface we specify

$$\tilde{\pi}_{ij} n_i v_j = \tilde{p} v_3 n_3 \qquad \text{on } S_2 \tag{4.7.30}$$

Thus, the pressure must be specified at $x_3 = 0$ and $x_3 = L$. It is clear that these two pressures determine the flow. The terms of Eq. (4.7.25) become

$$E^* = -\frac{1}{T} \int_A \tilde{p} \bigg|_{x_3=0} v_3 \, dx_1 \, dx_2 + \frac{1}{T} \int_A \tilde{p} \bigg|_{x_3=L} v_3 \, dx_1 \, dx_2$$

$$+ \int_A \int_0^L \left\{ -\frac{v_3^0}{T} \frac{\partial p}{\partial x_3} + \frac{\mu}{2T} \left[\left(\frac{\partial v_3}{\partial x_1} \right)^2 + \left(\frac{\partial v_3}{\partial x_2} \right)^2 \right] \right\} dx_1 \, dx_2 \, dx_3 \tag{4.7.31}$$

If we assume that the pressure drop is linear in x_3, then $\partial p/\partial x_3$ is a constant and the term $(v_3^0 T)(\partial p/\partial x_3)$ can not contribute more than a constant value to E^* and hence can be eliminated. Thus the following is the integral to be minimized by the proper choice of $v_3(x_1, x_2)$:

$$E^* = \frac{1}{T}\int_A v_3\, dx_1\, dx_2\, (\tilde{p}\mid_{x_3=L} - \tilde{p}\mid_{x_3=0}) + \frac{\mu}{2T}\int_A \int_0^L \left[\left(\frac{\partial v_3}{\partial x_1}\right)^2\right.$$

$$\left. + \left(\frac{\partial v_3}{\partial x_2}\right)^2\right] dx_1\, dx_2\, dx_3 \qquad (4.7.32)$$

Equation (4.7.32) is included in the Helmholtz theorem and is also clearly equivalent to minimum entropy production. Moreover, Eq. (4.7.32) is the same variational expression that we used in Sec. 3.2 to determine the velocity distribution in a square duct. This same equation has also been used by Sparrow and Siegel.[5] In the next chapter, we shall pursue the computational aspects using the principle of minimum entropy production.

EXAMPLE 4.7.4   The boundary conditions considered in the preceding three examples have been of type *B*. Let us now study a problem which has a type-*C* boundary condition. Again, let us view a simple problem in heat conduction so that Eq. (4.7.17) is valid.

$$\phi = -\int_S q_i \frac{\partial}{\partial t}\frac{1}{T} n_i\, dS + \int_V q_i \frac{\partial}{\partial t}\frac{\partial}{\partial x_i}\frac{1}{T}\, dV \le 0 \qquad (4.7.33)$$

Also, let us assume that

$$q_i n_i = K_H\left[\frac{1}{T} - \left(\frac{1}{T}\right)_e\right] \qquad (4.7.34)$$

is the imposed condition. We note that $(1/T)_e$ must be time-independent if the system is to come to a stationary state. Using Eq. (4.7.34), we write Eq. (4.7.17) as

$$\phi = \frac{\partial}{\partial t} E^*$$

where

$$E^* = -\int_S\left\{K_H^0\left[\frac{1}{T^0} - \left(\frac{1}{T}\right)_e\right]\frac{1}{T}\right\} dS + \int_V \frac{1}{2} L_{\theta\theta}(T^0)\frac{\partial T^{-1}}{\partial x_i}\frac{\partial T^{-1}}{\partial x_i}\, dV \qquad (4.7.35)$$

[5] E. M. Sparrow and R. Siegel, "Variational Methods for Fully-Developed Laminar Heat Transfer in Ducts," *J. Heat Transfer*, vol. 81, p. 157, 1959.

Here we assert that the temperature which renders E^* as small as possible and satisfies the auxiliary condition

$$T^0 = T \tag{4.7.36}$$

is the correct stationary state for the system being considered. Thus, we see that the type-C boundary conditions are easily included in the variational formulation of the problem in a systematic way. *One need only include the correct boundary condition into the surface contribution to the local potential.*

EXAMPLE 4.7.5   As our last example of this section, we study a problem which has type-D boundary conditions to be included. The system is a binary system (shown in Fig. 4.7.3). Here we see a two-phase (vapor-liquid) system through which there is a continuous heat flow. Because of thermal diffusion, there exist concentration gradients as well as temperature gradients. The sides of the vessel are well insulated, so that we only have to consider variations of both chemical potential and temperature in the x_3 direction. Moreover, the system is arranged so that there are no convection currents. Also, we will restrict our attention to a binary system. It is clear that we will have to study two subsystems, since the phenomenological coefficients are vastly different in the liquid phase from what they are in the vapor phase. For this special problem, Eq. (4.5.25) reduces to

$$\psi = \frac{\partial}{\partial x_3}\left[J_3^{(1)} \frac{\partial}{\partial t}\left(\frac{\mu_1}{T}\right) + J_3^{(2)} \frac{\partial}{\partial t}\left(\frac{\mu_2}{T}\right) - q_3 \frac{\partial}{\partial t} \frac{1}{T}\right]$$

$$- J_3^{(1)} \frac{\partial}{\partial t}\frac{\partial}{\partial x_3}\frac{\mu_1}{T} - J_3^{(2)} \frac{\partial}{\partial t}\frac{\partial}{\partial x_3}\frac{\mu_2}{T} + q_3 \frac{\partial}{\partial t}\frac{\partial}{\partial x_3}\frac{1}{T} \leq 0 \tag{4.7.37}$$

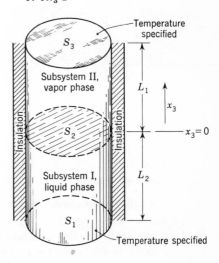

Fig. 4.7.3   Heat flow through a two-phase system.

which is valid for both phases in this form.   Since

$$J_3^{(1)} = -J_3^{(2)} \tag{4.7.38}$$

then

$$
\phi = \left[J_3^{(1)} \frac{\partial}{\partial t} \left(\frac{\mu_1}{T} - \frac{\mu_2}{T} \right) - q_3 \frac{\partial}{\partial t} \frac{1}{T} \right]^{I}_{x_3=0}
$$
$$
- \left[J_3^{(1)} \frac{\partial}{\partial t} \left(\frac{\mu_1}{T} - \frac{\mu_2}{T} \right) - q_3 \frac{\partial}{\partial t} \frac{1}{T} \right]^{II}_{x_3=0}
$$
$$
+ \int_{-L_2}^{0} \left[J_3^{(1)} \frac{\partial}{\partial t} \frac{\partial}{\partial x_3} \left(\frac{\mu_2}{T} - \frac{\mu_1}{T} \right) + q_3 \frac{\partial}{\partial t} \frac{\partial}{\partial x_3} \frac{1}{T} \right] dx_3
$$
$$
+ \int_{0}^{L_1} \left[J_3^{(1)} \frac{\partial}{\partial t} \frac{\partial}{\partial x_3} \left(\frac{\mu_2}{T} - \frac{\mu_1}{T} \right) + q_3 \frac{\partial}{\partial t} \frac{\partial}{\partial x_3} \frac{1}{T} \right] dx_3 \tag{4.7.39}
$$

where $[\ \ ]^{I}$ implies that the properties used in this expression are evaluated in subsystem I.

Here we have a structure in which the contribution to the surface integral comes from both subsystem I and subsystem II.   In addition there are two volume integrals (ordinary integrals in this case)—one for each phase.   The surface integrals vanish at the surfaces S_1 and S_3 because the temperature is fixed at these surfaces, and the mass fluxes vanish at both of the surfaces because the ends are not permeable to matter.   Now if we impose equality of fluxes and state at the common interface $x_3 = 0$, then the terms evaluated at $x_3 = 0$ cancel one another and we find an appropriate form of the local potential to be

$$E^* = \int_{-L_2}^{0} e^* \, dx_3 + \int_{0}^{L_1} e^* \, dx_3 \tag{4.7.40}$$

where

$$e^* = L_{1\theta}^0 \frac{\partial}{\partial x_3} \frac{1}{T} \frac{\partial \Lambda_{(1)}}{\partial x_3} + \frac{1}{2} L_{\theta\theta}^0 \left(\frac{\partial}{\partial x_3} \frac{1}{T} \right)^2 + \frac{1}{2} L_{11}^0 \left(\frac{\partial \Lambda_{(1)}}{\partial x_3} \right)^2$$

$$\Lambda_{(1)} = \frac{\mu_{(1)} - \mu_{(2)}}{T}$$

The natural boundary conditions arising from making E^* stationary are easily seen to be the equality of the fluxes and the state variables, which is the desired result.   The E^* defined by Eq. (4.7.40) is an acceptable variational principle describing the process selected for study.

In all cases studied, we note that the correct boundary conditions are added when developing E^*.   Then these boundary conditions are in a sense "imbedded" in the structure of E^* and appear as the natural boundary conditions necessary for E^* to be stationary.

CHAPTER 5
APPLICATIONS
TO TRANSPORT
PROBLEMS

5.1 INTRODUCTION A large class of important engineering problems is governed by the mass, momentum, and energy balance equations. The engineer must, therefore, synthesize techniques of studying the behavior of this set of equations as an economic alternative to constructing models and making experimental measurements. Of course, the availability of high-speed digital computers has sparked a wave of interest in the numerical methods of solution. These techniques usually result in the substitution of a large set of algebraic equations for the differential equations. The algebraic system is selected so that the behavior of the differential equations is approximated (hopefully) at discrete nodes. This approach has been very fruitful, and many successful studies of complex examples have been reported.

In this chapter we also want to concern ourselves with approximations to transport problems. However, here we shall confine our attention to the direct method of calculation applied to the solution of transport problems. This particular class of problems seems to merit special consideration because the variational principles describing the transport problems are unusual when viewed from the framework of the classical calculus of variations. In particular we note the structure of the local potential as developed in the last chapter. This quantity is a functional which depends on both functions which are subject to variation and functions which are to be held fixed. It is probably not clear that such a formalism has practical value. However, we shall see that all of the methods developed in Chap. 3 are applicable to the local potential.

As noted in Chap. 4, the local potential gives rise to a structure which includes a very general class of problem but the "price" of this generality was the loss of the means of developing bounds on the accuracy of the approximation. Thus we will also not be able to compare the relative quality of two solutions since we must know the true solution to use the local potential as a measure of the quality of an approximation. The last two examples presented in this chapter deal with the principle of minimum entropy production, and the advantages of the character of an extremal principle are put to full use.

It should be noted that all of the problems which are treated in this chapter are also amenable to numerical treatment. We have not made any effort to compare the various methods of solution, and, therefore, there are no recommendations to guide the reader down the "best route." However, it appears that for many problems crude approximations can best be found using variational methods. More refined approximations can be determined by numerical means, assuming that a computer is available.

5.2 CONCENTRATION PROFILE IN A CHEMICAL REACTOR

We begin our exploration of the applications of the methods developed in the last chapter by studying the isothermal chemical reactor. The reactor is depicted in Fig. 5.2.1, and the local concentration is described by the differential equation

$$V \frac{dc}{dx} = D \frac{d^2c}{dx^2} - kc^S \tag{5.2.1}$$

where V = velocity

c = concentration

D = diffusion coefficient

k and S = reaction rate parameters

The appropriate boundary conditions are

$$c = c_I \quad \text{at} \quad x = 0 \tag{5.2.2}$$

and

$$\frac{dc}{dx} = 0 \quad \text{at} \quad x = L \tag{5.2.3}$$

Equation (5.2.1) is a transport equation and can be represented in variational form if the local potential† is used. Indeed it can easily be verified that if

$$I = \int_0^L \left[Vc \frac{dc^0}{dx} + \frac{D}{2} \left(\frac{dc}{dx} \right)^2 + \frac{k}{S+1} c^{S+1} \right] dx \tag{5.2.4}$$

is stationary and if c^0 is given by the auxiliary equation

$$c = c^0 \tag{5.2.5}$$

† A variational principle in which local potential plays no role can also be developed (see Prob. 5.2.2). We shall not use this alternate formulation here since our aim is to illustrate the applications of the local potential.

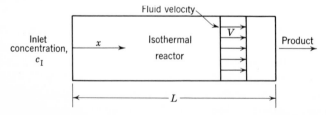

Fig. 5.2.1 Plugflow reactor.

then Eqs. (5.2.1) to (5.2.3) are satisfied.   Again the superscript zero denotes a function not subject to variation.   Our task is to develop an approximate solution for the concentration profile using a direct approach.   We shall assume

$$c = c_I(1 + a_1 x + a_2 x^2 + \cdots + a_n x^n) \tag{5.2.6}$$

with a_n chosen such that dc/dx vanishes at the end of the reactor.   How are we to satisfy the condition that the concentration c^0 is not to be varied but must be known?   To account for c^0, we shall assume

$$c^0 = c_I(1 + \alpha_1 x + \alpha_2 x^2 + \cdots + \alpha_n x^n) \tag{5.2.7}$$

where α_n is determined so that

$$\frac{dc^0}{dx} = 0 \qquad \text{at} \qquad x = L \tag{5.2.8}$$

Note that the expressions for c and c^0 have the same structure, but the parameters α_i and a_i are distinguishable.   We call this the self-consistent approximation.   We shall assume that the α_i are known and fixed but the a_i are to be determined so that

$$\frac{\partial I_n}{\partial a_i} = 0 \qquad i = 1, 2, \ldots, n \tag{5.2.9}$$

After performing this differentiation (equivalent to taking a variation), it is permissible, indeed necessary, to set

$$\alpha_i = a_i \qquad i = 1, 2, \ldots, n \tag{5.2.10}$$

which is equivalent to applying the auxiliary equation (5.2.5).

To make these considerations more definite, let us make a one-parameter approximation; that is, let us assume

$$c = c_I(1 + a_1 x + a_2 x^2) \tag{5.2.11}$$

with a_2 chosen such that

$$\left(\frac{dc}{dx}\right)_{x=L} = c_I(a_1 + 2a_2 L) = 0 \tag{5.2.12}$$

Therefore

$$a_2 = -\frac{a_1}{2L} \tag{5.2.13}$$

Hence, we find

$$\frac{dc}{dx} = c_I a_1 \left(1 - \frac{x}{L}\right) \tag{5.2.14}$$

Moreover by the same reasoning

$$\frac{dc^0}{dx} = c_I \alpha_1 \left(1 - \frac{x}{L}\right) \tag{5.2.15}$$

Thus, these approximations when substituted in Eq. (5.2.4) give

$$I_1 = \int_0^L \left\{ Vc_I^2 \left[1 + a_1 x \left(1 - \frac{x}{2L}\right)\right] \left[\alpha_1 \left(1 - \frac{x}{L}\right)\right] + \frac{D}{2} c_I^2 a_1^2 \left(1 - \frac{x}{L}\right)^2 \right.$$

$$\left. + \frac{k}{2} c_I^2 \left[1 + a_1 x \left(1 - \frac{x}{2L}\right)\right]^2 \right\} dx \tag{5.2.16}$$

for the special case of $S = 1$. Here the subscript on I is used to denote a one-parameter approximation to the true value. Also it should be stated that only $S = 1$ will be considered here, for in this case an analytical solution is available and can be used for comparison. In fact, it is easy to verify that

$$c = c_I \left\{ \frac{P_2 e^{P_2 L + P_1 x} - P_1 e^{P_1 L + P_2 x}}{P_2 e^{P_2 L} - P_1 e^{P_1 L}} \right\} \tag{5.2.17}$$

is the exact solution for $S = 1$ where

$$P_1 = \frac{V + \sqrt{V^2 + 4kD}}{2D} \tag{5.2.18}$$

and

$$P_2 = \frac{V - \sqrt{V^2 + 4kD}}{2D} \tag{5.2.19}$$

It is interesting to note that both α_1 and a_1 appear in the integral defining I_1. We now select a_1 so that

$$\left(\frac{\partial I_1}{\partial a_1}\right)_{\alpha_1} = 0 \tag{5.2.9}$$

or

$$\frac{\partial I_1}{\partial a_1} = \int_0^L c_I^2 \left[V x \alpha_1 \left(1 - \frac{x}{2L}\right)\left(1 - \frac{x}{L}\right) + D a_1 \left(1 - \frac{x}{L}\right)^2 \right.$$

$$\left. + kx\left(1 - \frac{x}{2L}\right) + k a_1 x^2 \left(1 - \frac{x}{2L}\right)^2 \right] dx = 0 \tag{5.2.20}$$

It is now permissible (after differentiation) to set $\alpha_1 = a_1$. Upon integration, we find

$$0 = \frac{VL}{8} + \frac{D}{3} + \frac{kL}{3a_1} + \frac{2}{15} kL^2 \tag{5.2.21}$$

or

$$a_1 = \frac{-5kL}{15\frac{5}{8} VL + 5D + 2kL^2}$$

(5.2.22)

This gives the first approximation to the concentration distribution in the reactor. The essential features of this simple analysis are characteristic of all the approximations which we shall consider in this chapter. First of all, we must distinguish between the two types of functions. This is done by assuming two different approximating functions having *precisely the same structure*, but different parameters. Then, after differentiating partially with respect to the parameters appearing in the functions subject to variation, all of the parameters can be adjusted so that the auxiliary conditions are satisfied.

We have developed a one-parameter approximation. Better approximations to the true solution can be found by introducing a larger number of parameters. For example, we can use a two-parameter equation such as

$$c = c_I\left[1 + a_1x\left(1 - \frac{x^2}{3L^2}\right) + a_2x^2\left(1 - \frac{2}{3}\frac{x}{L}\right)\right]$$

(5.2.23)

and

$$c^0 = c_I\left[1 + \alpha_1x\left(1 - \frac{x^2}{3L^2}\right) + \alpha_2x^2\left(1 - \frac{2}{3}\frac{x}{L}\right)\right]$$

(5.2.24)

Performing the steps as detailed above, we find

$$a_1(0.2222VL + 0.533330 + 0.215873kL^2)$$
$$+ a_2(0.14445VL^2 + 0.23333DL + 0.092858kL^3)$$
$$+ 0.416667kL = 0$$

(5.2.25)

and

$$a_1(0.07778VL + 0.23333D + 0.092858kL^2)$$
$$+ a_2(0.05556VL^2 + 0.13333DL + 0.041270kL^3)$$
$$+ 0.16667kL = 0$$

(5.2.26)

These two equations can be solved simultaneously for a_1 and a_2 in terms of V, D, k, and L. However, this will not be done. Instead we will simply compare the results of the approximation with the exact equation for a given set of physical parameters.

Before proceeding, we note that a three-parameter approximation can be expressed as follows:

$$c = c_I\left[1 + a_1x\left(1 - \frac{x^3}{4L^3}\right) + a_2x^2\left(1 - \frac{x^2}{L^2}\right) + a_3x^3\left(1 - \frac{3}{4}\frac{x}{L}\right)\right]$$

(5.2.27)

If this trial function is substituted into Eq. (5.2.4) and Eq. (5.2.9) is applied, there will result three simultaneous algebraic equations to be solved.   These equations are not written here.

To study the accuracy of the approximations, we selected the physical parameters shown in Table 5.2.1.   These values were chosen without any special a priori consideration.   The constants determined for this special case are shown in Table 5.2.2.   The concentration determined by each of these approximations is compared with the analytical results in Table 5.2.3.

The results given in Table 5.2.3 indicate that three parameters are required to obtain an adequate approximation.   This, of course, stems from the fact that we have used a power-series expansion to approximate the concentration, whereas the exact solution is exponential in character.   If we used some type of exponential approximation, better results could certainly be achieved with

TABLE 5.2.1 PARAMETERS SELECTED FOR COMPARISON STUDY

Parameter	Value	Dimensions
k	1.0	$(time)^{-1}$
D	0.1	$(length)^2/time$
V	0.1	$length/time$
L	1.0	$length$

TABLE 5.2.2 CONSTANTS

Integral	No. of constants	a_1	a_2	a_3
I_1	1	−0.1860	—	—
I_2	2	−1.326	0.2305	—
I_3	3	−2.664	3.345	−2.238

TABLE 5.2.3 COMPARISON OF APPROXIMATION WITH EXACT SOLUTION†

x	One parameter	Two parameters	Three parameters	Exact
0.1	0.9823	0.8670	0.7649	0.7642
0.3	0.9526	0.6279	0.4469	0.4478
0.5	0.9303	0.4300	0.2665	0.2664
0.75	0.9128	0.2486	0.1520	0.1511
1.0	0.9070	0.1928	0.1150	0.1159

† For $c_I = 1.0$.

fewer parameters.   However, our primary interest here has been to illustrate the application of the direct method using the local potential.   The next section gives a more complex illustration.

It should be noted here that convergence of this computational method is not assured.   If the true solution were known and substituted in the integrand of Eq. (5.2.4) for c^0, then we would know that by increasing the complexity of the approximating function, one would obtain nonincreasing values of the functional I.   However, the method suggested here approximates *both* the c^0 and c.   Therefore it can not be said that the functional will decrease with an increasing complexity of the trial function.   Indeed one can glean very little information regarding the quality of a given approximation by computing the value of the local potential with increasing numbers of free parameters in a trial solution.

Glansdorff[1] has recently studied the convergence of a nonlinear problem in heat conduction with the free parameters being selected as recommended here.   Glansdorff found that definite limits were to be imposed on the variation of the thermal conductivity with temperature if convergence was to be assured.   While the restrictions found by Glansdorff are not restrictive from the practical point of view, we can conclude that the convergence of the approximation to the true solution is not assured even though the physical problem is represented by a local potential.   Schechter[2] has discussed a method of direct search based on the local potential and Kruskal[3] has demonstrated that this method does not always converge.   Therefore we should be careful to perform all possible checks to verify our final result.

PROBLEM 5.2.1   Prove that the I defined by Eq. (5.2.4) and restricted by Eq. (5.2.5) is stationary if and only if Eqs. (5.2.1) to (5.2.3) are satisfied.

PROBLEM 5.2.2   Develop an alternate variational principle which has Eq. (5.2.1) and its associated boundary conditions, Eqs. (5.2.2) and (5.2.3), as the Euler-Lagrange equations.   Begin your analysis by finding an integrating factor $p(x)$ such that Eq. (5.2.1) can be written as

$$\frac{d}{dx} p(x) \frac{dc}{dx} = \frac{p(x)k}{D} c^S$$

[1] P. Glansdorff, Université Libre de Bruxelles, Belgium, personal communication (to appear in *Physica*), 1966.

[2] R. S. Schechter, "Variational Principles for Continuum Systems," R. J. Donnelly, R. Herman, and I. Prigogine (eds.) *Non-Equilibrium Thermodynamics—Variational Techniques and Stability*, The University of Chicago Press, Chicago, 1965, p. 55.

[3] M. Kruskal, "Convergence of Iteration Based on Prigogine's and Glansdorff's Generalized Variational Principle," R. J. Donnelly, R. Herman, and I. Prigogine (eds.), *Non-Equilibrium Thermodynamics—Variational Techniques and Stability*, The University of Chicago Press, Chicago, 1965, p. 287.

Then show that

$$I = \int_0^L \left[\frac{1}{2}\left(\frac{dc}{dx}\right)^2 + \frac{kc^{S+1}}{(S+1)D} \right] p(x)\, dx$$

is stationary if and only if Eq. (5.2.1) is satisfied.   Discuss the boundary conditions.

5.3 POISEUILLE FLOW WITH TEMPERATURE-DEPENDENT VISCOSITY

Viscous dissipation results in the generation of local temperature gradients in a flowing fluid.   If the viscosity of the fluid is highly sensitive to variations in temperature, these temperatures alter the flow to some extent.   Of course, in laminar flow the rate of dissipation is proportional to the viscosity, and the changing viscosity also gives rise to a variation in the temperature of the fluid.   The problem to be studied in this section concerns the slow, viscous, incompressible flow of a Newtonian fluid in a circular tube (as depicted in Fig. 5.3.1).   The wall temperature is assumed to be constant, and, with the exception of the viscosity, the variation of the physical properties with changes in temperature is ignored.   This problem is taken from the unpublished work of D. F. Hays.[1]   The presentation will closely follow that

[1] D. F. Hays, General Motors Research Laboratories, Warren, Michigan (personal communication), 1964.

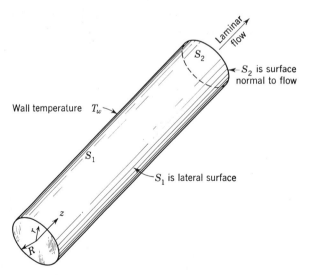

Fig. 5.3.1   Laminar flow in a circular tube with viscous dissipation.

given to the author by Hays.   Minor modifications will be made to smooth the transition from the preceding developments.

For the physical situation being studied, we note that

$$v_r = 0 \qquad v_\theta = 0$$

and

$$v_z = v_z(r)$$
$$T = T(r) \tag{5.3.1}$$

Thus, all of the stresses vanish with the exception of τ_{rz} which is given by

$$\tau_{rz} = -\mu \frac{dv_z}{dr} \tag{5.3.2}$$

for a Newtonian fluid.

It is now desirable to find a potential which defines the problem described above.   It should be reiterated that the analysis is applicable to the "fully developed" flow, that is, to the region far enough removed from the inlet so that the fluid has "forgotten" its initial state.   These considerations are reflected in the fact that both the temperature and the velocity are functions of the radial position but are independent of z.

To develop our potential, Eq. (4.6.24) provides a convenient starting point. This expression which was developed for a pure fluid in nonisothermal flow can be further reduced by neglecting the external forces ($F_i = 0$) and noting that the density assumed to be is a constant ($\partial\rho/\partial T = 0$, $\partial v_i/\partial x_i = 0$). Moreover, it is satisfying to introduce the usual transport coefficients—the viscosity μ ($\mu = M_{vv}/T$) and the thermal conductivity k ($T^2 k = L_{\theta\theta}$).   With these assumptions Eq. (4.6.24) reduces to

$$\psi = \frac{\partial}{\partial x_i}\left[\frac{\partial}{\partial t}\frac{v_i p}{T} + \frac{\tau_{ij}}{T}\frac{\partial v_j}{\partial t} - q_i\frac{\partial}{\partial t}\frac{1}{T} \right]$$

$$+ \tfrac{1}{2}kT^2 \frac{\partial}{\partial t}\frac{\partial}{\partial x_i}\frac{1}{T}\frac{\partial}{\partial x_i}\frac{1}{T} - \rho c_p v_i \frac{\partial T}{\partial t}\frac{\partial}{\partial x_i}\frac{1}{T}$$

$$+ \rho v_i \frac{v^2}{2}\frac{\partial}{\partial t}\frac{\partial}{\partial x_i}\frac{1}{T} - v_i\frac{\partial}{\partial t}\left(\frac{1}{T}\frac{\partial p}{\partial x_i}\right) - \rho v_i v_j \frac{\partial}{\partial t}\frac{\partial}{\partial x_i}\frac{v_j}{T}$$

$$- \frac{\partial}{\partial t}\left(p\frac{\partial}{\partial x_i}\frac{v_i}{T}\right) - \tau_{ij}\frac{\partial v_i}{\partial t}\frac{\partial}{\partial x_j}\frac{1}{T} + T\mu\frac{\partial}{\partial t}\frac{d_{ij}d_{ij}}{T^2}$$

$$+ \rho v_i \frac{\partial}{\partial t}\frac{\partial}{\partial x_i}\frac{v^2}{2T} \leq 0 \tag{5.3.3}$$

For problems with no diffusion it is often convenient to study $T\psi$ rather than ψ. For this case

$$
T\psi = \frac{\partial}{\partial x_i}\left[T\frac{\partial}{\partial t}\frac{v_i p}{T} + \tau_{ij}\frac{\partial v_j}{\partial t} - q_i T\frac{\partial}{\partial t}\frac{1}{T}\right]
$$

$$
- \frac{\partial}{\partial t}\left(\frac{v_i p}{T}\right)\frac{\partial T}{\partial x_i} - \frac{\tau_{ij}}{T}\frac{\partial v_j}{\partial t}\frac{\partial T}{\partial x_i} + q_i\frac{\partial T^{-1}}{\partial t}\frac{\partial T}{\partial x_i}
$$

$$
+ \frac{kT^3}{2}\frac{\partial}{\partial t}\left(\frac{\partial}{\partial x_i}\frac{1}{T}\frac{\partial}{\partial x_i}\frac{1}{T}\right) - T\rho c_p v_i\frac{\partial T^{-1}}{\partial x_i}\frac{\partial T}{\partial t}
$$

$$
+ T\rho v_i\frac{v^2}{2}\frac{\partial}{\partial t}\frac{\partial}{\partial x_i}\frac{1}{T} - Tv_i\frac{\partial}{\partial t}\left(\frac{1}{T}\frac{\partial p}{\partial x_i}\right)
$$

$$
- T\rho v_i v_j\frac{\partial}{\partial t}\frac{\partial}{\partial x_i}\frac{v_j}{T} - T\frac{\partial}{\partial t}\left(p\frac{\partial}{\partial x_i}\frac{v_i}{T}\right) + \frac{\tau_{ij}}{T}\frac{\partial T}{\partial x_j}\frac{\partial v_i}{\partial t}
$$

$$
+ T^2\mu\frac{\partial}{\partial t}\frac{d_{ij}d_{ij}}{T^2} + T\rho v_i\frac{\partial}{\partial t}\frac{\partial}{\partial x_i}\frac{v^2}{2T} \leq 0 \tag{5.3.4}
$$

To simplify this result somewhat, note that

$$
- \frac{\partial}{\partial t}\left(\frac{v_i p}{T}\right)\frac{\partial}{\partial x_i}T - Tv_i\frac{\partial}{\partial t}\left(\frac{1}{T}\frac{\partial p}{\partial x_i}\right) - T\frac{\partial}{\partial t}\left(p\frac{\partial}{\partial x_i}\frac{v_i}{T}\right)
$$

$$
= - \frac{\partial}{\partial x_i}\left(T\frac{\partial}{\partial t}\frac{v_i p}{T}\right) + \frac{\partial p}{\partial x_i}\frac{\partial v_i}{\partial t} \tag{5.3.5}
$$

and

$$
+ q_i\frac{\partial T^{-1}}{\partial t}\frac{\partial T}{\partial x_i} + \frac{kT^3}{2}\frac{\partial}{\partial t}\left(\frac{\partial}{\partial x_i}\frac{1}{T}\frac{\partial}{\partial x_i}\frac{1}{T}\right)
$$

$$
= \frac{k}{T^2}\frac{\partial T}{\partial t}\frac{\partial T}{\partial x_i}\frac{\partial T}{\partial x_i} + \frac{kT^3}{2}\frac{\partial}{\partial t}\left(\frac{1}{T^4}\frac{\partial T}{\partial x_i}\frac{\partial T}{\partial x_i}\right)
$$

$$
= \frac{kT}{2}\frac{\partial}{\partial t}\left(\frac{1}{T^2}\frac{\partial T}{\partial x_i}\frac{\partial T}{\partial x_i}\right) \tag{5.3.6}
$$

Substituting Eqs. (5.3.5) and (5.3.6) into Eq. (5.3.4), we find

$$
T\psi = \frac{\partial}{\partial x_i}\left(\tau_{ij}\frac{\partial v_j}{\partial t} + \frac{q_i}{T}\frac{\partial T}{\partial t}\right) + \frac{kT}{2}\frac{\partial}{\partial t}\left(\frac{1}{T^2}\frac{\partial T}{\partial x_i}\frac{\partial T}{\partial x_i}\right)
$$

$$
- T\rho c_p v_i\frac{\partial T}{\partial t}\frac{\partial}{\partial x_i}\frac{1}{T} + \rho v_i T\frac{v^2}{2}\frac{\partial}{\partial t}\frac{\partial}{\partial x_i}\frac{1}{T}
$$

$$
- T\rho v_i v_j\frac{\partial}{\partial t}\frac{\partial}{\partial x_i}\frac{v_j}{T} + T^2\mu\frac{\partial}{\partial t}\frac{d_{ij}d_{ij}}{T^2} + \frac{\partial p}{\partial x_i}\frac{\partial v_i}{\partial t}
$$

$$
+ T\rho v_j\frac{\partial}{\partial t}\frac{\partial}{\partial x_j}\frac{v^2}{2T} \leq 0 \tag{5.3.7}
$$

Forming the function ϕ

$$\phi = \int_V T\psi \, dV = \frac{\partial E^*}{\partial t} \tag{5.3.8}$$

where

$$
\begin{aligned}
E^* = \int_V &\left[\frac{k^0 T^0}{2T^2} \frac{\partial T}{\partial x_i} \frac{\partial T}{\partial x_i} - T^0 \rho c_p v_i^0 T \frac{\partial}{\partial x_i} \frac{1}{T^0} \right. \\
&+ \rho v_i^0 T^0 \frac{(v^0)^2}{2} \frac{\partial}{\partial x_i} \frac{1}{T} - T^0 \rho v_i^0 v_j^0 \frac{\partial}{\partial x_i} \frac{v_j}{T} \\
&\left. + \frac{\mu^0 (T^0)^2}{T^2} d_{ij} d_{ij} + v_i \frac{\partial p^0}{\partial x_i} + T^0 \rho v_j^0 \frac{\partial}{\partial x_j} \frac{v^2}{2T} \right] dV
\end{aligned} \tag{5.3.9}
$$

The surface part of E^* vanishes because on surface S_1, the lateral surface (see Fig. 5.3.1), the velocity and the temperature are fixed and on the open ends, surface S_2, the quantities q_z and τ_{zz} vanish. Equation (5.3.9) can be simplified still further by noting that

$$v_i^0 \frac{\partial}{\partial x_i} \frac{1}{T} = v_r^0 \frac{\partial}{\partial r} \frac{1}{T} + \frac{v_\theta^0}{r} \frac{\partial}{\partial \theta} \frac{1}{T} + v_z^0 \frac{\partial}{\partial z} \frac{1}{T} = 0 \tag{5.3.10}$$

because of Eq. (5.3.1). By using Eq. (5.3.10) and the condition of incompressibility ($\partial v_i/\partial x_i = 0$), we can reduce Eq. (5.3.9) to the simple form

$$E^* = \int_0^L \int_0^R \int_0^{2\pi} \left\{ \frac{k^0 T^0}{2T^2} \left(\frac{dT}{dr} \right)^2 + \frac{\mu^0 (T^0)^2}{2T^2} \left(\frac{dv_z}{dr} \right)^2 + v_z \frac{\partial p^0}{\partial z} \right\} r \, dr \, dz \, d\theta \tag{5.3.11}$$

The Euler-Lagrange equations for the integral defined by Eq. (5.3.11) to be stationary are

$$\frac{dp}{dz} = \frac{1}{r} \frac{d}{dr} r\mu \frac{dv_z}{dr} \tag{5.3.12}$$

and

$$0 = \frac{1}{r} \frac{d}{dr} rk \frac{dT}{dr} + \mu \left(\frac{dv_z}{dr} \right)^2 \tag{5.3.13}$$

with the boundary conditions T and v_z specified at $r = R$. Equations (5.3.12) and (5.3.13) are the momentum and energy balances, respectively. Thus, the same functions of r which simultaneously satisfy Eqs. (5.3.12) and (5.3.13) will also render E^* stationary. Note that the momentum and energy balances are coupled in that the temperature enters Eq. (5.3.12) through its effect on the viscosity, and the velocity appears in Eq. (5.3.13). It is the coupling which makes the problem difficult. We shall attempt to develop an approximate solution using the local potential, Eq. (5.3.11).

Before proceeding with our analysis, we can develop a more general result by defining the following dimensionless variables

$$\xi = \frac{r}{R}$$

$$\eta = \frac{z}{R}$$

$$\gamma = T_w \Gamma$$

$$\theta = \frac{T}{T_w}$$

$$u = v_z \sqrt{\frac{\mu^*}{kT_w}}$$

$$P = p \left(\frac{R^2}{kT_w \mu^*} \right)^{\frac{1}{2}}$$

$$(5.3.14)$$

in which the μ^* and Γ are parameters in the equation relating viscosity to temperature. Here

$$\mu = \mu^*[1 + \Gamma(T - T^*)] \qquad (5.3.15)$$

where T^* is a convenient reference temperature and μ^* is the viscosity at the reference temperature. Thus, we are approximating the temperature dependence of the viscosity by a linear relationship, and Γ is a viscosity-temperature coefficient. Introducing the dimensionless parameters into Eq. (5.3.11) gives

$$E^* = 2\pi L k T_w \int_0^1 \left\{ \frac{\theta^0}{2\theta^2} \left(\frac{d\theta}{d\xi} \right)^2 + \frac{[1 + \gamma(\theta^0 - \theta^{*0})](\theta^0)^2}{2\theta^2} \left(\frac{du}{d\xi} \right)^2 + u \frac{dP^0}{d\eta} \right\} \xi \, d\xi$$

$$(5.3.16)$$

As usual in the direct approach or Ritz method, the temperature and velocity distributions are assumed. In this case assume

$$\theta = a(1 - \xi^4) + 1 \qquad (5.3.17)$$

$$\theta^0 = \alpha(1 - \xi^4) + 1 \qquad (5.3.18)$$

and

$$u = b(1 - \xi^2) \qquad (5.3.19)$$

Equations (5.3.17) to (5.3.19) satisfy the boundary conditions at $\xi = 1$ for all values of a, α, and b. This is an elementary approximation, but we shall see that these expressions give an approximation which agrees well with the solution obtained by finite-difference methods (which, incidentally, are rather tedious trial-and-error calculations).

The only detail which remains to be settled before beginning the task of determining the constants is the selection of a suitable reference temperature. This temperature may be arbitrarily chosen.   In this case it is convenient to designate the reference temperature as the wall temperature, so that

$$\theta^* = 1 \qquad \theta^* = 1 \tag{5.3.20}$$

Here we designate

$$\theta_m = \theta(0)$$

The constants must be selected so that

$$\frac{\partial E^*}{\partial b} = 0 \tag{5.3.21}$$

and

$$\frac{\partial E^*}{\partial a} = 0 \tag{5.3.22}$$

with the auxiliary equation

$$a = \alpha \tag{5.3.23}$$

as was done in the previous example.

Differentiating Eq. (5.3.16) with respect to b, we find

$$\frac{\partial E^*}{\partial b} = 0 = \int_0^1 \left\{ \frac{[1 + \gamma(\theta^0 - \theta^*)](\theta^0)^2}{\theta^2} \frac{du}{d\xi} \frac{d}{db} \frac{du}{d\xi} + \frac{du}{db} \frac{dP^0}{d\eta} \right\} \xi \, d\xi \tag{5.3.24}$$

Using Eqs. (5.3.17) to (5.3.19) and (5.3.23), we find

$$\int_0^1 \left[4b\xi^2(1 - a\xi^4\gamma + a\gamma) + (1 - \xi^2) \frac{dP^0}{d\eta} \right] \xi \, d\xi = 0 \tag{5.3.25}$$

Integrating, we find

$$b = -\frac{1/4 \, (dP^0/d\eta)}{1 + \gamma a/2} = 0 \tag{5.3.26}$$

The second equation needed to determine a and b is found by differentiating Eq. (5.3.16) with respect to a

$$\frac{\partial E^*}{\partial a} = 0 = \int_2^1 \frac{\theta^0}{\theta^2} \left\{ -\frac{1}{\theta} \left(\frac{d\theta}{d\xi}\right)^2 \frac{d\theta}{da} + \frac{d\theta}{d\xi} \frac{d}{da} \frac{d\theta}{d\xi} \right.$$

$$\left. - [1 + \gamma(\theta^0 - \theta^*)] \left(\frac{du}{d\xi}\right)^2 \frac{d\theta}{da} \right\} \xi \, d\xi \tag{5.3.27}$$

TABLE 5.3.1 VALUES OF $\theta_m - 1$ AND u_m (COMPARABLE TO a AND b OF THE VARIATIONAL METHOD) OBTAINED BY THE NUMERICAL INTEGRATION OF THE MOMENTUM AND ENERGY EQUATIONS

	$\theta_m - 1$				u_m			
$\dfrac{dP^0}{d\eta}$ γ	0	−0.5	−1.0	−2.0	0	−0.5	−1.0	−2.0
−1.0	0.01563	0.01572	0.01581	0.01601	0.2500	0.2513	0.2527	0.2555
−2.0	0.06250	0.06404	0.06575	0.06984	0.5000	0.5109	0.5231	0.5520
−3.0	0.1406	0.1490	0.1599	0.2031	0.7500	0.7895	0.8409	1.045
−4.0	0.2500	0.2793	0.3346	—†	1.0000	1.492	1.299	—†

TABLE 5.3.2 VALUES OF a AND b (COMPARABLE TO $\theta_m - 1$ AND u_m OF THE EXACT EQUATIONS) OBTAINED FROM THE VARIATIONAL FORMULATION

	a				b			
$\dfrac{dP^0}{d\eta}$ γ	0	−0.5	−1.0	−2.0	0	−0.5	−1.0	−2.0
−1.0	0.01563	0.01567	0.01571	0.01579	0.2500	0.2510	0.2520	0.2540
−2.0	0.0625	0.06317	0.6389	0.06534	0.5000	0.5080	0.5165	0.5349
−3.0	0.1406	0.1441	0.1480	0.1570	0.750	0.7780	0.8099	0.8896
−4.0	0.2500	0.2617	0.2758	0.3138	1.000	1.070	1.160	1.457

† No stable flow was found for this case.

Using Eqs. (5.3.17) to (5.3.19) and (5.3.23) gives

$$\int_0^1 \frac{1}{1 + a(1 - \xi^4)}\left[-\frac{16a^2\xi^6(1 - \xi^4)}{1 + a(1 - \xi^4)} + 16a\xi^6 \right.$$

$$\left. -(1 - \gamma a\xi^4 + \gamma a)4\xi^2 b^2(1 - \xi^4) \right] \xi\, d\xi = 0 \tag{5.3.28}$$

Integrating Eq. (5.3.28) yields

$$2b^2\left(1 - \gamma + \frac{a\gamma}{2}\right) - \frac{1}{a}[8a + 2b^2(\gamma - 1)] \ln\frac{1}{a+1} - 8a = 0 \tag{5.3.29}$$

These two equations may now be solved simultaneously to find the value of both a and b as a function of the two parameters $dP^0/d\eta$ and γ. The $dP^0/d\eta$ is the dimensionless pressure drop, and the γ measures the variation of viscosity with temperature.

It is desirable to compare our approximations with a more laborious and more precise method of approximation. The differential equations (5.3.12) and (5.3.13) have been solved numerically by using an iterative scheme and the Runge-Kutta-Gill technique.[2]   Since

$$\theta_m - 1 = a \tag{5.3.30}$$

and

$$u_m = b \tag{5.3.31}$$

where θ_m is centerline temperature and u_m is the centerline velocity, the numerical results can be compared with those obtained from the direct calculation based on the variational formulation. In Table 5.3.1 the numerical values of $\theta_m - 1$ and $u_m - 1$ are given as a function of the parameters γ and $dP^0/d\eta$. These numbers are comparable to the values of a and b given in Table 5.3.2.   It is seen that the difference between the results of the variational method and the exact equations (solved numerically) increase with an increase in γ. This difference, however, is within the realm of "acceptable" engineering accuracy—the percentage error in u_m for a $dP^0/d\eta$ of -3.0 and a γ of -1.0 being 3.9 percent and the error for θ_m being but 6.2 percent. Thus, over the range of parameters considered, the variational method gives a reasonable approximation with a very few undetermined coefficients.   There is little doubt that the methods exhibited here will play an important role in engineering computations.

In the preceding analysis, we have seen how the general evolution criterion of Glansdorff and Prigogine can be applied.   The manipulations required to develop the variational principle were rather lengthy and somewhat involved.

---

[2] Hays gives A. D. Booth, "Numerical Methods," Academic Press Inc., New York, 1955, as his reference for this method.

In general, it is far simpler to begin with the differential equations, appropriately simplified, than to reduce Eq. (4.6.24) to the necessary form. We shall, for the most part, use the differential equations as the starting point, since this usually results in a structure which is less complex from the computational viewpoint.

To make these considerations more definite, let us reconsider the present example—Poiseuille flow with a temperature-dependent viscosity. The balance equations describing the process of interest are given by Eqs. (5.3.12) and (5.3.13). These equations can be written in dimensionless form as follows:

$$\frac{\rho}{\mu^*}\frac{\partial u}{\partial t} = \frac{1}{\xi}\frac{\partial}{\partial \xi}\,\xi\,\frac{\mu}{\mu^*}\frac{\partial u}{\partial \xi} - \frac{\partial P^0}{\partial \eta} \tag{5.3.32}$$

and

$$\frac{R^2\rho C_p}{k}\frac{\partial \theta}{\partial t} = \frac{1}{\xi}\frac{\partial}{\partial \xi}\,\xi\,\frac{\partial \theta}{\partial \xi} + \frac{\mu}{\mu^*}\left(\frac{\partial u}{\partial \xi}\right)^2 \tag{5.3.33}$$

where the time derivatives have been retained to "mark" our approach to the stationary state. Proceeding as in Chap. 4.4, we multiply Eq. (5.3.32) by $-\partial u/\partial t$ and Eq. (5.3.33) by $-\partial \theta/\partial t$ and add the resultant expressions. These manipulations yield

$$\psi' = -\frac{1}{\xi}\frac{\partial}{\partial \xi}\left(\xi\,\frac{\partial u}{\partial t}\frac{\mu}{\mu^*}\frac{\partial u}{\partial \xi}\right) + \frac{\partial P^0}{\partial \eta}\frac{\partial u}{\partial t} + \frac{1}{2}\frac{\mu}{\mu^*}\frac{\partial}{\partial t}\left(\frac{\partial u}{\partial \xi}\right)^2$$
$$- \frac{1}{\xi}\frac{\partial}{\partial \xi}\left(\xi\,\frac{\partial \theta}{\partial t}\frac{\partial \theta}{\partial \xi}\right) - \frac{\mu}{\mu^*}\frac{\partial \theta}{\partial t}\left(\frac{\partial u}{\partial \xi}\right)^2 + \frac{1}{2}\frac{\partial}{\partial t}\left(\frac{\partial \theta}{\partial \xi}\right)^2 \tag{5.3.34}$$

where

$$\psi' = -\left[\frac{\rho}{\mu^*}\left(\frac{\partial u}{\partial t}\right)^2 + \frac{R^2\rho C_p}{k}\left(\frac{\partial \theta}{\partial t}\right)^2\right] \le 0$$

We multiply ψ' by a volume element (simply $\xi\,d\xi$ in this case) and integrate over the volume of the system (0 to 1 in the present example). Then, using the concepts set forth in the last chapter, we can identify a potential as

$$E'^* = \int_0^1\left[-\frac{dP^0}{d\eta}u - \frac{1}{2}\left(\frac{\mu}{\mu^*}\right)^0\left(\frac{\partial u}{\partial \xi}\right)^2 + \theta\left(\frac{\mu}{\mu^*}\right)^0\left(\frac{\partial u^0}{\partial \xi}\right)^2 - \frac{1}{2}\left(\frac{\partial \theta}{\partial \xi}\right)^2\right]\xi\,d\xi \tag{5.3.35}$$

This formulation differs from the one found previously (Eq. (5.3.11); however, it is not difficult to show that a necessary condition for E'^* to be stationary subject to the subsidiary conditions $\theta^0 = \theta$ and $u^0 = u$ is that both Eqs. (5.3.32) and (5.3.33) be satisfied in the stationary state (left-hand side of these expressions then vanishes). Thus E'^* "describes" our problem, and there does not appear to be any test which can be applied in advance to determine which formulation will give the best approximation. Therefore, we have no basis for preferring Eq. (5.3.11). Since Eq. (5.3.35) differs to some extent from Eq. (5.3.11), the approximations found starting with the same trial functions will also be different. Moreover, we can not test the results by asking which trial function yields the smallest value of E'^*. Indeed, we know that the trial function giving the minimum of entropy production is not the correct solution (see Sec. 4.3). That the answer differs can be seen as follows. Substitute Eqs. (5.3.17) to (5.3.19), together with the following expression, into Eq. (5.3.35).

$$u^0 = \beta(1 - \xi^2)$$

Thus

$$E'^* =$$

$$\int_0^1 \left[-b \frac{dP^0}{d\eta} (1 - \xi^2) - 2b^2\xi^2 \left(\frac{\mu}{\mu^*}\right)^0 + (1 + a - a\xi^4) \left(\frac{\mu}{\mu^*}\right)^0 4\beta^2\xi^2 - 8a^2\xi^6 \right] \xi \, d\xi$$

(5.3.36)

where the viscosity ratio is defined by Eq. (5.3.15). If E'^* is to be stationary, then

$$\left(\frac{\partial E'^*}{\partial b}\right)_{\beta,a,\alpha} = 0$$

giving

$$b = - \frac{-(dP^0/d\eta)}{4(1 + a\gamma/2)}$$

(5.3.37)

This is the same result found before [Eq. (5.3.26)]. The condition

$$\left(\frac{\partial E'^*}{\partial a}\right)_{b,\beta,a} = 0$$

yields an expression which is considerably simpler than that found before. Indeed, after differentiating and setting $\alpha = a$ and $\beta = b$, a can be determined as

$$a = \frac{6b^2}{24 - 4\gamma b^2}$$

(5.3.38)

In comparing this with the previous results, we note that the values of b are the same as before and are then tabulated in Table 5.3.2. The values of a differ. Tabulated in Table 5.3.3 are values of a for $\gamma = -1$. These values can be compared with those given in Table 5.3.2 and can be seen to differ somewhat.   The numbers given in Table 5.3.2 appear to agree better with the more precise numerical results; however, it would be exceedingly dangerous to draw general conclusions from this single observation.

TABLE 5.3.3 VALUES OF a **DETERMINED BY SECOND METHOD** $(\gamma = -1.0)$

$\dfrac{dP^0}{d\eta}$	a
-1.0	0.01571
-2.0	0.06385
-3.0	0.1478
-4.0	0.2744

5.4 AN APPLICATION TO BOUNDARY-LAYER THEORY

To describe external flows at relatively large Reynolds numbers, we usually invoke a class of approximations known collectively as "boundary-layer theory."   The essential idea is to assume that the viscous effects are relegated to a very thin layer adjacent to the solid boundary.   In the fluid region external to the boundary layer, the motion is assumed to be described by the Euler equations.   It is not our purpose to delve deeply into boundary-layer theory.   The interested reader is referred to the treatise by Schlicting[1] for a penetrating discussion of this subject.   To understand the analysis presented in this section, we need only note that one first determines the pressure in the fluid adjacent to the boundary layer.   This pressure is then assumed to be the pressure in the boundary layer.   It is justified to assume that the external pressure is imposed onto the boundary layer if the boundary layer is very thin relative to some characteristic dimension of the solid body.   With the pressure fixed, there are but two variables which are to be determined in an incompressible flow—the two relevant components of velocity (we are going to limit our discussion to a two-dimensional flow such as that depicted in Fig. 5.4.1).   Thus to completely determine the boundary layer flows, it is necessary to retain only one of the component equations of the momentum balance and the continuity equation.   These relevant equations are

$$\rho\left(\frac{\partial v_x}{\partial t} + v_x\frac{\partial v_x}{\partial x} + v_y\frac{\partial v_x}{\partial y}\right) = -\frac{\partial p}{\partial x} + \mu\frac{\partial^2 v_x}{\partial y^2} \tag{5.4.1}$$

for the x component of momentum and the continuity equation.

[1] H. Schlicting, "Boundary Layer Theory," pp. 94–179, Pergamon Press, New York, 1955.

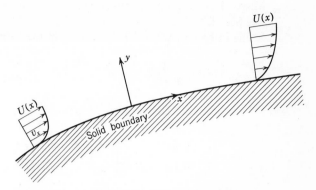

Fig. 5.4.1 Two-dimensional flow along a wall.

$$\frac{\partial v_x}{\partial x} + \frac{\partial v_y}{\partial y} = 0 \tag{5.4.2}$$

where v_x and v_y are the x and y components of velocity.   Equation (5.4.1) represents the equation of motion for an incompressible, Newtonian fluid in isothermal flow.   In writing Eq. (5.4.1), terms which are small in the special case of boundary-layer flow have been discarded.   The reader is again referred to Schlicting[1] for a more comprehensive discussion of the relevance of each term in these equations.

The simultaneous solution of Eqs. (5.4.1) and (5.4.2) is usually quite difficult even for the simplest geometry, since Eq. (5.4.1) is nonlinear.   Our aim is to construct a variational formulation which describes steady flows in an incompressible boundary layer.   The method of developing the local potential follows the technique introduced in Chap. 4.   Multiply Eq. (5.4.1) by $\partial v_x/\partial t$ and Eq. (5.4.2) by $-(\rho/2)(\partial v_y{}^2/\partial t)$ and add the resultant expressions. This gives

$$\psi = -\rho\left(\frac{\partial v_x}{\partial t}\right)^2 = \rho v_x \frac{\partial v_x}{\partial t}\frac{\partial v_x}{\partial x} + \rho v_y \frac{\partial v_x}{\partial t}\frac{\partial v_x}{\partial y} + \frac{\partial v_x}{\partial t}\frac{\partial p}{\partial x}$$

$$- \mu \frac{\partial^2 v_x}{\partial y^2}\frac{\partial v_x}{\partial t} - \frac{\rho}{2}\frac{\partial v_y{}^2}{\partial t}\left(\frac{\partial v_x}{\partial x} + \frac{\partial v_y}{\partial y}\right) \le 0 \tag{5.4.3}$$

Since Eqs. (5.4.1) and (5.4.2) describe a two-dimensional flow, the value of ψ will vary in the xy plane but will be independent of z.   Therefore it is necessary to consider a potential

$$\phi = \int_A \psi \, dx \, dy \le 0 \tag{5.4.4}$$

where A is an area in the xy plane and this area is bounded by curve C (see Sec. 1.7).

The integrand ψ can be rearranged in the form

$$
\begin{aligned}
\psi = {} & \frac{\partial}{\partial x}\left(\rho v_x v_x \frac{\partial v_x}{\partial t}\right) + \frac{\partial}{\partial y}\left(\rho v_x v_y \frac{\partial v_x}{\partial t}\right) + \frac{\partial v_x}{\partial t}\frac{\partial p}{\partial x} \\
& - \mu \frac{\partial}{\partial y}\left(\frac{\partial v_x}{\partial y}\frac{\partial v_x}{\partial t}\right) - \rho v_x \frac{\partial v_x}{\partial t}\left(\frac{\partial v_x}{\partial x} + \frac{\partial v_y}{\partial y}\right) - \rho v_x v_x \frac{\partial}{\partial t}\frac{\partial v_x}{\partial x} \\
& - \rho v_x v_y \frac{\partial}{\partial t}\frac{\partial v_x}{\partial y} + \frac{\mu}{2}\frac{\partial}{\partial t}\left(\frac{\partial v_x}{\partial y}\right)^2 - \frac{\rho}{2}\frac{\partial v_y^2}{\partial t}\left(\frac{\partial v_x}{\partial x} + \frac{\partial v_y}{\partial y}\right)
\end{aligned} \tag{5.4.5}
$$

Inequality (5.4.4) can be written as

$$
\begin{aligned}
0 \geq {} & \int_A\left[-\rho v_x v_x \frac{\partial}{\partial t}\frac{\partial v_x}{\partial x} - \rho v_x v_y \frac{\partial}{\partial t}\frac{\partial v_x}{\partial y} + \frac{\mu}{2}\frac{\partial}{\partial t}\left(\frac{\partial v_x}{\partial y}\right)^2\right. \\
& \left. - \rho\frac{1}{2}\frac{\partial v_x^2}{\partial t}\left(\frac{\partial v_x}{\partial x} + \frac{\partial v_y}{\partial y}\right) + \frac{\partial v_x}{\partial t}\frac{\partial p}{\partial x} - \frac{\rho}{2}\frac{\partial v_y^2}{\partial t}\left(\frac{\partial v_x}{\partial x} + \frac{\partial v_y}{\partial y}\right)\right]\,dx\,dy \\
& + \int_C\left(\rho v_x v_x \frac{\partial v_x}{\partial t}\,dy + \rho v_x v_y \frac{\partial v_x}{\partial t}\,dx - \mu\frac{\partial v_x}{\partial y}\frac{\partial v_x}{\partial t}\,dx\right)
\end{aligned} \tag{5.4.6}
$$

Near the stationary state, the concept of a local potential gives

$$
\begin{aligned}
0 \geq {} & \frac{\partial}{\partial t}\int_A\left[-\rho v_x^0 v_x^0 \frac{\partial v_x}{\partial x} - \rho v_x^0 v_y^0 \frac{\partial v_x}{\partial y} + \frac{\mu}{2}\left(\frac{\partial v_x}{\partial y}\right)^2\right. \\
& \left. - \rho\frac{v_x^2}{2}\left(\frac{\partial v_x^0}{\partial x} + \frac{\partial v_y^0}{\partial y}\right) + \frac{\partial p}{\partial x}v_x - \frac{\rho}{2}v_y^2\left(\frac{\partial v_x^0}{\partial x} + \frac{\partial v_y^0}{\partial y}\right)\right]\,dA \\
& + \frac{\partial}{\partial t}\int_C\left(\rho v_x^0 v_x v_x^0 \,dy + \rho v_x^0 v_y^0 v_x \,dx - \mu\frac{\partial v_x^0}{\partial y}v_x \,dx\right)
\end{aligned} \tag{5.4.7}
$$

where the superscript zero again denotes the value of the function at the stationary state. The value of the integral can only decrease with time, and at the stationary state the flow in the boundary layer is determined by the minimum of the functional

$$
\begin{aligned}
E^* = {} & \int_A\left[-\rho v_x^0 v_x^0 \frac{\partial v_x}{\partial x} - \rho v_x^0 v_y^0 \frac{\partial v_x}{\partial y} + \frac{\mu}{2}\left(\frac{\partial v_x}{\partial y}\right)^2 - \rho\left(\frac{v_x^2}{2} + \frac{v_y^2}{2}\right)\right. \\
& \left. \times \left(\frac{\partial v_x^0}{\partial x} + \frac{\partial v_y^0}{\partial y}\right) + v_x \frac{\partial p}{\partial x}\right]\,dA \\
& + \int_C\left(\rho v_x^0 v_x v_x \,dy + \rho v_x^0 v_x^0 v_x \,dx - \mu\frac{\partial v_x^0}{\partial y}v_x \,dx\right)
\end{aligned} \tag{5.4.8}
$$

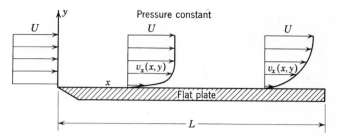

Fig. 5.4.2   Boundary-layer growth along a flat plate.

with the auxiliary conditions

$$v_x^0 = v_x \tag{5.4.9}$$

$$v_y^0 = v_y \tag{5.4.10}$$

This completes our task.   However, it is of interest to demonstrate a possible application of the variational principle.   Let us consider the boundary-layer flow along a flat plate, such as that depicted in Fig. 5.4.2.   For this case the pressure is a constant, and if the velocities are determined so that the continuity equation is always satisfied, Eq. (5.4.8) reduces to the following expression:

$$E^* = \int_0^L \int_0^\infty \left[-\rho v_x^0 v_y^0 \frac{\partial v_x}{\partial y} - \rho v_x^0 v_x^0 \frac{\partial v_x}{\partial x} + \frac{\mu}{2}\left(\frac{\partial v_x}{\partial y}\right)^2 \right] dy\, dx$$

$$+ \int_0^\infty \left(\rho v_x^0 v_x^0 v_x \bigg|_{x=L} - \rho U^3 \right) dy \tag{5.4.11}$$

The reduction of the boundary conditions (line integral) to the form shown in Eq. (5.4.11) is not obvious and requires further discussion.   First of all, the reader should note that the area of interest in studying the flow along a flat plate is a semi-infinite strip bounded by the lines $x = 0, L, y = 0$.   With this in mind, the contribution stemming from the line integral of Eq. (5.4.8) is

$$I_{\text{line}} = \int_C \left(\rho v_x^0 v_x^0 v_x\, dy + \rho v_x^0 v_y^0 v_x\, dx - \mu \frac{\partial v_x^0}{\partial y} v_x\, dx \right)$$

Expanding to fit our particular case,

$$I_{\text{line}} = \int_0^\infty \left(\rho v_x^0 v_x^0 v_x \bigg|_{x=L} - \rho v_x^0 v_x^0 v_x \bigg|_{x=0} \right) dy$$

$$+ \int_0^L \left(-\rho v_x^0 v_y^0 v_x \bigg|_{y=\infty} + \rho v_x^0 v_y^0 v_x \bigg|_{y=0} \right.$$

$$\left. + \mu \frac{\partial v_x^0}{\partial y} v_x \bigg|_{y=\infty} - \mu \frac{\partial v_x^0}{\partial y} v_x \bigg|_{y=0} \right) dx \tag{5.4.12}$$

Now we note that the boundary conditions are as follows:

$$v_x = 0 \quad \text{at} \quad y = 0 \qquad (5.4.13a)$$

$$v_y = 0 \quad \text{at} \quad y = 0 \qquad (5.4.13b)$$

$$v_x = U \quad \text{at} \quad y = \infty \qquad (5.4.13c)$$

$$v_x = U \quad \text{at} \quad x = 0 \qquad (5.4.13d)$$

Applying these conditions where appropriate in Eq. (5.4.12), we find

$$I_{\text{line}} = \int_0^\infty (\rho v_x{}^0 v_x{}^0 v_x \big|_{x=L} - \rho U^3) \, dy - \int_0^L \rho U^2 v_y{}^0 \big|_{y=\infty} \, dx \qquad (5.4.14)$$

However, the last term on the right does not contain a function subject to variation and therefore can be discarded without loss of generality. One can on the same grounds discard

$$-\int_0^\infty \rho U^3 \, dy$$

However, this term is very large (in fact infinite) and serves to cancel in part an equally large contribution from the first term in the integrand. Thus

$$I_{\text{line}} = \int_0^\infty (\rho v_x{}^0 v_x{}^0 v_x \big|_{x=L} - \rho U^3) \, dy \qquad (5.4.15)$$

is finite in this form. This last term does not contribute to the final results as we shall see. This is the boundary term appearing in Eq. (5.4.11).

Again we see that the local potential as defined for two-dimensional boundary layers is composed of two parts. Since the problem is two-dimensional, one part is an area contribution and the second stems from a line integral. The line integral enters because the velocity v_x is not specified at $x = L$, and hence the variation in velocity does not vanish at $x = L$ as it does for $x = 0$, $y = 0$, and $y = \infty$. Therefore, the boundary conditions at $x = L$ must be natural boundary conditions, and the addition contribution along the line $x = L$ arises so that the natural boundary conditions are also the correct physical conditions. In this particular case, the coefficient of δv_x at $x = L$ vanishes identically, giving no natural boundary condition. This is evidently correct, since the physics do not impose any restraints along line $x = L$. An approximation to the velocity distribution can now be developed. Assume

$$v_x = U \operatorname{erf}(fy) \qquad (5.4.16)\dagger$$

† A number of physical processes, described by an equation of the form

$$\frac{Dv_x}{Dt} = \mu \frac{\partial^2 v_x}{\partial y^2}$$

as is the case here, can be well represented by the error function provided the boundary conditions can be satisfied.

where f is an unspecified function of x and erf refers to the error function. The y component of velocity is fixed by the requirement that the continuity equation be satisfied.   It is not difficult to show that

$$v_y = \frac{Uf'}{\sqrt{\pi}f^2} [e^{-(yf)^2} - 1]$$

(5.4.17)

satisfies the continuity equation as well as the no-slip condition on the wall. The f' denotes the derivative of f with respect to x.   For the unvaried functions, it is convenient to choose

$$v_x^0 = U \operatorname{erf}(f^0 y)$$

(5.4.18)

and

$$v_y^0 = \frac{Uf^{0'}}{\sqrt{\pi}(f^0)^2} [e^{-(yf^0)^2} - 1]$$

(5.4.19)

The unvaried functions have the same structure as the functions subject to variation.   This is convenient, since the auxiliary restrictions are satisfied if

$$f = f^0$$

(5.4.20)

It should be noted that we intend to use the method of partial integration (see Chap. 3.3) to determine the velocity distribution.   More specifically, we aim to determine the $f(x)$ which will best fit the velocities.   The assumed form of the velocity distribution also satisfies the boundary conditions expressed by Eq. (5.4.13) provided

$$f(x) \to \infty \qquad \text{as} \qquad x \to 0$$

for then

$$v_x \to U \qquad \text{as} \qquad x \to 0$$

If Eqs. (5.4.16) to (5.4.18) are substituted into Eq. (5.4.11), one finds

$$E^* = \int_0^L \int_0^\infty \left\{ -\rho U^3 [\operatorname{erf}(yf^0)]^2 \frac{2}{\sqrt{\pi}} e^{-(yf)^2} yf' - \frac{\rho U^3}{\sqrt{\pi}} \operatorname{erf}(yf^0) \frac{f^{0'}}{(f^0)^2} [e^{-(yf^0)^2} - 1] \right.$$

$$\left. \cdot \frac{2}{\sqrt{\pi}} e^{-(yf)^2} f + \frac{2\mu}{\pi} U^2 f^2 e^{-2(yf)^2} \right\} dy\, dx$$

$$+ \int_0^\infty \rho U^3 \{ [\operatorname{erf}(f^0 y)]^2 \operatorname{erf}(fy) - 1 \} \Big|_{x=L} dy$$

(5.4.21)

As can be readily seen from the structure of Eq. (5.4.16), the y variation of the velocity has been selected a priori. ˙ The essential idea is to now select the best possible $f(x)$ to be associated with this particular choice of y dependence. This best choice of $f(x)$ is the one which renders E^* stationary.   Thus, it is necessary to take a variation of E^* with respect to $f(x)$ holding $f^0(x)$ fixed. This variation gives

$$\delta E^* = \int_0^L \int_0^\infty \left\{ \frac{-2\rho U^3}{\sqrt{\pi}} \left[\mathrm{erf}^2(yf^0)(y\,\delta f' - 2y^3 ff'\,\delta f)e^{-(yf)^2} \right.\right.$$

$$+ \mathrm{erf}(f^0 y)(e^{-(yf^0)^2} - 1)\frac{f^{0'}}{(f^0)^2}(1 - 2y^2 f^2)e^{-(yf)^2}\,\delta f \Bigg]$$

$$+ \frac{4\mu U^2}{\pi} f(1 - 2y^2 f^2)e^{-2(yf)^2}\,\delta f \Bigg\}\, dy\, dx$$

$$+ \int_0^\infty \rho U^3 \frac{2}{\sqrt{\pi}} e^{-(yf)^2} y\, \mathrm{erf}(yf^0)\,\delta f \bigg|_{x=L} dy \qquad (5.4.22)$$

At this point we are permitted to invoke the auxiliary condition $f^0 = f$, and after considerable algebraic manipulation, we obtain

$$\delta E^* = \int_0^L \left(\frac{\rho U^3}{\pi} C_1 \frac{f'}{f^3} + \frac{\mu U^2}{\sqrt{2\pi}} \right) \delta f\, dx \qquad (5.4.23)$$

The following identities are quite useful in the manipulations necessary to develop Eq. (5.4.23).

$$\int_0^\infty \mathrm{erf}(fy)e^{-(yf)^2} f^2 y^2\, dy = \frac{1}{2}\int_0^\infty \mathrm{erf}(fy)e^{-(yf)^2}\, dy + \frac{1}{4\sqrt{\pi}f} \qquad (5.4.24)$$

$$\int_0^\infty \mathrm{erf}(fy)e^{-2(yf)^2} f^2 y^2\, dy = \frac{1}{4}\int_0^\infty \mathrm{erf}(fy)e^{-2(yf)^2}\, dy + \frac{1}{12\sqrt{\pi}f} \qquad (5.4.25)$$

Also

$$\int_0^\infty \mathrm{erf}(fy)e^{-2(yf)^2}\, dy = \frac{1}{f}\int_0^\infty \mathrm{erf}(\lambda)e^{-2\lambda^2}\, d\lambda = \frac{C_1}{f} \qquad (5.4.26)$$

where

$$C_1 = \int_0^\infty \mathrm{erf}(\lambda)e^{-2\lambda^2}\, d\lambda \qquad (5.4.27)$$

If δE^* is to be 0 for all admissible variations, then Eq. (5.4.23) requires that

$$0 = \frac{\rho U^3}{\pi} C_1 \frac{f'}{f^3} + \frac{\mu U^2}{\sqrt{2\pi}} \qquad (5.4.28)$$

The solution of this differential equation which satisfies the boundary condition $f \to \infty$ as $x \to 0$ is

$$f = \left(\frac{C_1}{\sqrt{2\pi}} \right)^{\frac{1}{2}} \left(\frac{\rho U}{\mu x} \right)^{\frac{1}{2}} \qquad (5.4.29)$$

The constant C_1 can be approximated by expanding the error function into a Taylor series and integrating term by term. Performing these operations gives

$$C_1 = \frac{2}{\sqrt{\pi}} \sum_{n=0}^{\infty} \frac{(-1)^n}{(2n+1)n!} \int_0^{\infty} \lambda^{2n+1} e^{-2\lambda^2} \, d\lambda \tag{5.4.30}$$

If the series is truncated after six terms, an accuracy of three significant figures is obtained and

$$C_1 \cong \frac{2}{\sqrt{\pi}} \, 0.218 \tag{5.4.31}$$

so that the velocity profile is given as

$$\frac{v_x}{U} = \mathrm{erf}(0.313\eta) \tag{5.4.32}$$

where

$$\eta = y \left(\frac{\rho U}{\mu x} \right)^{\frac{1}{2}}$$

Table 5.4.1 shows a comparison of this velocity distribution with the more precise results of Howrath, which were obtained by using a numerical integration.   It is seen that the accuracy is acceptable for most engineering

TABLE 5.4.1   COMPARISON OF APPROX-
IMATE VELOCITIES WITH PRECISE
NUMERICAL VALUES

$y\left(\dfrac{\rho U}{\mu x}\right)^{\frac{1}{2}}$	$\dfrac{v_x}{U}$	$\dfrac{v_x}{U}$ †
	approximate	*numerical*
0	0	0
0.2	0.0705	0.0664
0.6	0.209	0.199
1.0	0.342	0.330
1.6	0.521	0.517
2.0	0.624	0.630
3.0	0.816	0.846
∞	1.0	1.0

† The numbers in this column are given by L. Howrath, *Proc Roy. Soc.* (*London*) *Ser. A.*, vol. 164, p. 547, 1938.

approximations.   The method exhibited here has the further advantage of giving an analytical answer, rather than a table of results, as is usually produced in a purely numerical computation.   The velocity distribution, Eq. (5.4.32), can be used to determine the drag force acting on the plate.   For

$$F = W \int_0^L -\tau_{xy}\bigg|_{y=0} dx \tag{5.4.33}$$

where τ_{xy} = local shearing stress acting on the plate

$\qquad W$ = width of plate

$\qquad F$ = drag force

For a Newtonian fluid,

$$F = W \int_0^L \mu \frac{\partial v_x}{\partial y}\bigg|_{y=0} dx \tag{5.4.34}$$

or for the velocity given by Eq. (5.4.32)

$$F = 0.706 WUV\sqrt{\mu\rho LU} \tag{5.4.35}$$

The answer found by the numerical method is

$$F = 0.664 WUV\sqrt{\mu\rho LU} \tag{5.4.36}$$

The approximate drag differs from the correct answer by approximately 7 percent.   This seems to be entirely adequate, especially in view of the great difficulty one would have in developing the numerical solution rather than using the method exhibited in this section.

5.5   THE THERMAL ENTRY REGION

In this section problems of heat transfer in the thermal entry region are to be studied using variational techniques.   Such problems are encountered by design engineers, and, frequently, only an approximate answer is required. If such is the case, then direct calculations should prove to be quite useful. To illustrate the potential of these methods as applied to thermal problems, we shall study two different problems employing two distinct methods of analysis.   However, in both analyses it will be assumed that the velocity is everywhere specified.   Thus in developing an appropriate form of the local potential defining the thermal state of the system, we can assert that the velocities are time-independent, specified functions of position.   Moreover, the fluid will be assumed incompressible, and our starting point, Eq. (4.6.24), can be written as

$$\psi = \frac{\partial}{\partial x_i}\left(v_i p \frac{\partial}{\partial t}\frac{1}{T} - q_i \frac{\partial}{\partial t}\frac{1}{T}\right) + \frac{1}{2}L_{\theta\theta}\frac{\partial}{\partial t}\left(\frac{\partial}{\partial x_i}\frac{1}{T}\frac{\partial}{\partial x_i}\frac{1}{T}\right)$$

$$- \rho c_p v_i \frac{\partial T}{\partial t}\frac{\partial}{\partial x_i}\frac{1}{T} + \rho v_i \frac{v^2}{2}\frac{\partial}{\partial t}\frac{\partial}{\partial x_i}\frac{1}{T} - v_i \frac{\partial p}{\partial x_i}\frac{\partial}{\partial t}\frac{1}{T}$$

$$- \rho v_i v_j \frac{\partial}{\partial x_i}v_j \frac{\partial}{\partial t}\frac{1}{T} - p v_i \frac{\partial}{\partial t}\frac{\partial}{\partial x_i}\frac{1}{T} + M_{vv}d_{ij}d_{ij}\frac{\partial}{\partial t}\frac{1}{T^2}$$

$$+ \rho v_j \frac{\partial}{\partial t}\frac{\partial}{\partial x_j}\frac{v^2}{2T} \le 0 \tag{5.5.1}$$

In developing Eq. (5.5.1), we have used the equalities $\partial v_i/\partial t = 0$, $\partial p/\partial t = 0$, and $\partial v_i/\partial x_i = 0$. The following identities are valid for this special case:

$$\rho v_i \frac{v^2}{2}\frac{\partial}{\partial t}\frac{\partial}{\partial x_i}\frac{1}{T} - \rho v_i v_j \frac{\partial}{\partial x_i}v_j \frac{\partial}{\partial t}\frac{1}{T} + \rho v_j \frac{\partial}{\partial t}\frac{\partial}{\partial x_j}\frac{v^2}{2T} = 0 \tag{5.5.2}$$

and

$$-v_i \frac{\partial p}{\partial x_i}\frac{\partial}{\partial t}\frac{1}{T} - p v_i \frac{\partial}{\partial x_i}\frac{\partial}{\partial t}\frac{1}{T} = -\frac{\partial}{\partial x_i}p v_i \frac{\partial}{\partial t}\frac{1}{T} \tag{5.5.3}$$

Using Eqs. (5.5.2) and (5.5.3), Eq. (5.5.1) reduces to

$$\psi = -\frac{\partial}{\partial x_i}q_i \frac{\partial}{\partial t}\frac{1}{T} + \frac{1}{2}L_{\theta\theta}\frac{\partial}{\partial t}\left(\frac{\partial}{\partial x_i}\frac{1}{T}\frac{\partial}{\partial x_i}\frac{1}{T}\right) - \rho c_p v_i \frac{\partial T}{\partial t}\frac{\partial}{\partial x_i}\frac{1}{T}$$

$$+ M_{vv}d_{ij}d_{ij}\frac{\partial}{\partial t}\frac{1}{T^2} \le 0 \tag{5.5.4}$$

If we neglect the effect of viscous dissipation in determining the temperature profiles, we can neglect the last term on the right-hand side of Eq. (5.5.4). Thus

$$0 \ge \psi = -\frac{\partial}{\partial x_i}q_i \frac{\partial}{\partial t}\frac{1}{T} + \frac{kT^2}{2}\frac{\partial}{\partial t}\left(\frac{\partial}{\partial x_i}\frac{1}{T}\frac{\partial}{\partial x_i}\frac{1}{T}\right)$$

$$- \rho c_p v_i \frac{\partial T}{\partial t}\frac{\partial}{\partial x_i}\frac{1}{T} \tag{5.5.5}$$

Here we have used the thermal conductivity in place of the phenomenological coefficient $L_{\theta\theta}$ ($kT^2 = L_{\theta\theta}$), with k being defined so that

$$q_i = -k \frac{\partial T}{\partial x_i} \tag{5.5.6}$$

If the thermal conductivity, rather than $L_{\theta\theta}$ is used, it is more convenient to study $T^2\psi$. This function is

$$T^2\psi = -T^2\frac{\partial}{\partial x_i}\left(k\frac{\partial T}{\partial x_i}\frac{\partial T}{\partial t}\frac{1}{T^2}\right) + \frac{k}{2}\frac{\partial}{\partial t}\left(\frac{\partial T}{\partial x_i}\frac{\partial T}{\partial x_i}\right)$$

$$-\frac{2k}{T}\frac{\partial T}{\partial t}\frac{\partial T}{\partial x_i}\frac{\partial T}{\partial x_i} + \rho c_p v_i\frac{\partial T}{\partial t}\frac{\partial T}{\partial x_i} \leq 0 \tag{5.5.7}$$

or after some reduction

$$T^2\psi = -\frac{\partial}{\partial x_i}k\frac{\partial T}{\partial x_i}\frac{\partial T}{\partial t} + \frac{k}{2}\frac{\partial}{\partial t}\frac{\partial T}{\partial x_i}\frac{\partial T}{\partial x_i} + \rho c_p v_i\frac{\partial T}{\partial t}\frac{\partial T}{\partial x_i} \leq 0 \tag{5.5.8}†$$

Equation (5.5.8) represents the form of the potential sought. This inequality gives rise to a definition of the local potential which will govern the evolution of temperatures in any entry region.

For our first example, let us consider the thermal entry region for the parabolic flow between two semi-infinite parallel plates as shown in Fig. 5.5.1. The fluid enters with a zero temperature and contacts a heated wall at $x_1 = 0$ which is maintained at $T = 1$. As an approximation assume that the thermal energy penetrates only a finite distance into the fluid. This distance of penetration $q(x_1)$ increases for increasing distances from the inlet, as depicted in Fig. 5.5.1. This distance of penetration becomes equal to the half-width of the plate spacing at the axial position $x_1 = L$. We are interested in determining the mean fluid temperature as a function of

† We could have developed this same result starting with the differential balance equation describing the flow of heat into a fluid which is incompressible and flowing in such a way that the viscous dissipation is negligible. This differential equation is

$$\rho c_p\frac{\partial T}{\partial t} + \rho c_p v_i\frac{\partial T}{\partial x_i} = \frac{\partial}{\partial x_i}\left(k\frac{\partial T}{\partial x_i}\right)$$

Multiply both sides of the equation by $\partial T/\partial t$ and rearrange to obtain

$$-\rho c_p\left(\frac{\partial T}{\partial t}\right)^2 = \rho c_p v_i\frac{\partial T}{\partial t}\frac{\partial t}{\partial x_i} - \frac{\partial}{\partial x_i}\left(k\frac{\partial T}{\partial t}\frac{\partial T}{\partial x_i}\right) - \frac{k}{2}\frac{\partial}{\partial t}\left(\frac{\partial T}{\partial x_i}\frac{\partial T}{\partial x_i}\right) \leq 0$$

which is identical to Eq. (5.5.8), provided we identify

$$T^2\psi = -\rho c_p\left(\frac{\partial T}{\partial t}\right)^2$$

Clearly, in most cases it is easier to begin the development of a potential with the final form of the differential balance equations representing the particular system under study. One needs however to retain the time-dependent character of the equations when forming the potential.

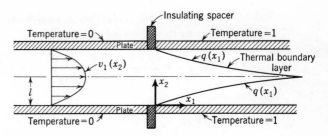

Fig. 5.5.1   Heat transfer in an entry region.

axial position for the region $0 \leq x_1 \leq L$; $0 \leq x_2 \leq l$.   This calculation will depend on the temperature being adequately approximated by the polynomial

$$T = 1 - \frac{10}{7}\frac{x_2}{q} + \frac{5}{7}\left(\frac{x_2}{q}\right)^4 - \frac{2}{7}\left(\frac{x_2}{q}\right)^5 \qquad (5.5.9)$$

This expression was developed by expanding T into a fifth-degree polynomial in x_2 with the coefficients being fixed by the conditions

$$T = 1 \qquad \frac{\partial^2 T}{\partial x_2{}^2} = 0 \qquad \frac{\partial^3 T}{\partial x_2{}^3} = 0 \qquad \text{for} \qquad x_2 = 0 \qquad (5.5.10)$$

and

$$T = 0 \qquad \frac{\partial T}{\partial x_2} = 0 \qquad \frac{\partial^3 T}{\partial x_2{}^3} = 0 \qquad \text{for} \qquad x_2 = q \qquad (5.5.11)$$

The boundary conditions imposed at the wall ($x_2 = 0$) are easily verified using the energy balance and the velocity distribution†

$$v_1 = V_{\text{av}} \frac{3}{l}\left(x_2 - \frac{x_2{}^2}{2l}\right) \qquad (5.5.12)$$

The temperature vanishes at $x_2 = q$, and the other conditions imposed at this "interface" are simply "smooth-fit conditions," which can not be rigorously justified.

To simplify the calculations, we shall assume that the heat flux in the axial direction q_1 is small compared with the rate of convective energy transport $\rho c_p v_1 T$.   Noting that $v_1(x_2)$ is the only surviving component of velocity

† The energy balance is

$$\rho c_p v_1(x_2) \frac{\partial T}{\partial x_1} = k \frac{\partial^2 T}{\partial x_2{}^2}$$

so that $(\partial^2 T/\partial x_2{}^2)_{x_2=0} = 0$ because both $v_1(x_2)$ and $\partial T/\partial x_1$ vanish on the surface of the wall.   Differentiating the energy balance with respect to x_2 and evaluating the resultant expression at the wall, one finds that $\partial^3 T/\partial x_2{}^3$ also vanishes.

and that derivatives with respect to x_3 vanish, our potential defined by Eq. (5.5.8) reduces to the following expression:

$$0 \geq T^2\psi = -\frac{\partial}{\partial x_2}\, k\frac{\partial T}{\partial x_2}\frac{\partial T}{\partial t} + \frac{k}{2}\frac{\partial}{\partial t}\left(\frac{\partial T}{\partial x_2}\right)^2 + \rho c_p v_1\frac{\partial T}{\partial t}\frac{\partial T}{\partial x_1} \tag{5.5.13}$$

Define

$$\phi = \int_0^L\int_0^q \psi T^2\, dx_2\, dx_1 \leq 0 \tag{5.5.14}$$

giving

$$\phi = \int_0^L\int_0^q \left[\frac{k}{2}\frac{\partial}{\partial t}\left(\frac{\partial T}{\partial x_2}\right)^2 + \rho c_p v_1\frac{\partial T}{\partial t}\frac{\partial T}{\partial x_1}\right] dx_2\, dx_1 \leq 0 \tag{5.5.15}$$

since the temperature is time-independent at both $x_2 = 0$ and $x_2 = q$. Using the concept of the local potential near the stationary state, we write

$$\phi = \frac{\partial}{\partial t}\, E^* \tag{5.5.16}$$

where

$$E^* = \int_0^L\int_0^{q^0} \left[\frac{k}{2}\left(\frac{\partial T}{\partial x_2}\right)^2 + \rho c_p v_1 T\frac{\partial T^0}{\partial x_1}\right] dx_2\, dx_1 \tag{5.5.17}$$

is a minimum in the stationary state. Note that the q appearing in the limits of integration is an unvaried function. This identification was necessary to interchange the order of differentiation with respect to time and the integration done in deriving Eq. (5.5.16) starting from Eq. (5.5.15).

Substituting Eq. (5.5.9) into Eq. (5.5.17) gives

$$\begin{aligned}
E^* = \int_0^L\int_0^{q^0} \Bigg\{ &\frac{50k}{49q^2}\left[-1 + 2\left(\frac{x_2}{q}\right)^3 - \left(\frac{x_2}{q}\right)^4\right]^2 \\
&+ \frac{3V_{av}\rho c_p}{l}\left(x_2 - \frac{x_2^2}{2l}\right)\frac{1}{q^0}\frac{dq^0}{dx_1}\left[1 - \frac{10}{7}\frac{x_2}{q} + \frac{5}{7}\left(\frac{x_2}{q}\right)^4\right. \\
&\left. - \frac{2}{7}\left(\frac{x_2}{q}\right)^5\right]\left[\frac{10}{7}\frac{x_2}{q^0} - \frac{20}{7}\left(\frac{x_2}{q^0}\right)^4 + \frac{10}{7}\left(\frac{x_2}{q^0}\right)^5\right]\Bigg\}\, dx_1\, dx_2
\end{aligned} \tag{5.5.18}$$

Let us take the variation of E^* with respect to q, remembering to hold q^0 fixed. This step gives

$$\begin{aligned}
\delta E^* = \int_0^L\int_0^{q^0} \Bigg\{ &\frac{100k}{49}\left(-\frac{1}{q} + \frac{2x_2^3}{q^4} - \frac{x_2^4}{q^5}\right)\left(\frac{1}{q^2} - \frac{8x_2^3}{q^5} + \frac{5x_2^4}{q^6}\right) \\
&+ \frac{3V_{av}\,\rho c_p}{l}\left(x_2 - \frac{x_2^2}{2l}\right)\frac{1}{q^0}\frac{dq^0}{dx_1}\frac{100}{49}\left(\frac{x_2}{q^2} - \frac{2x_2^4}{q^5} + \frac{x_2^5}{q^6}\right) \\
&\left[\frac{x_2}{q^0} - \frac{2x_2^4}{(q^0)^4} + \left(\frac{x_2}{q^0}\right)^5\right]\Bigg\}\, dx_1\, dx_2\, \delta q
\end{aligned} \tag{5.5.19}$$

We need not distinguish between the varied and unvaried q, since the process of variation is now complete.   Dropping the superscript and integrating on the x_2 coordinate, we find

$$\frac{49}{100} \delta E^* = \int_0^L \left(-\frac{k}{q^2}\frac{367}{1260} + \frac{3V_{\mathrm{av}}\rho c_p}{l}\frac{223}{4620}\frac{dq}{dx_1} \right.$$
$$\left. -\frac{3V_{\mathrm{av}}\rho c_p}{l}\frac{379}{12870}\frac{q}{2l}\frac{dq}{dx_1} \right) \delta q \, dx_1 \tag{5.5.20}$$

Since δE^* must vanish for all δq,

$$0 = -k\frac{367}{1260} + \frac{V_{\mathrm{av}}\rho c_p}{l}\frac{223}{4620}\frac{d}{dx_1}q^3 - \frac{3V_{\mathrm{av}}\rho c_p}{8l^2}\frac{379}{12870}\frac{d}{dx_1}q^4 \tag{5.5.21}$$

Integrating this differential equation subject to the boundary condition $q = 0$ at $x_1 = 0$ gives the boundary-layer thickness q as a function of the axial position:

$$\left(\frac{q}{l}\right)^3 - 0.2288\left(\frac{q}{l}\right)^4 - 24.14\frac{1}{N_{\mathrm{Pe}}}\frac{x_1}{2l} = 0 \tag{5.5.22}$$

Here N_{Pe} is the Peclet number defined for this case as

$$N_{\mathrm{Pe}} = \frac{2lV_{\mathrm{av}}\rho c_p}{k} \tag{5.5.23}$$

The relationship between the thermal boundary-layer thickness and the axial position is shown in Fig. 5.5.2.   We see that the boundary layers,

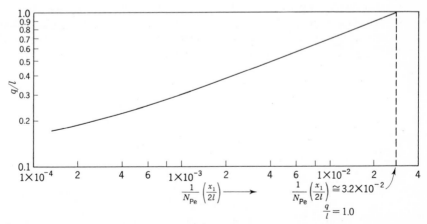

Fig. 5.5.2   Thermal boundary-layer thickness.

penetrating from both the upper and lower walls, meet at an axial position given by

$$\frac{1}{N_{Pe}}\frac{x_1}{2l} \cong 0.032 \tag{5.5.24}$$

Our approximation is not applicable for axial positions greater than those defined by Eq. (5.5.24). However, as we shall see, the region of greatest interest is included within the range of validity encompassed by our approximation. To put the results to practical use, define the mean temperature as

$$\langle T \rangle = \frac{\int_0^q v_1(x_2)T\,dx_2}{\int_0^l v_1(x_2)\,dx_2} \tag{5.5.25}$$

This "cup mixing" temperature is then a function of $q(x_1)$ as given by the following expression:

$$\langle T \rangle = \frac{15}{49}\frac{q^2}{l^2} - \frac{25}{392}\frac{q^3}{l^3} \tag{5.5.26}$$

The Nusselt number is defined as

$$N_{Nu} = -\frac{1}{1 - \langle T \rangle}\left(\frac{\partial T}{\partial x_2}\right)_{x_2=0} 2l \tag{5.5.27}$$

which, in terms of q, reduces to

$$N_{Nu} = \frac{20}{7}\frac{l}{q}\frac{1}{1 - \langle T \rangle} \tag{5.5.28}$$

The mean temperature and the Nusselt number are given in Table 5.5.1. The results are seen to be in good agreement with the values found by a conventional mathematical analysis using separation of variables.[1] Certainly the accuracy is more than adequate for most design purposes. It should also

[1] J. A. W. Van Der Does De Bye and J. Schenk, "Heat Transfer in Laminar Flow between Parallel Plates," *Appl. Sci. Res. Sec. A*, vol. 3, p. 308, 1953.

TABLE 5.5.1   HEAT-TRANSFER CHARACTERISTICS

$\dfrac{x_1}{2l}\dfrac{1}{N_{Pe}}$	$\langle T \rangle$	N_{Nu}	$\langle T \rangle^{(1)}$ exact	$N_{Nu}^{(1)}$ exact
0.005	0.07	5.98	0.08	5.78
0.01	0.11	4.86	0.13	5.00
0.025	0.21	3.94	0.24	4.10

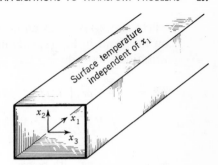

Fig. 5.5.3 Coordinate system in heated
duct.

be noted that the Nusselt number approaches a constant value of 3.77 as x_1
becomes large. Therefore our approximation is valid over the region of
the duct where the Nusselt number varies.

The technique used to treat this particularly simple problem can also be
applied to more complex systems. It appears that the most useful applications
of this method are to complex systems using a somewhat simpler temperature
profile in place of Eq. (5.5.9). The simplification of the assumed form of the
temperature reduces the amount of numerical work necessary to develop the
approximate solution.

Our second example is illustrated in Fig. 5.5.3. Here we see a duct heated
so that the temperature varies on the surface; however, this variation is
presumed to be independent of axial position x_1. It is clear that the fluid
introduced at $x_1 = 0$ will begin to lose and gain heat such that a stationary
distribution of temperatures will be approached. Our task is to estimate the
length required for the fluid to achieve the stationary thermal configuration.

We begin our study by writing the local potential governing the heat flow
(developed from Eq. 5.5.8) as

$$E^* = \int_0^\infty dx_1 \int_A \left\{ \rho c_p v_1(x_2, x_3) T \frac{\partial T^0}{\partial x_1} + \frac{k}{2} \left[\left(\frac{\partial T}{\partial x_1} \right)^2 + \left(\frac{\partial T}{\partial x_2} \right)^2 \right. \right.$$
$$\left. \left. + \left(\frac{\partial T}{\partial x_3} \right)^2 \right] \right\} dx_2 \, dx_3 \tag{5.5.29}$$

where A is the area normal to flow. In writing Eq. (5.5.29) we have assumed
that the velocity is directed along the x_1 axis and is a function of x_2 and x_3
but is independent of x_1. The essential idea of the computation is to assume
that any inlet configuration can be expressed as a sum of Fourier components
and that each component will decay independently. Thus we write

$$T = f(x_2, x_3) e^{-\lambda x_1} \tag{5.5.30}$$

and

$$T^0 = f^0(x_2, x_3) e^{-\lambda^0 x_1} \tag{5.5.31}$$

where $f(x_2,x_3)$ is as yet an unspecified function. Again the superscript zero on the terms in Eq. (5.5.31) implies that these quantities are not subject to variation. Introducing Eqs. (5.5.30) and (5.5.31) into Eq. (5.5.29) we have

$$E^* = \frac{-\lambda^0}{\lambda^0 + \lambda}\, \rho c_p \int_A v_1 f f^0 \, dx_2 \, dx_3 + \frac{k}{4\lambda} \int_A \left[\left(\frac{\partial f}{\partial x_2} \right)^2 \right.$$

$$+ \left. \left(\frac{\partial f}{\partial x_3} \right)^2 \right] dx_2 \, dx_3 + \frac{k\lambda}{4} \int_A f^2 \, dx_2 \, dx_3 \qquad (5.5.32)$$

after integrating with respect to x_1.

Since E^* is to be stationary, we should select λ such that $\partial E^*/\partial \lambda$ vanishes. Thus

$$\frac{\partial E^*}{\partial \lambda} = 0 = \frac{\lambda^0}{(\lambda + \lambda^0)^2}\, \rho c_p \int_A v_1 f f^0 \, dx_2 \, dx_3$$

$$- \frac{k}{4\lambda^2} \int_A \left[\left(\frac{\partial f}{\partial x_2} \right)^2 + \left(\frac{\partial f}{\partial x_3} \right)^2 \right] dx_2 \, dx_3 + \frac{k}{4} \int_A f^2 \, dx_2 \, dx_3 \qquad (5.5.33)$$

We now impose the usual auxiliary restrictions by letting

$$\lambda^0 = \lambda \qquad (5.5.34)$$

$$f^0 = f \qquad (5.5.35)$$

If we neglect conduction in the axial direction [this is equivalent to discarding the last term on the right-hand side of Eq. (5.5.33)], we can write

$$\lambda = \frac{k \int_A \left[\left(\dfrac{\partial f}{\partial x_2} \right)^2 + \left(\dfrac{\partial f}{\partial x_3} \right)^2 \right] dx_2 \, dx_3}{\rho c_p \int_A v_1 f^2 \, dx_2 \, dx_3} \qquad (5.5.36)$$

It should be stressed that one need not neglect the conduction in the x_1 direction except as a matter of convenience in this presentation. The computations for a specific problem are not complicated by leaving axial conduction in the final result.

Equation (5.5.36) has a structure which seems to be analogous to Rayleigh's principle in mechanics.[2] The numerator is proportional to the production of entropy owing to the decay of the initial temperature configuration $f(x_2,x_3)$, whereas the denominator is the rate at which entropy is convected in the axial direction. If λ is large, inlet disturbances will not penetrate far into the system. On the other hand, a small generation (or dissipative) mechanism relative to the rate of transport will yield a small λ, and considerable distance will be required to achieve the equilibrium distribution.

[2] G. Temple and W. G. Bichley, "Rayleigh's Principle," pp. 1–9, Dover Publications, Inc., New York, 1956.

Approximations for λ are possible using a technique similar to that employed in conjunction with Rayleigh's quotient (see Chap. 3.4). To illustrate the method and the results, let us focus our attention on the rectangular duct shown in Fig. 5.5.3. Furthermore, let us assume that the velocity is a constant; that is,

$$v_1(x_2,x_3) = V_{av} \tag{5.5.37}$$

Let

$$f(x_2,x_3) = f_{mn}(x_2,x_3) = \sin\frac{m\pi x_2}{a}\sin\frac{n\pi x_3}{aE} \tag{5.5.38}$$

Then substituting Eqs. (5.5.37) and (5.5.38) into Eq. (5.5.36) we obtain after some integration

$$\lambda_{mn} = \frac{k^2\pi^2}{a^2\rho c_p V_{av}}\frac{m^2E^2 + n^2}{E^2} \tag{5.5.39}$$

which is, of course, the exact result. One can easily verify Eq. (5.5.39) by finding the eigenvalues associated with the simple energy balance equation

$$V_{av}\rho c_p\frac{\partial T}{\partial x_1} = k\left(\frac{\partial^2 T}{\partial x_2{}^2} + \frac{\partial^2 T}{\partial x_3{}^2}\right) \tag{5.5.40}$$

The eigenvalue is found by substituting

$$T = e^{-\lambda_{mn}x_1}\sin\frac{m\pi x_2}{a}\sin\frac{n\pi x_3}{aE} \tag{5.5.41}$$

into Eq. (5.5.40). When this computation is performed, Eq. (5.5.39) will be verified.

If the velocity is not constant, the method of determining the exact eigenvalues is a laborious and complex procedure. This is discussed by Mitchell[3] and by Dennis, Mercer, and Poots.[4] However, Eq. (5.5.36) can still be used to obtain an approximation for λ. When the velocity is expanded into a Fourier series

$$v_1(x_2,x_3) = V_{av}\Bigg(G_{11}\sin\frac{\pi x_2}{a}\sin\frac{\pi x_3}{aE} + G_{13}\sin\frac{\pi x_2}{a}\sin\frac{3\pi x_3}{aE}$$

$$+ G_{31}\sin\frac{3\pi x_2}{a}\sin\frac{\pi x_3}{aE} + G_{33}\sin\frac{3\pi x_2}{a}\sin\frac{3\pi x_3}{aE}$$

$$+ G_{15}\sin\frac{\pi x_2}{a}\sin\frac{5\pi x_3}{a} + G_{51}\sin\frac{5\pi x_2}{a}\sin\frac{\pi x_3}{aE}\Bigg) \tag{5.5.42}$$

[3] J. W. Mitchell, Master's thesis, "An Extension of Variational Principles to the Solutions of Non-linear Differential Equations," Department of Chemical Engineering, University of Texas, Austin, Tex., 1963.

[4] Dennis, Mercer, and Poots, "Forced Heat Convection in Laminar Flow through Rectangular Ducts," *Quart. Appl. Math.*, vol. 17, p. 285, 1959.

the appropriate coefficients for power-law fluids flowing in rectangular ducts are given by Schechter.[5]   The values for a Newtonian fluid are given in Table 5.5.2.   Since Mitchell and Dennis et al., have computed the eigenvalues associated with the transfer of heat from the wall of a rectangular duct, it will be interesting to compare the approximate values obtained using Eq. (5.5.36) with their more precise values.   If we let

$$f(x_2, x_3) = \sin \frac{\pi x_2}{a} \sin \frac{\pi x_3}{aE} \tag{5.5.43}$$

and the values of G taken for a Newtonian fluid and for $E = 1.0$, we find after integration and summation

$$\lambda_{11} = \frac{12.0k}{V_{\mathrm{av}} \rho c_p a^2} \tag{5.5.44}$$

whereas Mitchell gives

$$\lambda_{11} = \frac{11.87k}{V_{\mathrm{av}} \rho c_p a^2} \tag{5.5.45}$$

The accuracy of the approximate value is far better than that required for most engineering computations.   Since the decay of the temperature with axial position goes as $e^{-\lambda x_1}$, the entry length is defined and the designer can estimate the length required for the fluid to "forget" its inlet temperature. For $E = 0.5$ the approximate value is

$$\lambda_{11} = \frac{30.7k}{a^2 V_{\mathrm{av}} \rho c_p}$$

[5] R. S. Schechter, "On the Steady Flow of a Non-Newtonian Fluid in Cylinder Ducts," *J. Am. Inst. Chem. Engrs.*, vol. 7, p. 445, 1961.

TABLE 5.5.2 CONSTANTS FOR VELOCITY DISTRIBUTION OF NEWTONIAN FLUIDS [Eq. (5.5.40)]

	$E = 1.0$	$E = 0.5$
G_{11}	2.346	2.311
G_{13}	0.156	0.296
G_{31}	0.156	0.104
G_{33}	0.0289	0.0285
G_{15}	0.0360	0.0303
G_{51}	0.0360	0.0795

and for this case Mitchell finds

$$\lambda_{11} = \frac{30.37k}{a^2 V_{av} \rho c_p}$$

A comparison of the second eigenvalues is also shown in Table 5.5.3. It is clear that the approximate values obtained using the equation developed from the local potential are sufficiently accurate for most engineering problems. Furthermore, it is clear that other entry effects, such as momentum entry regions, can also be defined using the techniques outlined in this section. It appears that the extended variational principles based on the concept of local potential are of real significance in defining entry effects.

TABLE 5.5.3 COMPARISON OF EIGENVALUES

	Approximate	Mitchell
$E = 1.0, \lambda_{11}$	12.0	11.87
$E = 0.5, \lambda_{11}$	30.7	30.37
$E = 0.5, \lambda_{13}$	95.3	91.78

5.6 DIFFUSION IN CONCENTRATED SUSPENSIONS OR POROUS MEDIA

The examples presented thus far in this chapter have been devoted almost entirely to demonstrating the use of the local potential in making direct calculations. This example was selected to illustrate a different application of the principles discussed in the previous chapter. The principle of minimum entropy production will be invoked to fix an upper bound on the effective diffusion coefficient associated with the diffusional flow of a solute in a solution embedded within the interstices of a collection of solid particles. The analysis is due to Prager,[1,2] and the presentation closely follows that given by Prager.

The geometric configuration of the system is characterized by a stochastic function of position $g(x_i)$, which is defined to be unity if the point x_i lies in a region occupied by fluid and defined to be 0 if x_i falls inside one of the solid particles. We can not hope to know $g(x_i)$ for *any* system; however, it is possible to measure some of the correlations which can be generated. For example, it is clear that the porosity ϵ is determined by

$$\epsilon = \frac{1}{V} \int_V g(x_i) \, dV = \langle g(x_i) \rangle \tag{5.6.1}$$

[1] S. Prager, "Diffusion and Viscous Flow in Concentrated Suspensions," *Physica*, vol. 29, p. 129, 1963.

[2] S. Prager, "Viscous Flow through Porous Media," *Phys. of Fluids*, vol. 4, p. 1477, 1961.

Also a two-point correlation can be defined as

$$S(r_i) = \langle g(x_i)g(x_i + r_i)\rangle \tag{5.6.2}$$

The physical significance of $S(r_i)$ will become somewhat more transparent by developing the two limiting values. As r_i becomes small, both $g(x_i)$ and $g(x_i + r_i)$ have a high probability of being identical. Thus

$$\lim_{r_i \to 0} S(r_i) \to \epsilon \tag{5.6.3}$$

Moreover, as r_i becomes large, the $g(x_i)$ are not correlated; that is, a knowledge of g at one point is not useful in predicting g at a second point.

$$\lim_{r_i \to \infty} S(r_i) = \langle g(x_i)\rangle\langle g(x_i + r_i)\rangle = \epsilon^2 \tag{5.6.4}$$

From these considerations it is clear that $S(r_i)$ is a measure of the probability that two points separated by a distance $|r_i|$ will both lie within the fluid. A method of measuring $S(r_i)$ based on light-scattering experiments has been proposed.[3]

There are other averages which can be defined; however, for our purposes, it is necessary to assume the availability of the three-point average

$$G(r_i, r_i') = \langle g(x_i)g(x_i + r_i)g(x_i + r_i')\rangle \tag{5.6.5}$$

Values of the three-point average can be written down for a number of limiting cases. For example,

$$G(r_i, r_i') = \begin{cases} \epsilon S(r_i) & \text{as } r_i' \to \infty, \, r_i \text{ finite} \\ \epsilon S(r_i') & \text{as } r_i \to \infty, \, r_i' \text{ finite} \\ \epsilon^3 & \text{as } r_i, r_i', \, |r_i - r_i'| \to \infty \\ S(r_i) & \text{as } r_i' \to 0, \, r_i \text{ finite} \end{cases} \tag{5.6.6}$$

Techniques of measuring $G(r_i, r_i')$ have not yet been suggested, but we shall assume that $G(r_i, r_i')$ is known. The problem is to use this partial description of the system geometry to determine a rigorous upper bound for the effective diffusion coefficient. The analysis to follow is limited to isotropic configurations, so that $S(r_i)$ depends only on the magnitude of r_i and $G(r_i, r_i')$ is a function of the magnitude of both r_i and r_i' as well as the angle between them. We imagine a system in which there is no flow (or a very slow flow so that the convection of matter can be neglected) and an ideal system; thus the rate of entropy production (see Sec. 5.4.3) can be written as

$$E = \left\langle D(x_i) \frac{\partial c}{\partial x_i} \frac{\partial c}{\partial x_i}\right\rangle \tag{5.6.7}$$

[3] P. Debye and A. M. Bueche, "Scattering by an Inhomogeneous Solid," *J. Appl. Phys.*, vol. 20, p. 518, 1949.

where

$$D(x_i) = g(x_i)D_0 \tag{5.6.8}$$

and D_0 is the molecular diffusion of the solute in the solvent. To avoid difficulties arising from discontinuities in the concentration, we assume to begin with that the solute is distributed in both the solid and the liquid with a distribution coefficient k, which is unity. The use of Eq. (5.6.8) for the molecular-diffusion coefficient has the effect of making the diffusion coefficient in the solid vanish (since $g(x_i) = 0$ when x_i is in solid) and gives the molecular-diffusion coefficient to the liquid. The entropy production E is to be minimized subject to the restriction that a certain mean concentration gradient

$$\alpha_i = \left\langle \frac{\partial c}{\partial x_i} \right\rangle \tag{5.6.9}$$

be fixed.

Owing to the imposed mean concentration gradient, we have a mean flux

$$\bar{J}_i = - \left\langle D(x_i) \frac{\partial c}{\partial x_i} \right\rangle \tag{5.6.10}$$

which is just the steady-state flux of solute that would be observed in a normal diffusion experiment. The quantity of interest is the effective diffusion coefficient D_e defined as

$$\bar{J}_i = - D_e \alpha_i \tag{5.6.11}$$

To relate D_e to E, we split the local solute concentration into two parts

$$\frac{\partial c}{\partial x_i} = \alpha_i + \frac{\partial c'}{\partial x_i} \tag{5.6.12}$$

where c' is a fluctuation about the mean. Substituting Eq. (5.6.12) into (5.6.7) gives

$$E = D_0 \left[\epsilon \alpha^2 + 2\alpha_i \left\langle g(x_i) \frac{\partial c'}{\partial x_i} \right\rangle + \left\langle g(x_i) \frac{\partial c'}{\partial x_i} \frac{\partial c'}{\partial x_i} \right\rangle \right] \tag{5.6.13}$$

where $\alpha^2 = \alpha_i \alpha_i$. Now we remember E is to be a minimum so that we assume a fluctuation of the form

$$c'(x_i) = \lambda \bar{c}'(x_i) \tag{5.6.14}$$

where $\bar{c}'(x_i)$ is the fluctuation in concentration which minimizes E and λ is an adjustable parameter whose optimum value (in the sense of minimizing entropy production) will be unity.   The entropy production for a variation about the optimal ($\lambda = 1$) is

$$E = D_0\left[\epsilon\alpha^2 + 2\alpha_i\lambda\left\langle g(x_i)\frac{\partial\bar{c}'}{\partial x_i}\right\rangle + \lambda^2\left\langle g(x_i)\frac{\partial\bar{c}'}{\partial x_i}\frac{\partial\bar{c}'}{\partial x_i}\right\rangle\right] \qquad (5.6.15)$$

Since E is to be a minimum at $\lambda = 1$, we must have

$$\left(\frac{\partial E}{\partial\lambda}\right)_{\lambda=1} = 0 \qquad (5.6.16)$$

giving

$$\alpha_i\left\langle g(x_i)\frac{\partial\bar{c}'}{\partial x_i}\right\rangle = -\left\langle g(x_i)\frac{\partial\bar{c}'}{\partial x_i}\frac{\partial\bar{c}'}{\partial x_i}\right\rangle$$

Therefore, substituting this result into Eq. (5.6.15), we find

$$E = -\alpha_i\bar{J}_i \qquad (5.6.17)$$

This is a very interesting and useful result.   For we see that the minimum entropy production can be computed rigorously from a knowledge of the mean gradient and the associated mass flux.   Since we do not know, and can never hope to calculate, the true concentration distribution, we shall always be forced to use some approximate concentration—a trial function. Of course, the approximate entropy production will be greater than the true minimum value, and Eq. (5.6.17) becomes the inequality

$$D_e\alpha^2 \leq E \qquad (5.6.18)$$

If $c'(x_i)$ is an approximate trial function, others can be constructed in the form $\lambda c'(x_i)$ and the λ chosen such that E is minimized.   It should be noted that the λ giving the smallest E is not necessarily unity, since $c'(x_i)$ is not the true concentration fluctuation, but some assumed trial function.   The "best" choice for λ associated with a given trial function is determined from Eq. (5.6.16) (except λ is not necessarily unity) and gives

$$\lambda = -\frac{\alpha_i\langle g(x_i)(\partial c'/\partial x_i)\rangle}{\langle g(x_i)(\partial c'/\partial x_i)(\partial c'/\partial x_i)\rangle} \qquad (5.6.19)$$

Substituting into Eq. (5.6.15) gives

$$D_e \leq D_0\left\{\epsilon - \frac{[\alpha_i\langle g(x_i)(\partial c'/\partial x_i)\rangle]^2}{\alpha^2\langle g(x_i)(\partial c'/\partial x_i)(\partial c'/\partial x_i)\rangle}\right\} \qquad (5.6.20)$$

An immediate consequence of our analysis is

$$D_e \leq D_0\epsilon \qquad (5.6.21)$$

which is itself an interesting limit.   We can assert at once [using Eq. (5.3.11)] the well-known inequality

$$- J_i \leq D_0 \epsilon \alpha_i$$

A diffusional flux computed using the molecular diffusion coefficient gives a result which is always greater than the observable flux owing to the tortuosity of the diffusional path.   In this inequality the ϵ appears to account for the fact that only a fraction ϵ of a unit area is free to accommodate mass flow.   To improve on Eq. (5.6.21), we must introduce a trial function $c'(x_i)$.   It seems evident that these fluctuations are due to the variations in the geometry of the system and that this $c'(x_j)$ is related to the $g(x_j)$. However, some care must be taken in choosing this relationship.   For if the average $\langle g(x_j)(\partial c'/\partial x_i)(\partial c'/\partial x_i) \rangle$ is to exist, then $c'(x_i)$ must be continuous at all points, including the solid-liquid interface, where g is discontinuous.   In addition the trial function must satisfy the equation

$$\left\langle \frac{\partial c'}{\partial x_i} \right\rangle = 0 \tag{5.6.22}$$

since we have agreed to impose a mean gradient α_i.   A simple trial function satisfying all of these restrictions is

$$c'(x_i) = \int h(\rho_i)[g(x_i + \rho_i) - \epsilon] \, d\boldsymbol{\rho} \tag{5.6.23}†$$

where $h(\rho_i)$ is a weighting function and the integration extends over all of space.   We should choose $h(\rho_i)$ such that E is as small as possible.   With this trial function, the averages appearing in Eq. (5.6.20) become

$$\left\langle g(x_i) \frac{\partial c'}{\partial x_i} \right\rangle = \left\langle g(x_i) \int h(\rho_i) \frac{\partial}{\partial x_i} [g(x_i + \rho_i) - \epsilon] \, d\boldsymbol{\rho} \right\rangle$$

$$= \int h(\rho_i) \left\langle g(x_i) \frac{\partial}{\partial \rho_i} [g(x_i + \rho_i) - \epsilon] \, d\boldsymbol{\rho} \right\rangle$$

$$= \int h(\rho_i) \frac{\partial S^*(\rho_i)}{\partial \rho_i} \, d\boldsymbol{\rho} \tag{5.6.24}$$

where

$$S^*(\rho_i) = S(\rho_i) - \epsilon^2$$

Similarly

$$\left\langle g(x_i) \frac{\partial c'}{\partial x_j} \frac{\partial c'}{\partial x_j} \right\rangle = \int \int h(\rho_i) h(\rho_i') \frac{\partial}{\partial \rho_i} \frac{\partial}{\partial \rho_i'} G^*(\rho_i, \rho_i') \, d\boldsymbol{\rho} \, d\boldsymbol{\rho}' \tag{5.6.25}$$

† Here $d\boldsymbol{\rho}$ denotes a volume element, say
$$d\boldsymbol{\rho} = d\rho_1 \, d\rho_2 \, d\rho_3$$
in rectangular cartesian coordinates.

with

$$G^*(\rho_i,\rho_i') = G(\rho_i,\rho_i') - \epsilon S(\rho_i) - \epsilon S(\rho_i') + \epsilon^3$$

The concentration c' must be a linear homogeneous function of the mean concentration gradient α_i, for the fluctuations vanish if the gradients vanish. As the gradient increases, so do the fluctuations. It follows that h must depend on α_i in the same way. Moreover, since the system is isotropic, the dependence of h on ρ_i and α_i must be independent of coordinate rotations. The most general function satisfying these requirements is

$$h(\rho_i) = H(\rho)\rho_i\alpha_i \tag{5.6.26}$$

where $H(\rho)$ is any function of the magnitude of ρ_i.

If $h(\rho_i)$ has the structure given by Eq. (5.6.26), the vectors $\langle g(x_i)(\partial c'/\partial x_i)\rangle$ and α_i will be collinear. This can be seen as follows. Substituting Eq. (5.6.26) into Eq. (5.6.24) and expanding for a particular component of the vector, say component 1, we find

$$\left\langle g(x_i)\frac{\partial c'}{\partial x_1}\right\rangle = \alpha_1\int \rho_1 H(\rho)\frac{\partial}{\partial \rho_1}S^*(\rho)\,d\mathbf{\rho} + \alpha_2\int \rho_2 H(\rho)\frac{\partial}{\partial \rho_1}S^*(\rho)\,d\mathbf{\rho}$$

$$+ \alpha_3\int \rho_3 H(\rho)\frac{\partial}{\partial \rho_1}S^*(\rho)\,d\mathbf{\rho} \tag{5.6.27}$$

Let us convert to a spherical coordinate system defined by the following transformation:

$$\rho_1 = \rho\sin\theta\sin\phi$$
$$\rho_2 = \rho\sin\theta\cos\phi$$
$$\rho_3 = \rho\cos\theta$$

Then the second term on the right-hand side of Eq. (5.6.27) becomes

$$\int \rho_2 H(\rho)\frac{\partial}{\partial \rho_1}S^*(\rho)\,d\mathbf{\rho} = \int_0^\infty\int_0^\pi\int_0^{2\pi}\rho^3\sin^3\theta\cos\phi\sin\phi\,H(\rho)\frac{dS^*}{d\rho}\,d\phi\,d\theta\,d\rho$$

if we use the volume element $d\mathbf{\rho} = \rho^2\sin\theta\,d\phi\,d\theta\,d\rho$ and recall that S^* depends only on ρ, the magnitude of ρ_i, for an isotropic porous medium. This integral vanishes, since

$$\int_0^{2\pi}\sin\phi\cos\phi\,d\phi = 0$$

Similarly, the third term on the right-hand side of Eq. (5.6.27) can be shown to vanish. Thus the x_1 component of the vector $\langle g(x_i)\,\partial c'/\partial x_i\rangle$ is proportional to the x_1 component of α_i as shown below:

$$\left\langle g(x_i)\frac{\partial c'}{\partial x_1}\right\rangle = \alpha_1\int \rho_1 H(\rho)\frac{\partial}{\partial \rho_1}S^*(\rho)\,d\mathbf{\rho} = \frac{4}{3}\pi\alpha_1\int_0^\infty \rho^3 H(\rho)\frac{dS^*}{d\rho}\,d\rho \tag{5.6.28}$$

By a similar argument, the x_2 and x_3 components of these two vectors can be shown to be proportional. Therefore $\langle g(x_i)\,\partial c'/\partial x_i \rangle$ and α_i are collinear and

$$\left[\alpha_i \left\langle g(x_i)\frac{\partial c'}{\partial x_i} \right\rangle \right]^2 = \alpha^2 \left\langle g(x_i)\frac{\partial c'}{\partial x_i} \right\rangle \left\langle g(x_i)\frac{\partial c'}{\partial x_i} \right\rangle \tag{5.6.29}$$

Substituting Eqs. (5.6.24), (5.6.25), and (5.6.29) into Eq. (5.6.20) gives

$$D_e < D_0 \left\{ \epsilon - \frac{\int h(\rho_i)[\partial S^*(\rho_i)/\partial \rho_i]\,d\boldsymbol{\rho}\int h(\rho_i)[\partial S^*(\rho_i)/\partial \rho_i]\,d\boldsymbol{\rho}}{\int\int h(\rho_i)h(\rho_i')\dfrac{\partial}{\partial \rho_i}\dfrac{\partial}{\partial \rho_i'}\,G^*(\rho_i,\rho_i')\,d\boldsymbol{\rho}\,d\boldsymbol{\rho}'} \right\} \tag{5.6.30}$$

This inequality provides an upper bound on D_e, which no longer involves a stochastic quantity. Since the best choice of $h(\rho_i)$ is that which minimizes E, we can apply the Euler-Lagrange equation to find the following integral equation.

$$\int h(\rho_i')\frac{\partial}{\partial \rho_i}\frac{\partial}{\partial \rho_i'}\,G^*(\rho_i,\rho_i')\,d\boldsymbol{\rho}' = -\alpha_i\frac{\partial S^*(\rho_i)}{\partial \rho_i} \tag{5.6.31}$$

Here we see that the best choice of $h(\rho_i)$ hinges on the two- and three-point averages of the stochastic variable $g(x_i)$. To determine the upper bound on the effective diffusion coefficient, we must know these two averages. However, at the present time, methods of determining the three-point average do not exist.

To demonstrate the usefulness of this result we must, therefore, make an additional approximation and note that the inequality expressed by Eq. (5.6.20) is reinforced if we replace the $g(x_i)$ appearing in the denominator by 1. Then Eq. (5.6.20) reduces to

$$D_e < D_0 \left\{ \epsilon - \frac{[\alpha_i\langle g(x_i)(\partial c'/\partial x_i)\rangle]^2}{\alpha^2\langle(\partial c/\partial x_i)(\partial c/\partial x_i)\rangle} \right\} \tag{5.6.32}$$

Then, using Eq. (5.6.23) as our trial function,

$$\left\langle \frac{\partial c'}{\partial x_i}\frac{\partial c'}{\partial x_i} \right\rangle = \int\int h(\rho_i)h(\rho_i')\left\langle \frac{\partial}{\partial x_i}[g(x_i+\rho_i)-\epsilon]\right.$$
$$\left. \times \frac{\partial}{\partial x_i}[g(x_i+\rho_i')-\epsilon] \right\rangle d\boldsymbol{\rho}\,d\boldsymbol{\rho}' \tag{5.6.33}$$

or

$$\left\langle \frac{\partial c'}{\partial x_i}\frac{\partial c'}{\partial x_i} \right\rangle = \int\int h(\rho_i)h(\rho_i')\frac{\partial}{\partial \rho_i}\frac{\partial}{\partial \rho_i'}\,S^*(\rho_i-\rho_i')\,d\boldsymbol{\rho}\,d\boldsymbol{\rho}' \tag{5.6.34}\dagger$$

$\dagger\ \langle g(x_i+\rho_i)g(x_i+\rho_i')\rangle = \langle g(x_i)g(x_i+\rho_i'-\rho_i)\rangle$
$$= S(\rho_i'-\rho_i)$$

So that the entropy production is minimized, $h(\rho_i)$ should satisfy the Euler-Lagrange equation

$$\int h(\rho_i') \frac{\partial}{\partial \rho_i} \frac{\partial}{\partial \rho_i} S^*(\rho_i - \rho_i') \, d\rho' = -\alpha_i \frac{\partial S^*(\rho_i)}{\partial \rho_i} \tag{5.6.35}$$

Equation (5.6.35) can be solved to give

$$h(\rho_i) = (1/4\pi) \frac{a_i \rho_i}{\rho^3} \tag{5.6.36}$$

where

$$\rho^3 = |\rho_i|^3$$

Using Eq. (5.6.35) gives

$$\iint h(\rho_i) h(\rho') \frac{\partial}{\partial \rho_i} \frac{\partial}{\partial \rho_i'} S^*(\rho_i - \rho_i') \, d\rho' \, d\rho = -\alpha_i \int h(\rho_i) \frac{\partial S^*}{\partial \rho_i} \, d\rho \tag{5.6.37}$$

We can orient our coordinate system so that the only surviving component of the vector α_i is the x_1 component.   There is no loss in generality associated with this assertion.   Thus

$$D_e < D_0 \left\{ \epsilon + \frac{1}{\alpha_1} \int \left[h(\rho_j) \frac{\partial S^*}{\partial \rho_1} \, d\rho \right] \right\} \tag{5.6.38}$$

Substituting into Eq. (5.6.36), we find

$$\frac{1}{\alpha_1} \int h(\rho_j) \frac{\partial S^*}{\partial \rho_1} \, d\rho = \frac{1}{4\pi} \int \frac{\rho_1}{\rho^3} \frac{\partial S^*}{\partial \rho_1} \, d\rho \tag{5.6.39}$$

Comparing this with Eq. (5.6.28), we can clearly reduce this expression to

$$\frac{1}{\alpha_1} \int h(\rho_j) \frac{\partial S^*}{\partial \rho_1} \, d\rho = \frac{1}{3} \int_0^\infty \frac{\partial S^*}{\partial \rho} \, d\rho \tag{5.6.40}$$

Since

$$\lim_{\rho \to \infty} S^*(\rho) = 0$$

and

$$\lim_{\rho \to 0} S^*(\rho) = \epsilon(1 - \epsilon)$$

Then we can write

$$\frac{1}{\alpha_1} \int h(\rho_j) \frac{\partial S^*}{\partial \rho_1} d\rho = -1/3(1 - \epsilon)\epsilon$$

Putting this result into Eq. (5.6.38),

$$D_e < D_0 \epsilon [1 - \tfrac{1}{3}(1 - \epsilon)] \tag{5.6.41}$$

This is a very general result, and is independent of the configuration of the solids.

Thus, we have seen that the principle of minimum entropy production leads to an important inequality which governs the magnitude of the effective diffusion coefficient in a porous material or a suspension of solids. This seems to be a very powerful method.

5.7 VISCOUS DRAG[1]

Our study of diffusion in concentrated suspensions utilized the principle of minimum entropy production to aid in the development of approximating functions describing fluctuations in concentration and to put an upper bound on the diffusion coefficient. This latter application, that of giving limits for certain physically important parameters, has not yet been exploited to the extent that its importance merits. The reason for this apparent omission is, of course, that the local potential is not an extremum when used in establishing approximations. However, if the principle of minimum entropy production is valid (see Chap. 4.3 for a statement of the necessary conditions), then one can give limits.

In this section we are going to put limits on the drag force which arises when a solid body V_s is translated through a quiescent fluid at a uniform velocity U_i. The motion is assumed to be so slow that we can neglect the inertia terms in the equation of motion. Also we assume that the temperature is constant and the fluid is both incompressible and Newtonian. As was noted in Chap. 4.3, these restrictions insure that the principle of minimum entropy production is valid. Thus the actual steady-state fluid motion must be such that

$$E = \int_V \sigma \, dV \tag{5.7.1}$$

is a minimum. The integration noted in Eq. (5.7.1) is taken over the fluid which is completely contained within rigid boundaries at rest or extends to

---

[1] R. Hill and G. Power, "Extremum Principles for Slow Viscous Flow and the Approximate Calculation of Drag," *Quart. J. Mech. Appl. Math.*, vol. 9, p. 313, 1956.

infinity in one or more directions and the boundary of the moving solid.   The rate of entropy production (Chap. 4.2) is given by

$$E = -\frac{1}{T}\int_V \tau_{ij}d_{ij}\,dV \qquad (5.7.2)$$

Since the fluid is incompressible, $d_{ij}\delta_{ij} = 0$ and

$$\pi_{ij}d_{ij} \equiv \tau_{ij}d_{ij}$$

where π_{ij} contains the pressure.   Moreover, π_{ij} is symmetric and thus

$$E = -\frac{1}{T}\int_V \pi_{ij}d_{ij}\,dV = -\frac{1}{T}\int_V \frac{\partial v_i}{\partial x_j}\pi_{ij}\,dV \qquad (5.7.3)$$

Using Gauss' theorem,

$$E = -\frac{1}{T}\int_S U_i\pi_{ij}n_j\,dS + \frac{1}{T}\int_V v_i\frac{\partial \pi_{ij}}{\partial x_j}\,dV \qquad (5.7.4)$$

The surface integration is only taken over the surface of the solid body. The integration over the other surfaces bounding the fluid vanish, since v_i is zero on these surfaces.   The volume integral in Eq. (5.7.4) vanishes at the stationary state because of the equation of motion which reduces to

$$\frac{\partial \pi_{ij}}{\partial x_j} = 0 \qquad (5.7.5)$$

if the inertia terms are negligible.   The drag force (force of fluid on solid body) is given by

$$F_i = -\int_S \pi_{ij}n_j\,dS \qquad (5.7.6)$$

or

$$E = \frac{1}{T}\,F_iU_i \qquad (5.7.7)$$

Thus the inner product of the drag force and the velocity of the solid body divided by the temperature is identically the rate of entropy production.   It is interesting to note that a solid body which is constrained to move at a certain velocity U_i, relative to the fluid, should always orient itself so that the drag force is a minimum.   Thus a weather vane points in the direction of the wind, since this is configuration of minimum drag.   On the other hand, a motion for which the drag force is fixed, such as a body falling in gravitational field, gives an orientation of the body so that the required drag is attained at the lowest velocity.   A feather falls flat rather than turning its sharp edge when dropped.   To prove these latter observations one should, in fact, include the possibility of a rotational, as well as a translational, motion of the solid body.   These remarks are of a qualitative nature.   Our aim is to fix limits on the drag force F_i without making extensive calculations based on the equation of motion.   If we take any function $v_i^*(x_j)$ which satisfies the boundary conditions (that is, vanishes at infinity or on walls of the container and is U_i at solid surface) and the continuity equation, then

$$E^* \geq E = \frac{1}{T} F_i U_i \qquad (5.7.8)$$

where E^* is the approximate entropy production computed using $v_i^*(x_j)$ in the following way

$$d_{ij}^* = \frac{1}{2}\left(\frac{\partial v_i^*}{\partial x_j} + \frac{\partial v_j^*}{\partial x_i}\right) \qquad (5.7.9)$$

and

$$\tau_{ij}^* = -2\mu d_{ij}^* \qquad (5.7.10)$$

Equation (5.7.9) is simply the definition of the strain-rate tensor (Chap. 4.2) and Eq. (5.7.10) defines the viscosity (Chap. 4.2) of a Newtonian fluid.   Substituting Eqs. (5.7.9) and (5.7.10) into Eq. (5.7.2) gives an approximation of the entropy production, E^*.   Since the true entropy production E is a minimum, it must be less than or equal to E^*.   Thus Eq. (5.7.8) gives us our upper limit on the drag force.   (Actually, to obtain the force, we must note that U_i and F_i are parallel in stationary state.)

Before illustrating the application of Eq. (5.7.8), let us find a lower limit. Consider the following obvious inequality:

$$(d_{ij}' - d_{ij})(d_{ij}' - d_{ij}) \geq 0 \qquad (5.7.11)$$

Rearranging,

$$d_{ij}' d_{ij}' - 2d_{ij} d_{ij}' \geq -d_{ij} d_{ij} \qquad (5.7.12)$$

Multiplying both sides by $-2\mu/T$ ($T > 0$, $\mu > 0$),

$$\frac{\tau_{ij}' d_{ij}'}{T} - \frac{2d_{ij}\tau_{ij}'}{T} \leq -\frac{\tau_{ij} d_{ij}}{T} \qquad (5.7.13)$$

This expression is valid without any restrictions other than the definition of the Newtonian viscosity.   However, we should like to restrict our attention to the stresses π_{ij}' which satisfy the equation of motion (i.e., $\partial \pi_{ij}/\partial x_j = 0$) and are symmetric but are not necessarily derivable from a velocity field and, hence, are not necessarily the true stresses.   Let d_{ij}' in Eq. (5.7.13) be computed from Eq. (5.7.10).   Moreover, identify τ_{ij}, π_{ij}, and d_{ij} as the true solutions.   Since Eq. (5.7.13) applies at each point in the fluid,

$$\frac{1}{T}\int_V \tau_{ij}' d_{ij}' \, dV - 2\frac{1}{T}\int_V d_{ij}\pi_{ij}' \, dV \leq E \qquad (5.7.14)$$

Remembering that d_{ij} is the true solution and using Gauss' theorem, we can rearrange this expression into the form

$$-E' + \frac{2F_i' U_i}{T} \leq E \tag{5.7.15}$$

which yields an upper limit on the drag. It is interesting to note that in Chap. 4.2, we developed bounds on the volumetric flow rate of a Newtonian fluid passing through a duct. The lower bound was associated with a function satisfying the boundary conditions and the upper limit with a function satisfying the differential equation. This situation will recur in Chap. 6.3, in which reciprocal variational principles will be discussed further.

Let us apply our limits to the translated motion of a sphere in an infinite fluid.

EXAMPLE 5.7.1: THE STOKES PROBLEM   Let us consider the drag on a slowly translated sphere in an infinite fluid. The coordinate system most convenient for these calculations is spherical polar coordinates relative to the center of the sphere and its direction of motion (see Fig. 5.7.1). The components of velocity on the surface of the translated sphere are

$$\left. \begin{array}{l} U_r = U \cos \theta \\[2mm] U_\theta = -U \sin \theta \end{array} \right\} \quad \text{at} \quad r = a \tag{5.7.16}$$

where a is the radius of the sphere. Let us first select appropriate velocity trial functions which vanish as r goes to infinity and reduces to Eq. (5.7.16) at $r = a$. Furthermore, the trial function must satisfy the continuity equation, which in spherical polar coordinates can be written as[2]

$$\frac{1}{r^2} \frac{\partial}{\partial r} r^2 v_r + \frac{1}{r \sin \theta} \frac{\partial}{\partial \theta} v_\theta \sin \theta = 0 \tag{5.7.17}$$

A simple set of trial functions is

$$v_r^* = U \left(\frac{2a}{r} - \frac{a^2}{r^2} \right) \cos \theta$$

$$v_\theta^* = -U \frac{a \sin \theta}{r} \tag{5.7.18}$$

In spherical polar coordinates

$$E^* = \frac{1}{T} \int_a^\infty \int_0^\pi 2\mu [(d_{rr}^*)^2 + 2(d_{r\theta}^*)^2 + (d_{\theta\theta})^2 + (d_{\phi\phi})^2] 2\pi r^2 \sin \theta \, dr \, d\theta \tag{5.7.19}$$

[2] R. B. Bird, W. E. Stewart, and E. N. Lightfoot, "Transport Phenomena," pp. 83–91, John Wiley & Sons, Inc., New York, 1960.

where[2]

$$d_{rr}^* = \frac{\partial v_r^*}{\partial r} = U\left(-\frac{2a}{r^2} + \frac{2a^2}{r^3}\right)\cos\theta$$

$$d_{r\theta}^* = \frac{1}{2}\left(r\frac{\partial}{\partial r}\frac{v_\theta^*}{r} + \frac{1}{r}\frac{\partial v_r^*}{\partial\theta}\right) = +U\frac{1}{2}\frac{a^2}{r^3}\sin\theta$$

$$d_{\theta\theta}^* = \frac{1}{r}\frac{\partial v_\theta^*}{\partial\theta} + \frac{v_r^*}{r} = +U\left(\frac{a}{r^2} - \frac{a^2}{r^3}\right)\cos\theta$$

$$d_{\phi\phi}^* = \frac{v_r^*}{r} + \frac{v_\theta^*\cot\theta}{r} = U\left(\frac{a}{r^2} - \frac{a^2}{r^3}\right)\cos\theta†$$

Substituting these approximate strain rates into Eq. (5.7.19) and integrating,

$$E^* = \frac{1}{T}\frac{56}{9}\pi\mu a U^2 \tag{5.7.20}$$

To find a lower limit, we must select a set of stresses satisfying the equation of motion, but not necessarily derivable from a velocity. In spherical polar coordinates, the relevant equations of motion are[2]

r component $$0 = -\frac{\partial p}{\partial r} - \left(\frac{1}{r^2}\frac{\partial}{\partial r}r^2\tau_{rr} + \frac{1}{r\sin\theta}\frac{\partial}{\partial\theta}\tau_{r\theta}\sin\theta\right.$$

$$\left. -\frac{\tau_{\theta\theta} + \tau_{\phi\phi}}{r}\right) \tag{5.7.21}$$

θ component $$0 = -\frac{1}{r}\frac{\partial p}{\partial\theta} - \left(\frac{1}{r^2}\frac{\partial}{\partial r}r^2\tau_{r\theta} + \frac{1}{r\sin\theta}\frac{\partial}{\partial\theta}\tau_{\theta\theta}\sin\theta\right.$$

$$\left. +\frac{\tau_{r\theta}}{r} - \frac{\cot\theta}{r}\tau_{\phi\phi}\right) \tag{5.7.22}$$

A few simple calculations will show that we cannot satisfy these equations with functions which are linear in sine and cosine of θ if $\tau_{\theta\theta}$ or $\tau_{\phi\phi}$ exists. Therefore, we arbitrarily set both $\tau_{\phi\phi}$ and $\tau_{\theta\theta} \equiv 0$, our only justification being that the computations are simplified. Then we set

$$p' = g(r)\cos\theta \tag{5.7.23a}$$

$$\tau_{r\theta}' = h(r)\sin\theta \tag{5.7.23b}$$

$$\tau_{rr}' = l(r)\cos\theta \tag{5.7.23c}$$

† The ϕ component of velocity is assumed here to be zero as are all changes with respect to ϕ.

since functions of these forms will satisfy the θ dependence in Eqs. (5.7.21) and (5.7.23). Again, no physical considerations were applied; mathematical convenience is the governing condition. Equations (5.7.21) and (5.7.22) now have the appearance

$$\frac{dg}{dr} + \frac{1}{r^2}\frac{d}{dr}r^2 l + \frac{2}{r}h = 0 \qquad (5.7.21a)$$

and

$$\frac{1}{r}g - \frac{1}{r^2}\frac{d}{dr}r^2 h - \frac{1}{r}h = 0 \qquad (5.7.22a)$$

We have three unknown functions and two equations. Let us select one function arbitrarily. The others then follow. Choose

$$l = \frac{A}{r^3} \qquad (5.7.24)$$

where A is a constant. Then we can solve Eqs. (5.7.21a) and (5.7.22a) simultaneously for $h(r)$ and $g(r)$. It is not difficult to verify that

$$g = \frac{B}{r^2} \qquad (5.7.25)$$

and

$$h = \frac{B}{r^2} + \frac{A}{2r^3} \qquad (5.7.26)$$

We will choose the constants A and B such that the best possible bound based on Eqs. (5.7.23) is found. There are two terms to be evaluated in Eq. (5.7.15). The quantity $F_i' U_i$ is found by integrating the forces over the surface as noted in Eq. (5.7.6). Thus

$$F_i' U_i = U\left(2\pi\int_0^\pi -p'\,\big|_{r=a}\cos\theta\,a^2\sin\theta\,d\theta - 2\pi\int_0^\pi \tau_{rr}'\,\big|_{r=a}\cos\theta\,a^2\sin\theta\,d\theta \right.$$
$$\left. + 2\pi\int_0^\pi \tau_{r\theta}'\,\big|_{r=a}\sin\theta\,a^2\sin\theta\,d\theta\right)$$

Substituting the approximations for p', τ_{rr}', and $\tau_{r\theta}'$ and integrating yields

$$\frac{1}{T}F_i' U_i' = a^2\frac{U(2\pi)}{T}\left[-\frac{2}{3}g(a) - \frac{2}{3}l(a) + \frac{4}{3}h(a)\right]$$

or

$$\frac{1}{T}F_i' U_i' = \frac{4\pi U B}{3T} \qquad (5.7.27)$$

The second term in Eq. (5.7.15) to be evaluated is given by

$$-E' = + \frac{1}{T} \int_V \tau'_{ij} d'_{ij} dV = - \frac{1}{2\mu} \frac{1}{T} \int_V \tau'_{ij} \tau'_{ij} dV$$

or

$$-E' = - \frac{\pi}{\mu T} \int_a^\infty \int_0^\pi [l^2(r) \cos^2 \theta + 2h^2(r) \sin^2 \theta] r^2 \sin \theta \, d\theta \, dr \qquad (5.7.28)$$

Using the values of l and h specified by Eq. (5.7.24) and (5.7.26),

$$-E' = - \frac{\pi}{\mu T} \frac{1}{a^3} \left(\frac{4}{9} A^2 + \frac{4}{3} aAB + \frac{8}{3} a^2 B^2 \right) \qquad (5.7.29)$$

Thus the lower bound is

$$- \frac{1}{T} \frac{\pi}{\mu} \frac{1}{a^3} \left(\frac{4}{9} A^2 + \frac{4}{3} aAB + \frac{8}{3} a^2 B^2 \right) + \frac{8\pi UB}{3T}$$

Select A and B such that this limit is as large as possible. We choose

$$A = -\tfrac{6}{5} a^2 \mu U$$

and

$$B = \tfrac{4}{5} a \mu U$$

giving

$$\frac{16}{15} \frac{\pi \mu U^2 a}{T} \le E \le \frac{56}{6} \frac{\pi \mu a U^2}{T} \qquad (5.7.30)$$

These bounds are not close. The lower bound has a numerical coefficient of roughly 1 and the upper is slightly greater than 9. The true answer is 6. We could improve the lower bound by using a different set of trial functions. For example

$$\tau'_{rr} = \left(\frac{A}{r^3} + \frac{C}{r^2} \right) \sin \theta$$

$$\tau'_{r\theta} = \left(\frac{B}{r^2} + \frac{A}{2r^3} \right) \sin \theta$$

$$p' = \frac{B}{r^2} \cos \theta$$

represents a valid set of trial functions and gives a lower bound of $2\pi\mu U^2 a/T$, which narrows the limits somewhat. Assuming more complicated trial functions (in the sense of having more adjustable parameters) will, of course, provide even better bounds.

One can also prove certain theorems comparing the drag forces for two different systems. For example, suppose that we have two solid bodies, one of which has a shape such that it can be completely contained within the other (that is, the body enclosed by surface S_2 can be enclosed by S_1). If these two bodies are translated in the same system at the same velocity, then

$$F_1 \geq F_2 \tag{5.7.31}$$

The proof is not difficult. We know that the true velocity distribution associated with the translation of body 1 is an admissible trial function for v_i^* in the system containing body 2 provided that we assume that the velocity of the fluid between $S_1 - S_2$ is U_i. This trial function gives, from Eq. (5.7.8),

$$E^* > E_2 \tag{5.7.32}$$

Since the entropy production vanishes between $S_1 - S_2$ where we have a constant velocity U_i, the entropy production denoted by E^* must be

$$E^* \equiv E_1 \tag{5.7.33}$$

Since $E_1 = F_1 U/T$ and $E_2 = F_2 U/T$, we have a proof of Eq. (5.7.31). Note that one must have the steady-state and a drag force directed along U_i for the proof to be valid.

EXAMPLE 5.7.2: DRAG ON AN OBLATE SPHEROID   Estimate the drag on an oblate spheroid whose major axis is $2a$ and minor axis is $\sqrt{2a}$. This body can be contained with a sphere of radius a and can contain a sphere having a radius $a/\sqrt{2}$. Therefore the drag must be bounded as follows:

$$\frac{6\pi a\mu U}{\sqrt{2}} < F < 6\pi a\mu V \tag{5.7.34}$$

Thus

$$F \cong 3 \frac{1 + \sqrt{2}}{\sqrt{2}} \pi a\mu U \pm 3 \frac{\sqrt{2 - 1}}{\sqrt{2}} \pi a\mu U$$

or

$$F \cong 5.12\pi a\mu U \pm 0.89\pi a\mu V$$

Our answer is certainly correct to within 20 percent.   Lamb[3] gives the drag on the oblate spheroid of the shape described here as

$$F = 4\sqrt{2}\pi\mu aV \cong 5.67\pi\mu aU \tag{5.7.35}$$

PROBLEM 5.7.1   Prove that the drag on a body in slow translated motion tends to be increased by the presence of a second fixed body S_2.

PROBLEM 5.7.2   Prove that the drag on a given body in slow translational motion through a fluid in a rigid stationary container is greater than or equal to the drag on the same body moving at the same velocity through any other container which will completely enclose the first.

[3] H. Lamb, "Hydrodynamics," 6th ed., secs. 338, 339, and 344, Cambridge University Press, London, 1953.

CHAPTER 6
OTHER METHODS OF REPRESENTING CONTINUUM SYSTEMS

6.1 INTRODUCTION Thus far in our studies of continuum systems, we have concentrated our attention on variational principles for the stationary state which are related, or closely related, to the rate of entropy production. In this context we sought to define those processes which are governed by the principle of minimum entropy production and, by using the concept of a local potential, to define a generalized dissipation function so that a far larger class of systems would be included. In this chapter we shall consider other variational approaches to the same problem without imposing the restrictions.

The Galerkin method will be discussed first. Although this method does not stem from a variational formulation, it yields results which are closely related to those found using variational principles. Moreover, this method is widely used in determining approximate solutions. Because of this range of application and its relationship to variational calculations, the Galerkin method is discussed here. However, it should be noted that many methods of approximation have been omitted because they are not applications of the variational calculus. As noted in previous chapters, the most notable omission in the broad area of approximations is the method of finite differences.

The last two sections of this chapter are devoted to a discussion of various methods of formulating certain transport problems in variational terms.

6.2 THE GALERKIN METHOD

This text would not be complete if the Galerkin method of approximation were omitted, since this important technique is closely related to the Ritz method. The Galerkin method can be described as follows.[1,2] Suppose that a solution of the equation

$$L\{u\} = 0 \qquad (6.2.1)$$

is required, where u is a function of position satisfying homogeneous boundary conditions and L is a differential operator. For convenience, imagine u to depend on two independent variables x and y which define a

[1] L. Collatz, "The Numerical Treatment of Differential Equations," 3d ed., pp. 31, 413, Springer-Verlag OHG, Berlin, 1960.

[2] L. V. Kantorovich and V. I. Krylov, "Approximate Methods of Higher Analysis," p. 258–262, Interscience Publishers, Inc., New York, 1958.

point in a planar region A bounded by a curve Γ.   The function u is approximated by a trial function having the form

$$\tilde{u} = \sum_{i=1}^{N} C_i v_i(x,y) \tag{6.2.2}$$

as in the Ritz method (see Chap. 3.2).   The functions $v_i(x,y)$ have been selected so that each member of the set $\{i = 1, 2, \ldots, N\}$ satisfies the homogeneous boundary conditions.   Thus Eq. (6.2.2) satisfies the boundary conditions for all values of C_i.   Furthermore, if possible, the functions v_i should be members of a larger class of functions which is complete in the sense that any arbitrary continuous function can be represented by a linear combination of this set in the region A.   The constants C_i are undetermined. Certainly, if $L\{\tilde{u}\} = 0$ for a certain set of values, then we have an exact solution because the approximation would satisfy both the differential equation and the boundary conditions.   However, if $\tilde{u}$ does not satisfy Eq. (6.2.1) at every point in A for any choice of the C_i, how can we select these parameters such that a good approximation to the true solution is achieved?   The Galerkin method requires that the constants be selected so that the following N equations (algebraic) be satisfied.

$$\int_A L\{u\} v_i \, dx \, dy = 0 \qquad i = 1, 2, \ldots, N \tag{6.2.3}$$

This method is applicable to both linear and nonlinear problems even when a classical variational principle does not exist.   However, if a variational principle does exist, it will be shown (in subsequent paragraphs) that the Galerkin method is closely related to the Ritz method.   In fact, in some cases, the two methods produce identical results.

Before developing this comparison between the Galerkin and Ritz methods, let us consider an example which should illustrate the essential aspects of the method.

EXAMPLE 6.2.1   Let

$$L\{u\} \equiv \frac{\partial^2 u}{\partial x^2} + \frac{\partial^2 u}{\partial y^2} - (1 - x^2) = 0 \tag{6.2.4}$$

subject to the boundary conditions

$$u = 0 \qquad \text{on } \Gamma \tag{6.2.5}$$

where Γ is the boundary of the square region defined by $x = \pm 1$ and $y = \pm 1$.   This equation could represent several physical problems, as for example, the conduction of heat in a rectangular region with internal generation.   Here the boundaries would be cooled to zero temperature.

Let us consider an approximation of the form

$$\tilde{u} = C_1(1 - x^2)(1 - y^2) + C_2(1 - x^2)(1 - y^2)x^2 \tag{6.2.6}$$

We can identify v_1 and v_2 as the functional coefficients of C_1 and C_2, respectively. Note that both v_1 and v_2 satisfy the homogeneous boundary condition. Following the prescription set forth by Galerkin, one first substitutes the trial function into the differential equation. In this case we find

$$L\{\tilde{u}\} = -2(1 - y^2)(C_1 - C_2 + 6C_2x^2)$$
$$-2(C_1 + C_2x^2 - C_1x^2 - C_2x^4) - (1 - x^2) \tag{6.2.7}$$

An examination of this result shows clearly that there do not exist two values of C_1 and C_2 which will cause Eq. (6.2.7) to vanish for all x and y. Thus the trial function cannot be an exact solution. Thus C_1 and C_2 are to be determined as indicated by Eq. (6.2.3). Imposing this condition gives the following two equations which fix C_1 and C_2:

$$\int_{-1}^{1}\int L\{\tilde{u}\}(1 - x^2)(1 - y^2)\, dx\, dy = 0 \tag{6.2.8a}$$

and

$$\int_{-1}^{1}\int L\{\tilde{u}\}(1 - x^2)(1 - y^2)x^2\, dx\, dy = 0 \tag{6.2.8b}$$

If we substitute Eq. (6.2.7) into Eqs. (6.2.8) and integrate we find the following two algebraic equations.

$$4C_1 + {}^{24}\!/_{35}C_2 = -1 \tag{6.2.9a}$$

and

$${}^{24}\!/_{5}C_1 + {}^{76}\!/_{15}C_2 = -1 \tag{6.2.9b}$$

Solving,

$$C_1 = \frac{-575}{2228} \quad \text{and} \quad C_2 = \frac{105}{2228}$$

These constants, together with Eq. (6.2.6), give us an approximation to the solution of the original problem. This approximation can be checked in several ways. First of all, in this case an exact solution can be found† and

† This exact solution is a double Fourier series

$$u = \sum_{m,n=0}^{\infty} A_{mn} \cos \frac{2m + 1}{2} \pi x \cos \frac{2n + 1}{2} \pi y$$

where

$$A_{mn} = \frac{512(-1)^{m+n+1}}{\pi^6(2m + 1)^3(2n + 1)[(2m + 1)^2 + (2n + 1)^2]}$$

compared with the approximation. We shall not present this comparison, since our primary purpose is to develop the rudiments of the Galerkin method.

However, before proceeding with the further discussion of the Galerkin method, it is perhaps of some interest to note that bounds can be developed for this particular problem. Indeed our work in Sec. 3.2 already provides the answer. For if we define w so that

$$L\{w\} = 0 \tag{6.2.10}$$

but w does not necessarily vanish on the boundary ($w = \frac{1}{2}x^2 - \frac{1}{12}x$) is a possible function), then

$$M(w,w) \geq M(u,u) \geq \frac{[M(\tilde{u},w)]^2}{M(\tilde{u},\tilde{u})} \tag{6.2.11}$$

where

$$M(\tilde{u},w) = \int_{-1}^{1}\int \left(\frac{\partial \tilde{u}}{\partial x}\frac{\partial w}{\partial x} + \frac{\partial \tilde{u}}{\partial y}\frac{\partial w}{\partial y}\right) dx\, dy$$

The development of these limits is discussed in Sec. 3.2 and will not be pursued here.

In the preceding example, we described what Collatz[3] calls the interior method; that is, the trial function satisfies the boundary conditions but not the differential equation. A boundary method using the Galerkin technique can also be applied. Here one develops an approximation which satisfies the differential equation but not the boundary conditions. Represent the approximate solution as

$$\tilde{u} = w(x,y) + \sum_{i=1}^{N} C_i v_i(x,y) \tag{6.2.12}$$

where $w(x,y)$ is defined by Eq. (6.2.10) and the v_i satisfy the homogeneous part of the operator. With this construction, $\tilde{u}$ will satisfy the differential equation for all values of C_i. Suppose that the boundary conditions are represented as

$$G(u) = 0 \quad \text{on } \Gamma \tag{6.2.13}$$

and in general

$$G(\tilde{u}) \neq 0 \quad \text{on } \Gamma$$

[3] L. Collatz, "The Numerical Treatment of Differential Equations," 3d ed., p. 28, Springer-Verlag OHG, Berlin, 1960.

Let us select the parameters so that

$$\int_\Gamma G(\tilde{u})v_i \, ds = 0 \qquad \text{for} \qquad i = 1, 2, \ldots, N \tag{6.2.14}$$

This is the boundary method.

EXAMPLE 6.2.2   Let us consider the problem of Example 2.1 using the boundary method.   Consider a single-parameter approximation of the form:

$$\tilde{u} = \tfrac{1}{2}x^2 - \tfrac{1}{12}x^4 + C_1(x^4 - 6x^2y^2 + y^4) \tag{6.2.15}$$

The functional coefficient of C_1 satisfies the Laplace equation; that is,

$$\frac{\partial^2 v_1}{\partial x^2} + \frac{\partial^2 v_1}{\partial y^2} = 0 \tag{6.2.16}$$

A sequence of such functions can be generated by noting that both the ψ and η defined by the equation

$$\psi + i\eta = (x + iy)^n \qquad \text{where} \qquad i = \sqrt{-1} \tag{6.2.17}$$

satisfy Eq. (6.2.16).   Indeed the coefficient of C_1 shown in Eq. (6.2.15) is ψ for $n = 4$.   Since our problem is symmetric in both x and y [$u(-x,y) = u(x,y)$ and $u(x,-y) = u(x,y)$], we have not included the odd powers in our expansion.   Equation (6.2.14) requires

$$\int_{-1}^{1} (\tilde{u}v_1)_{x=-1} \, dy + \int_{-1}^{1} (\tilde{u}v_1)_{y=1} \, dx - \int_{1}^{-1} (\tilde{u}v_1)_{x=1} \, dy - \int_{1}^{-1} (\tilde{u}v_1)_{y=-1} \, dx = 0 \tag{6.2.18}$$

Noting that

$$(\tilde{u}v_1)_{y=1} = (\tilde{u}v_1)_{y=-1}$$

and

$$(\tilde{u}v_1)_{x=1} = (\tilde{u}v_1)_{x=-1}$$

Equation (6.2.18) becomes

$$4\int_0^1 [\tfrac{5}{12} + C_1(1 - 6y^2 + y^4)](1 - 6y^2 + y^4) \, dy + 4\int_0^1 [\tfrac{1}{2}x^2 - \tfrac{1}{12}x^4$$
$$+ C_1(1 - 6x^2 + x^4)](1 - 6x^2 + x^4) \, dx = 0 \tag{6.2.19}$$

Integrating and solving for C_1 yields

$$C_1 = \frac{307}{2832} \tag{6.2.20}$$

Equation (6.2.19) is the key to the boundary calculation, for here we see that the line integration around the perimeter of the region (in this case, a square) is being made to vanish.   This condition ultimately yields a value for the free parameter C_1.   Clearly, the boundary method can be easily extended to include the adjustment of additional free parameters.

PROBLEM 6.2.1   Improve the approximation to the mathematical problem posed in Example 6.2.2 by using the two-parameter approximation

$$\tilde{u} = \tfrac{1}{2}x^2 - \tfrac{1}{12}x^4 + C_1 v_1 + C_2 v_2 \tag{6.2.21}$$

where

$$v_1 = \text{Re}\,(x + iy)^4 \tag{6.2.22}$$

and

$$v_2 = \text{Re}\,(x + iy)^6 \tag{6.2.23}$$

Since $\tilde{u}$ satisfies the differential operator in the region of interest, one would use the boundary method to find the improved solution.

PROBLEM 6.2.2   Some indication of the validity of the approximate solution can be found by computing both upper and lower bounds as proposed by Eq. (6.2.11). We note that the function w appearing in this equation corresponds to a trial function suitable for use with the boundary method. For example, Eq. (6.2.19) would certainly be an appropriate choice for a w function. The $\tilde{u}$ appearing in this equation [Eq. (6.2.11)] is restricted so that the boundary condition is satisfied. Thus Eq. (6.2.6) would be an acceptable form. Using Eqs. (6.2.6) and (6.2.15) in place of the $\tilde{u}$ and w, respectively, find an upper and lower bound for $M(u,u)$.

Collatz[3] also defines a mixed method in which neither the boundary condition nor the differential operator is satisfied by the trial function. Snyder, Spriggs, and Stewart[4] have discussed this situation relative to application of the Galerkin method. These authors have noted that an overdetermined system results in this case. For example, suppose the trial function depended on N free parameters. Since neither the differential equation nor the boundary conditions are satisfied, the set of N constants determined by Eq. (6.2.3) is, in general, different from that determined from Eq. (6.2.14). Clearly, we cannot satisfy *both* sets of N equations with just N free parameters at our disposal. Snyder et al. suggest that the choice of which N of the $2N$ equations that are selected to determine the free parameters is somewhat arbitrary as long as the equations are independent. Although this situation may exist when the Galerkin method is used for mixed problems, it should be noted here that the variational principles developed in Chap. 4 have the boundary conditions embedded in the statement of the problem. One has, in the general case of a stationary state, a *sum* of volumetric and surface terms which gives the appropriate boundary conditions as *natural boundary conditions* if the dependent variable is not fixed on the boundary. If a trial

[4] L. J. Snyder, T. W. Spriggs, and W. E. Stewart, "Solution of the Equations of Change by Galerkin's Method," *J. Am. Inst. Chem. Engrs.*, vol. 10, p. 535, 1964.

function is substituted into the variational principle, then the condition that the functional be stationary leads to N equations found by requiring that the derivatives of the functional with respect to the free parameters $C_i \, (i = 1, 2, \ldots, N)$ vanish. These N equations contain a sum of surface and volume integrals which arise naturally from the variational principle. Thus there is no ambiguity about the means of selecting the best (best in the sense of yielding a stationary functional) values for our free parameters. The variational principles present a unified "picture" of the problem in the sense that the boundary conditions are part of the functional. Although it will be seen in the following paragraphs that the Galerkin method is closely associated with a variational principle when such exists, it should be remembered that associating the boundary conditions directly to the statement of the problem is advantageous.

To see the relationship between the Galerkin method and variational principles whether classical or based on the concept of the local potential, let us consider an example. The remarks to be presented here can be extended to more general situations in a straightforward way. Suppose that we wish to solve the equation

$$L\{u\} = 0 \qquad \text{in } A \tag{6.2.24}$$

with

$$u = 0 \qquad \text{or } \Gamma \tag{6.2.25}$$

where, as before, Γ is the curve bounding A. Suppose that this same system of equations is the system of Euler-Lagrange equations which define u if the functional

$$E^*(u, u^0) = \int_A \mathcal{L}(u, u_x, u_y, u^0, u_x{}^0, u_y{}^0) \, dA \tag{6.2.26}$$

is to be stationary. Here u^0 is not to be varied, but must satisfy the auxiliary condition

$$u^0 = u \tag{6.2.27}$$

If we form the variation of E^*, then after an integration by parts and assuming that the function is specified on the boundary

$$\delta E^* = \int_A \left(\frac{\partial \mathcal{L}}{\partial u} - \frac{\partial}{\partial x} \frac{\partial \mathcal{L}}{\partial u_x} - \frac{\partial}{\partial y} \frac{\partial \mathcal{L}}{\partial u_y} \right) \delta u \, dA \tag{6.2.28}$$

Setting $u^0 = u$, we note that the integrand must vanish everywhere; therefore

$$\frac{\partial \mathcal{L}}{\partial u} - \frac{\partial}{\partial x} \frac{\partial \mathcal{L}}{\partial u_x} - \frac{\partial}{\partial y} \frac{\partial \mathcal{L}}{\partial u_y} = W(u)L\{u\} = 0 \tag{6.2.29}$$

where $\dagger W(u)$ is a weighting function which is different from zero. This relationship stems from the assumption made at the onset equating Eq. (6.2.24) to the Euler-Lagrange equation.

Let us now develop an approximate solution by the trial function

$$\tilde{u} = \sum_{i=1}^{N} C_i v_i(x,y) \tag{6.2.30}$$

where the v_i vanish on Γ. If u^0 also appears in the integrand, let us use the self-consistent approximation (see Chap. 5.2)

$$\tilde{u}^0 = \sum_{i=1}^{N} C_i{}^0 v_i(x,y) \tag{6.2.31}$$

Treating the problem in the way prescribed in Chap. 5, we find that

$$\frac{\partial E^*}{\partial C_j} = \int_A \left(\frac{\partial \mathscr{L}}{\partial \tilde{u}} - \frac{\partial}{\partial x} \frac{\partial \mathscr{L}}{\partial \tilde{u}_x} - \frac{\partial}{\partial y} \frac{\partial \mathscr{L}}{\partial \tilde{u}_y} \right) v_j(x,y) \, dA \tag{6.2.32}$$

Using the relationship which exists between the differential equation and the Euler-Lagrange equation if these two modes of expression represent the same physical problem, we find

$$\frac{\partial E^*}{\partial C_j} = \int_A W(\tilde{u}) L\{\tilde{u}\} v_j \, dA = 0 \qquad j = 1, 2, \ldots, N \tag{6.2.33}$$

Comparing this equation with Eq. (6.2.3), we see that the two expressions are the same except for the weighting factor. Thus the relationship between the approximations stemming from the variational principle and those produced by the Galerkin method is clearly defined.

Before completing this section, we should note two things. First of all, if one broadens his definition of the Galerkin method, it can be made to include some of the other calculations which we have discussed in Chap. 5. However, we shall not consider any examples here, since the general techniques which have been established in Chap. 4 include the Galerkin technique with the added advantage of treating the boundary conditions directly. Furthermore, in those cases where a classical variational principle exists, at least one, and sometimes two, bounds can be established to measure the quality of the solution. An excellent discussion of the method of weighted residuals and its relation to the Galerkin method has been published.[5]

† This weighting function can depend on u and its derivatives as well as on both x and y explicitly.

[5] B. A. Finlayson and L. E. Scriven, "The Method of Weighted Residuals and Its Relation to Certain Variational Principles for Analysis of Transport Process," *Chem. Engr. Sci.*, vol. 20, p. 395, 1965.

6.3 VARIATIONAL PRINCIPLES FOR CREEPING FLOW OF NON-NEWTONIAN FLUIDS

In this section, we summarize, in a somewhat different form, the interesting and important results which have been reported by Johnson.[1]   Our attention will be focused on fluids which have a stress-strain rate relationship of the form

$$\tau_{ij} = \frac{\partial \Gamma(d_{km})}{\partial d_{ij}} \tag{6.3.1}$$

where τ_{ij} are the components of the reduced stress tensor as defined in Sec. 4.2, and the d_{ij} are the components of the deformation rate tensor

$$d_{ij} = \frac{1}{2}\left(\frac{\partial v_i}{\partial x_j} + \frac{\partial v_j}{\partial x_i}\right) \tag{6.3.2}$$

(see also Sec. 4.6).   It should be noted that Eq. (6.3.1) is not so restrictive as to leave the following analysis devoid of any practical interest.   Indeed, it is not difficult to show that

$$\Gamma = -\mu d_{km}d_{km} \tag{6.3.3}$$

for Newtonian fluids with μ being the Newtonian viscosity.   This can be seen as follows.   Since

$$\frac{\partial d_{km}}{\partial d_{ij}} = \delta_{ki}\delta_{jm} \tag{6.3.4}†$$

$$\frac{\partial}{\partial d_{ij}}(-\mu d_{km}d_{km}) = -2\mu d_{ij} = \tau_{ij}$$

giving the Newtonian relationship between stress and rate of deformation.   Moreover,

$$\Gamma = -\int_0^{\mathrm{II}} \eta(\lambda)\, d\lambda \tag{6.3.5}$$

gives[2] the constitutive equation for the so-called generalized Newtonian fluid

$$\tau_{ij} = -2\eta(\mathrm{II})\, d_{ij} \tag{6.3.6}$$

Here, as in Sec. 4.6 [see especially Eq. (6.6.5)], II represents the second invariance of the deformation tensor.   Recall that

$$\mathrm{II} = d_{ij}d_{ij}$$

---

[1] W. W. Johnson, Jr., "Some Variational Theorems for Non-Newtonian Flow," *Phys. of Fluids*, vol. 3, p. 871, 1960.

† $\delta_{ki} = 0$ if $i \neq k$ and $\delta_{ki} = 1$ if $i = k$.

[2] R. B. Bird, "New Variational Principle for Incompressible Non-Newtonian Flow," *Phys. of Fluids*, vol. 3, p. 539, 1960.

The analysis to follow is restricted to steady incompressible flow

$$\frac{\partial v_i}{\partial x_i} = 0 \tag{6.3.7}$$

and to situations in which the inertia terms can be neglected giving the following equation of motion

$$-\frac{\partial \tau_{ij}}{\partial x_j} + \rho F_i - \frac{\partial p}{\partial x_i} = 0 \tag{6.3.8}$$

It should be noted that the inertia terms have yet to be included in a classical variational principle. In our previous work, we have considered inertial effects within the framework of the local potential. In the next section a second method of treating the inertia terms will be presented.

To further define our system, let us study a volume of fluid V which is enclosed by stationary, nonoverlapping surfaces S_U and S_T distinguished by the fact that different boundary conditions apply on each surface as follows:

$$v_i = U_i \qquad \text{on } S_U \tag{6.3.9}$$

and

$$\tau_{ij}n_j + pn_i = T_i \qquad \text{on } S_T \tag{6.3.10}$$

where U_i and T_i are prescribed vector functions on the bounding surfaces S_U, and S_T, respectively. In these equations n_i are the components of the outward-drawn normal.

Consider the functional

$$J = \int_V \left\{ \left[\frac{1}{2}\left(\frac{\partial v_i}{\partial x_j} + \frac{\partial v_j}{\partial x_i} \right) - d_{ij} \right] \tau_{ij} + \rho F_i v_i + \Gamma(d_{km}) \right.$$
$$\left. + p\frac{\partial v_i}{\partial x_i} \right\} dV - \int_{S_T} T_i v_i \, dS \tag{6.3.11}$$

If we impose no admissibility conditions other than assuring the differentiability of the quantities appearing in Eq. (6.3.11), insist that the v_i satisfy Eq. (6.3.9), and note that both the d_{ij} and τ_{ij} are symmetric tensors, we should vary all quantities appearing in Eq. (6.3.11) independently. The variation equation $\delta J = 0$ has Eqs. (6.3.1), (6.3.2), (6.3.7), and (6.3.8) as its Euler-Lagrange equations, and Eq. (6.3.10) appears as a natural boundary condition. This assertion should be checked by the reader. We shall not work through the details here.

It is interesting and, as we shall see, significant, to note that an alternate variational theorem can be proposed provided a function Γ can be found such that

$$d_{ij} = \frac{\partial \Gamma}{\partial \tau_{ij}} \tag{6.3.12}$$

Assuming that such a function exists, we can develop a useful transformation property. Multiply Eq. (6.3.1) by $d(d_{ii})$ and Eq. (6.3.12) by $d(\tau_{ij})$. Add the resultant expressions.

$$\tau_{ij}\, d(d_{ij}) + d_{ij}\, d(\tau_{ij}) = \frac{\partial \Gamma}{\partial \tau_{ij}}\, d(\tau_{ij}) + \frac{\partial \Gamma}{\partial d_{ij}}\, d(d_{ij})$$

or

$$d(\tau_{ij} d_{ij}) = d\Gamma + d\Gamma$$

Apart from a constant, we can write

$$\Gamma - \tau_{ij} d_{ij} = -\Gamma \tag{6.3.13}$$

which is the transformation we sought. Substitute Eq. (6.3.13) into the integrand of Eq. (6.3.11):

$$H = \int_V \left[\frac{1}{2}\left(\frac{\partial v_i}{\partial x_j} + \frac{\partial v_j}{\partial x_i} \right) \tau_{ij} + \rho F_i v_i - \Gamma + p \frac{\partial v_i}{\partial x_i} \right] dV \tag{6.3.14}$$
$$- \int_{S_T} T_i v_i\, ds$$

It is not difficult to show that setting $\delta H = 0$ for all admissible variations gives the Euler-Lagrange equations

$$-\frac{\partial \tau_{ij}}{\partial x_j} + \rho F_i - \frac{\partial p}{\partial x_i} = 0 \tag{6.3.8}$$

$$\frac{1}{2}\left(\frac{\partial v_i}{\partial x_j} + \frac{\partial v_j}{\partial x_i} \right) = \frac{\partial \Gamma}{\partial \tau_{ij}} \tag{6.3.12}$$

$$\frac{\partial v_i}{\partial x_i} = 0 \tag{6.3.7}$$

with the natural boundary condition

$$\tau_{ij} n_j + p n_i = T_i \qquad \text{on } S_T \tag{6.3.10}$$

Thus the necessary conditions for both J and H to be extremals are the same—the equation of motion, the constitutive equation, the continuity equation, and the natural boundary condition on S_T. We shall now prove that in a restricted sense the two variational principles provide an upper and lower bound.

We first want to prove that if the true extremalizing velocities and stress are substituted into the integrands defining J and H, the two functionals become identical. In other words, at the stationary point, J and H both have *the same value*. Examine J first. We find at the stationary point

$$J^* = \int_V (\rho F_i v_i + \Gamma)\, dV - \int_{S_T} T_i v_i\, ds \tag{6.3.15}$$

because both Eqs. (6.3.2) and (6.3.7) must be satisfied by the velocities which extremalize J. On the other hand,† H^* is given by

$$H^* = \int_V (d_{ij}\tau_{ij} + \rho F_i v_i - \Gamma) \, dV - \int_{S_T} T_i v_i \, ds \qquad (6.3.16)$$

H^* can be shown to be identically J^* if we substitute Eq. (6.3.13) into Eq. (6.3.16). Thus, when using trial functions to compute H and J, one will find that these two numbers will approach each other as the trial provides a better and better approximation.

We next would like to examine the possibility of finding H to be a maximum when J is a minimum (or vice versa). Clearly, this would be useful, since we would then have limits to test the quality of our approximations. To investigate the character of the extremal, we must consider the second variation (see Sec. 1.2). It can be shown that

$$\delta^2 J = \int_V \left(\delta\tau_{ij} \frac{\partial}{\partial x_j} \delta v_i - \delta d_{ij} \, \delta\tau_{ij} + \frac{1}{2} \frac{\partial^2 \Gamma}{\partial d_{ij} \, \partial d_{kl}} \delta d_{ij} \, \delta d_{kl} + \delta p \frac{\partial}{\partial x_i} \delta v_i \right) dV \qquad (6.3.17)$$

We now insist that all trial functions for the velocities satisfy Eqs. (6.3.2) and (6.3.7) before they are admitted for testing as possible extremalizing functions. Trial functions satisfying these conditions will be called velocity-conditioned. If we restrict our attention to such functions, then

$$(\delta^2 J)_{\text{v.c.}} = \int_V \frac{1}{2} \frac{\partial^2 \Gamma}{\partial d_{ij} \, \partial d_{kl}} \delta d_{ij} \, \delta d_{kl} \, dV \qquad (6.3.18)‡$$

If the integrand can be shown to be positive (negative) for all velocity-conditioned functions, then we can assert that J is a local minimum (maximum). Before investigating the sign of this integrand in special cases, let us compute $\delta^2 H$. Proceeding as above,

$$\delta^2 H = \int_V \left(\delta\tau_{ij} \frac{\partial}{\partial x_j} \delta v_i - \frac{1}{2} \frac{\partial^2 \Gamma}{\partial \tau_{ij} \, \partial \tau_{kl}} \delta\tau_{ij} \, \delta\tau_{kl} + \delta p \frac{\partial}{\partial x_i} \delta v_i \right) dV \qquad (6.3.19)$$

Applying Gauss' theorem,

$$\delta^2 H = \int_V \left(-\frac{\partial}{\partial x_j} \delta\tau_{ij} - \frac{\partial}{\partial x_i} \delta p \right) \delta v_i \, dV - \frac{1}{2} \int_V \frac{\partial^2 \Gamma}{\partial \tau_{ij} \, \partial \tau_{kl}} \delta\tau_{ij} \, \delta\tau_{kl} \, dV$$
$$+ \int_{S_T} (\delta\tau_{ij} n_j \, \delta v_i + n_i \, \delta v_i \, \delta p) \, ds \qquad (6.3.20)$$

---

† The asterisk denotes value at stationary point.

‡ The notation $(\delta^2 J)_{v.c.}$ and $(\delta^2 H)_{s.c.}$ should be read as "second variations restricted to velocity- and stress-conditioned trial functions." This is important because these second variations are not general and depend on the trial function satisfying certain admissibility conditions.

We now define a stress-conditioned test function as one which obeys both Eq. (6.3.8) and Eq. (6.3.10). For stress-conditioned test functions,

$$(\delta^2 H)_{\text{s.c.}} = -\frac{1}{2} \int_V \frac{\partial^2 \Gamma}{\partial \tau_{ij}\, \partial \tau_{kl}}\, \delta\tau_{ij}\, \delta\tau_{kl}\, dV \qquad (6.3.21)\dagger$$

We want to prove that $(\delta^2 H)_{\text{s.c.}} = -(\delta^2 J)_{\text{v.c.}}$. For if this equality is valid, then $(J)_{\text{v.c.}}$ is a maximum when $(H)_{\text{s.c.}}$ is a minimum or vice versa. Then we will have generated a computational scheme whereby one can place upper and lower bounds on J or H (they are equivalent at the true stationary point). The proof is not difficult. The first variation of d_{ij} can be defined using Eq. (6.3.12). Recognizing that variations in d_{ij} give rise to changes in τ_{ij}, we find

$$\delta d_{ij} = \frac{\partial^2 \Gamma}{\partial \tau_{ij}\, \partial \tau_{kl}}\, \delta\tau_{kl} \qquad (6.3.22)$$

Similarly, using Eq. (6.3.1),

$$\delta\tau_{ij} = \frac{\partial^2 \Gamma}{\partial d_{ij}\, \partial d_{kl}}\, \delta d_{kl} \qquad (6.3.23)$$

Substituting both Eqs. (6.3.22) and (6.3.23) into (6.3.21),

$$(\delta^2 H)_{\text{s.c.}} = -\frac{1}{2} \int_V \frac{\partial^2 \Gamma}{\partial d_{ij}\, \partial d_{kl}}\, \delta d_{kl}\, \delta d_{ij}\, dV \qquad (6.3.24)$$

Comparing this result with Eq. (6.3.18) gives

$$-(\delta^2 H)_{\text{s.c.}} = +(\delta^2 J)_{\text{v.c.}} \qquad (6.3.25)$$

Thus if J is a local maximum, then H is a local minimum and we have our bounds. For a Newtonian fluid,

$$\frac{\partial^2 \Gamma}{\partial d_{ij}\, \partial d_{kl}} = -\mu \delta_{ij}\delta_{kl} \qquad (6.3.26)$$

giving

$$(\delta J)_{\text{v.c.}} = -\int_V \mu\, \delta d_{ij}\, \delta d_{ij}\, dV \le 0 \qquad (6.3.27)$$

provided $\mu \ge 0$. In this case J is a local maximum.

The generalized Newtonian fluid yields

$$\frac{\partial^2 \Gamma}{\partial d_{ij}\, \partial d_{kl}} = -4 \frac{\partial \eta}{\partial \text{II}}\, d_{ij}d_{kl} - 2\eta \delta_{ik}\delta_{jl} \qquad (6.3.28)$$

or

$$(\delta^2 J)_{\text{v.c.}} = -\int_V \left[\frac{\partial \eta}{\partial \text{II}}\, (\delta d_{ij}d_{ij})^2 + \eta\, \delta d_{ij}\, \delta d_{ij} \right] dV \qquad (6.3.29)$$

Thus the sufficient conditions for a maximum are

$$\frac{\partial \eta}{\partial \text{II}} > 0 \tag{6.3.30a}†$$

and

$$\eta > 0 \tag{6.3.30b}$$

EXAMPLE 6.3.1   The results developed here are particularly interesting in the case of a Newtonian fluid. We shall see that the bounds are closely related to the limits previously derived (see Sec. 3.2).

Consider flow along the axis of a tube whose generators are parallel to the x_3 axis. The velocity vector has the following components in steady, rectilinear, laminar flow:

$$v_1 = v_2 = 0 \tag{6.3.31}$$
$$v_3 = v_3(x_1, x_2)$$

We want to focus our attention on the volume of fluid bounded by the tube and by two imaginary surfaces ($S_T = S_1$ and S_2) drawn perpendicular to x_3 and located a distance L apart. The tube forms a surface of class S_U, since the velocity must vanish on this surface. The two cross sections S_1 and S_2 are surfaces in class S_T, since we shall specify the stress on these surfaces as follows:

$$\left.\begin{array}{l} T_1 = T_2 = 0 \\ T_3 = -p(0) \end{array}\right\} \quad \text{on } S_1 \text{ at } x_3 = 0 \tag{6.3.32}$$

with

$$\left.\begin{array}{l} T_1 = T_2 = 0 \\ T_3 = p(L) \end{array}\right\} \quad \text{on } S_2 \text{ at } x_3 = L \tag{6.3.33}$$

These give for *velocity-conditioned trial functions*

$$J_{\text{v.c.}} = \int_0^L \int_{S_1} [\rho F_3 v_3 - 2\mu(d_{13}{}^2 + d_{23}{}^2)]\, dx_1\, dx_2\, dx_3 - [p(L)$$
$$- p(0)]\int_{S_1} v_3\, dx_1\, dx_2$$

Since the integrand does not depend on x_3, we can write

$$(J)_{\text{v.c.}} = -\frac{L\mu}{2}\int_{S_1}\left[\left(\frac{\partial v_3}{\partial x_1}\right)^2 + \left(\frac{\partial v_3}{\partial x_2}\right)^2\right] dx_1\, dx_2 - [p(L) - P(0)]$$
$$- \rho F_3]\int_{S_1} v_3\, dx_1\, dx \tag{6.3.34}$$

† For pseudoplastic materials, $\eta(\text{II})$ decreases for increasing strain rates (II), and condition (6.3.30a) would not be satisfied. For this fluid, we would not be able to conclude that J is a local minimum.

The reader will recall that $(J)_{\text{v.c.}}$ is a maximum, and thus any trial function which is velocity-conditioned but not the exact solution of the boundary-value problem will necessarily give a *smaller* value of J than the actual velocity. Thus approximations in $(J)_{\text{v.c.}}$ give lower limits.

The upper limit is provided by $H_{\text{s.c.}}$. For the particular case under consideration

$$H = \int_0^L \int_{S_1} \left(\frac{\partial v_3}{\partial x_1} \tau_{31} + \frac{\partial v_3}{\partial x_2} \tau_{32} + \frac{1}{2\mu} (\tau_{13}^2 + \tau_{23}^2) + \rho F_3 v_3 \right) dx_1\, dx_2\, dx_3$$

$$- [p(L) - p(0)] \int_{S_1} v_3\, dx_1\, dx_2$$

Again noting that the integrand is independent of x_3 and using the fact that v_3 vanishes on the boundary

$$H = L \int_{S_1} \left[v_3 \left(-\frac{\partial \tau_{31}}{\partial x_1} - \frac{\partial \tau_{32}}{\partial x_2} + \rho F_3 \right) + \frac{1}{2\mu} (\tau_{13}^2 + \tau_{23}^2) \right] dx_1\, dx_2$$

$$- [p(L) - p(0)] \int_{S_1} v_3\, dx_1\, dx_2 \qquad (6.3.35)$$

If we impose only stress-conditioned trial functions, then

$$(H)_{\text{s.c.}} = L \int_{S_1} \left[v_3 \frac{\partial p}{\partial x_3} + \frac{1}{2\mu} (\tau_{13}^2 + \tau_{23}^2) \right] dx_1\, dx_2$$

$$- [p(L) - P(0)] \int_{S_1} v_3\, dx_1\, dx_2$$

Since the pressure is a linear function of x_3, this expression reduces to

$$(H)_{\text{s.c.}} = \frac{L}{2\mu} \int_{S_1} (\tau_{23}^2 + \tau_{23}^2)\, dx_1\, dx_2 \qquad (6.3.36)$$

This expression provides our upper bound, since $(H)_{\text{s.c.}}$ is a minimum at the stationary state. These equations have been applied by Stewart[3] to obtain upper and lower bounds for flow in a square duct (see Prob. 6.3.1). In his note, Stewart shows how appropriate trial functions for the stress can be developed. This same problem was discussed in a seemingly different context in Sec. 3.2. Sani[4] has proven that the bounds found in Sec. 3.2 are better than those given in this example. We should note, however, that this example, the discussion found in Sec. 3.2, and Sani's arguments are all applicable to Newtonian flow, whereas the development found in this section applies to a large class of non-Newtonian fluids as well as to Newtonian fluids.

[3] W. E. Stewart, "Application of Reciprocal Variational Principles to Laminar Flow in Uniform Ducts," *J. Am. Inst. Chem. Engrs.*, vol. 8, p. 425, 1962.

[4] R. L. Sani, "Dual Variational Statements Viewed from Function Space," *J. Am. Inst. Chem. Engrs.*, vol. 9, p. 277, 1963.

PROBLEM 6.3.1   Prove that for the case considered in Example 6.3.1

$$H = J = -\tfrac{1}{2}L\left(\frac{\partial p}{\partial x_3} - \rho F_3\right)Q \tag{6.3.37}$$

at the stationary point where Q is the volumetric flow rate defined as

$$Q = \int_{S_1} v_3 \, dx_1 \, dx_2$$

PROBLEM 6.3.2   Use the results of Example 6.3.1 and Prob. 6.3.1 to find limits on the volumetric flow of a Newtonian fluid in a square duct which is of length $2a$ on a side.   If the coordinate system is positioned in the center of the duct, a suitable velocity-conditioned function (satisfying both the continuity equation and the boundary conditions) is

$$v_3(x_1, x_2) = C_1\left[1 - \left(\frac{x_1}{a}\right)^2\right]\left[1 - \left(\frac{x_2}{a}\right)^2\right]$$

where C_1 is a constant to be determined.

As a stress-conditioned trial function, choose

$$\tau_{13} = m\frac{x_1}{2} + \frac{\partial F}{\partial x_2}$$

and

$$\tau_{23} = m\frac{x_2}{2} + \frac{\partial F}{\partial x_1}$$

where

$$F = C_2(x_1{}^3 x_2 - x_2{}^3 x_1)$$

and m is to be selected so that the equation of motion [Eq. (6.3.8)] is satisfied.

How does one select C_1 and C_2?   What is the value of m?   Show the upper and lower limit on the volumetric flow rate and discuss methods of bringing the limits together.

PROBLEM 6.3.3   The variational principles $(H)_{\text{s.c.}}$ and $(J)_{\text{v.c.}}$ would be termed reciprocal if the admissibility conditions of one are the Euler-Lagrange equations of the other and vice versa.   Show that $(H)_{\text{s.c.}}$ and $(J)_{\text{v.c.}}$ are reciprocal variational principles.

6.4   ASSOCIATED FUNCTIONS

Morse and Feshbach[1] have proposed the concept of an image system to be associated with each dissipative process in such a way that the frictional

---

[1] P. M. Morse and H. Feshbach, "Methods of Theoretical Physics," part 1, p. 298, McGraw-Hill Book Company, New York, 1953.

dissipation of mechanical energy in the real process appears as a generation term in the image system. To be explicit, consider the simple mechanical system in which the displacement from equilibrium $x(t)$ is governed by the second-order equation

$$M \frac{d^2x}{dt^2} + R \frac{dx}{dt} + Kx = 0 \qquad (6.4.1)$$

where t = time

$\quad M$ = mass

$\quad R$ = resistance

$\quad K$ = restoring force constant

This system is dissipative because of the existence of the resistance term. Its corresponding image system would be governed by the differential equation

$$M \frac{d^2x^*}{dt^*} - R \frac{dx^*}{dt} + Kx^* = 0 \qquad (6.4.2)$$

where x^* is the associated function. The frictional force of the real system appears as an accelerating force in Eq. (6.4.2). What has been gained by introducing the image system? How are the two systems really related? The principal application to be noted is the existence of a functional which is stationary if both Eqs. (6.4.1) and (6.4.2) are simultaneously satisfied.

This functional can be formed as

$$E = \int_{t_2}^{t_1} \left(-M \frac{dx}{dt} \frac{dx^*}{dt} - Rx \frac{dx^*}{dt} + Kxx^* \right) dt \qquad (6.4.3)$$

Clearly, Eqs. (6.4.1) and (6.4.2) are necessary conditions for δE to vanish with respect to variations in x and x^*. Thus, by introducing the associated function x^*, we have been able to construct a variational principle which governs the behavior of the dissipative system.

There are several interesting features to be noted. First of all, we see the associated function $x^*(t)$ does not appear to have physical significance. This variable is "associated" with a particular physical system but is not measurable in the vibrating mechanical system. This lack of a physical "handle" is indeed a handicap in the chore of generating approximate solutions. As we have seen in our previous work, physical intuition has been one of our most valuable guides. This particular point will trouble us throughout our work on associated functions and represents one of the primary difficulties encountered in applying the method.

It is interesting to see that Eq. (6.4.2) can be evolved from Eq. (6.4.1) by reversing the sign of time, that is, by putting $-t$ for t in Eq. (6.4.1). For a nondissipative process, such a transformation would leave the equations invariant. However, the mechanical system considered here is dissipative, and reversing the sign of time yields the associated equation. Unfortunately, this procedure does not produce correct results in general cases. For continuous systems, the associated functions become rather complex and cannot be generated by reversing the sign of time.

A general process expressible by the macroscopic balance equations can be represented by use of image systems. Several variational principles relying on this concept have been reported.[2-4] To exhibit the essential features of the method relative to its applications to continuum systems, consider the simple process of steady-state heat conduction in a solid body having a temperature-sensitive thermal conductivity. Assume that the temperature is specified on the boundary. The balance equation describing this process is

$$\frac{\partial}{\partial x_i}\left(k\frac{\partial T}{\partial x_i}\right) = 0 \quad \text{in } V \tag{6.4.4}$$

This is a dissipative process (entropy is generated), and we define an associated function T^* by requiring that the functional

$$E = \int_V \left[k(T)\frac{\partial T}{\partial x_i}\frac{\partial T^*}{\partial x_i}\right] dV \tag{6.4.5}$$

be stationary with respect to variations in both T and T^*. The Euler-Lagrange equations are

$$\delta T^* = 0 \quad \text{on } S \tag{6.4.6}$$

and

$$\frac{\partial^2 T^*}{\partial x_i\,\partial x_i} = 0 \quad \text{in } V \tag{6.4.7}$$

We see that T^* must be specified on S and must satisfy Laplace's equation in V. However, the T^* is not completely determined, since the boundary condition, Eq. (6.4.6), does not give us any reason to prefer one set of boundary values over any other. We shall come back to this point in Example 6.4.1.

[2] H. L. Dryden, F. P. Murnaghan, and H. Bateman, "Hydrodynamics," p. 168, Dover Publications, Inc., New York, 1956.

[3] J. C. Slattery, "A Widely Applicable Type of Variational Integral I: Development," *Chem. Engr. Sci.*, vol. 19, p. 801, 1964.

[4] R. W. Flumerfelt and J. C. Slattery, "A Widely Applicable Type of Variational Integral II: Newtonian Flow Past a Sphere," *Chem. Engr. Sci.*, vol. 20, p. 157, 1965.

A rather perplexing situation exists when one uses the Ritz method to determine an approximate solution. If one uses the exact expression for T^*, then the functional δE vanishes for all values of the constants appearing in an approximating function such as the following:

$$T \simeq T_s(x_i) + \sum_{\delta=1}^{N} C_\delta v_\delta(x_i) \tag{6.4.8}$$

where

$$T = T_s \quad \text{on } S$$

Thus Eq. (6.4.5) does not yield numerical values for the C_δ. This state of affairs can be seen by substituting Eq. (6.4.8) into Eq. (6.4.5) and differentiating with respect to one of the free parameters, say C_γ. We find

$$\frac{\partial E}{\partial C_\gamma} = \int_V \left(\frac{\partial k}{\partial \tilde{T}} v_\gamma \frac{\partial \tilde{T}}{\partial x_i} \frac{\partial T^*}{\partial x_i} + k \frac{\partial v_\gamma}{\partial x_i} \frac{\partial T^*}{\partial x_i} \right) dV \tag{6.4.9}$$

This expression can be rearranged as

$$\frac{\partial E}{\partial C_\gamma} = \int_V \left[\frac{\partial}{\partial x_i} \left(k v_\gamma \frac{\partial T^*}{\partial x_i} \right) - k v_\gamma \frac{\partial^2 T^*}{\partial x_i \, \partial x_i} \right] dV \tag{6.4.10}$$

The first term in the integrand can be converted to a surface integral and vanishes because v_γ is 0 on the surface. The second term is also 0, since we have asserted at the onset that T^* be an exact solution of the associated equation. Thus

$$\frac{\partial E}{\partial C_\gamma} = 0 \tag{6.4.11}$$

for all values of C_δ, and we are unable to find an approximation.

EXAMPLE 6.4.1   Consider the stationary temperature distribution in a heated slab bounded by the planes $x = 0, 1$. Suppose that the thermal conductivity depends linearly on the temperature

$$k = \alpha T \tag{6.4.12}$$

with α being constant. Let the temperature be 1 at $x = 0$ and 2 at $x = 1$. Approximate T as

$$T \simeq 1 + x + C_1 x(1 - x) = \tilde{T} \tag{6.4.13}$$

which satisfies boundary conditions for all C_1. Let

$$T^* = x \tag{6.4.14}$$

which is an exact solution of Eq. (6.4.7).

$$E_1 = \alpha \int_0^1 \{[1 + x + C_1 x(1 - x)][1 + C_1(1 - 2x)]\} \, dx \tag{6.4.15}$$

or

$E_1 = 3\alpha/2$ for all C_1

To find an approximation to T, we will have to use an imperfect T^*. Assume T^* to be

$$T^* = \tfrac{1}{2}x^2 + C_1^* \sin \pi x \tag{6.4.16}$$

This form has two merits. First of all, it does *not* satisfy Eq. (6.4.7) and secondly, the boundary values of T^* are unchanged with respect to changes in C_1^*. This condition is necessary to satisfy Eq. (6.4.6). Substituting Eqs. (6.4.13) and (6.4.16) into Eq. (6.4.5) yields

$$E = \alpha \int_0^1 \{[1 + x + C_1(x)(1 - x)][1 + C_1(1 - 2x)][x + \pi C_1^* \cos \pi x]\}\, dx$$

or

$$E = \alpha \left\{ \frac{C_1^*}{\pi} \left[-2 + 6C_1 + \left(\frac{24}{\pi^2} - 2\right) C_1^2 \right] + \frac{5}{6} - \frac{C_1}{4} - \frac{C_1^2}{60} \right\} \tag{6.4.17}$$

or

$$\frac{\partial E}{\partial C} = 0 = -2 + 6C_1 + \left(\frac{24}{\pi^2} - 2\right) C_1^2$$

Solving,

$$C_1 = \frac{-3 + \sqrt{5 + 48/\pi^2}}{24/\pi^2 - 2}$$

where we have selected the positive sign before the radical because the temperature must never fall below 1. There is one last feature to be noted. It is generally true that the arbitrary constants appearing in the associated trial function can never influence the parameters of the physical system. Thus in this example, the value of C_1 was quite independent of the value of C_1^*. (See Prob. 6.4.2.)

PROBLEM 6.4.1 Find the constant C_1 of Example 6.4.1 for both $T^* = x^2$ and x^3. Compare the approximate temperature profiles with the one obtained by integrating the heat-conduction equation pertaining to the problem described in this example.

PROBLEM 6.4.2 Prove that if

$$E = \int_V \zeta(T, T^*)\, dV \tag{6.4.18}$$

is stationary with respect to variations in both T and T^*, and the Euler-Lagrange equation evolved by taking the variation of E with respect to

T^* is the expression defining the physical variable, which cannot contain T^*, then

$$\frac{\partial E}{\partial C_\delta^*} \text{ is independent of } C_\delta^* \qquad \delta = 1, 2, \ldots, N$$

The C_δ^* are parameters in the equation

$$\tilde{T}^* = T_s^* + \sum_{\delta=1}^{N} C_\delta^* v_\delta^*(x_i) \tag{6.4.19}$$

with $v_\delta^* = 0$ on S. Also

$$\tilde{T} = T_s + \sum_{\delta=1}^{N} C_\delta v_\delta(x_i) \tag{6.4.20}$$

Thus if $\partial E/\partial C_\gamma^*$ is independent of C_δ^*, $\delta = 1, 2, \ldots, N$, then the C_γ are independent of the C_δ^*.

Our work with the image as associated functions applied to continuum systems has shown that the behavior is quite complex. Indeed, there is considerable research which must be done to assess the practical value of this method. For example, a second look at Prob. 6.4.2 will show that the constants C_δ are determined from the N equations for

$$\int_V L(\tilde{T}) v_\delta^*(x_i) \, dV = 0 \qquad \delta = 1, 2, \ldots, N \tag{6.4.21}$$

where $L(\tilde{T})$ is the differential operator applied to the approximate function. This structure is quite closely associated with the Galerkin method, although it is not in exact correspondence with that technique. The function v_δ^* would have to be replaced by v_δ to make the two methods identically the same.

As a final remark, we should note that in more complex problems than the example considered above, the associated equation is coupled to the physical problem. Of course, the associated function cannot appear in the Euler-Lagrange equation defining the physical variable. However, the reverse situation, in which the physical variable appears in the associated equation, often occurs. This complicates the search for an adequate trial function. This coupling is shown in the next example.

EXAMPLE 6.4.2 Let us examine the flow of a heated fluid in a system in which the temperature is specified on those boundaries S_T through which there may also be a flow of mass. On a second portion of the total surface enclosing the system, the radiation boundary condition applies. This surface S_R is assumed to be a solid impermeable boundary so that the velocity vanishes on this surface. Let us further assume for simplicity that the fluid is incompressible and all the physical properties are constant except the thermal conductivity, which is a function of the temperature. The velocity is a specified function of position. This process is defined by the condition that the functional

$$E = \int_V \left[\frac{\rho C_p}{2} v_j \left(T \frac{\partial T^*}{\partial x_j} - T^* \frac{\partial T}{\partial x_j} \right) - k \frac{\partial T}{\partial x_j} \frac{\partial T^*}{\partial x_j} \right] dV + \int_{S_R} h T T^* \, dS$$

$$(6.4.22)$$

be stationary. For

$$\delta E = \int_V \left(-\rho C_p v_j \frac{\partial T}{\partial x_j} + \frac{\partial}{\partial x_j} k \frac{\partial T}{\partial x_j} \right) \delta T^* \, dV$$

$$+ \int_V \left(\rho C_p v_j \frac{\partial T^*}{\partial x_j} + k \frac{\partial^2 T^*}{\partial x_j \partial x_j} \right) \delta T \, dV$$

$$+ \int_{S_T} \left(\frac{\rho C_p}{2} v_j n_j T - k \frac{\partial T}{\partial x_j} n_j \right) \delta T^* \, dS$$

$$+ \int_{S_R} \left(-k \frac{\partial T}{\partial x_j} n_j + h T \right) \delta T^* \, dS$$

$$+ \int_{S_R} \left(-k \frac{\partial T^*}{\partial x_j} n_j + h T^* \right) \delta T \, dS \qquad (6.4.23)$$

As usual, the coefficient of δT^*, the variation of the associated function, is the differential equation of the physical system—in this case the heat-conduction equation. The differential equation defining the associated function is the coefficient of δT. The essential feature to be noted is that T appears in this equation through the temperature dependence of the thermal conductivity. Thus the associated equation is coupled to the physical variable.

Finally, as an exercise, we write the boundary conditions which T^* must satisfy.

$$\delta T^* = 0 \qquad \text{on } S_T \qquad (6.4.24)$$

and

$$-k \frac{\partial T^*}{\partial x_j} n_j + h T^* = 0 \qquad \text{on } S_R \qquad (6.4.25)$$

since δT does not vanish on this surface. Thus the associated function must also satisfy the radiation boundary conditions on S_R.

CHAPTER 7
TIME-DEPENDENT PROCESSES AND HYDRODYNAMIC STABILITY

7.1 GENERAL PRINCIPLES OF THE ANALYSIS OF STABILITY

Although a certain stationary state may satisfy all of the governing equations and then be acceptable on purely mathematical grounds, that state may not be observed in practice. For example, the laminar velocity distribution satisfies the momentum balance for all Reynolds numbers; however, at large Reynolds numbers, such a flow is not observed. The laminar flow is said to be unstable because at sufficiently high Reynolds numbers, a small perturbation will cause the flow to change from laminar to turbulent. Clearly, it is important to be able to predict the existence of such behavior in a given system. In this chapter, we first indicate a means of studying time-dependent processes using variational techniques. After developing the capability of so formulating unsteady-state problems and achieving some understanding of the applications, we shall develop a technique for approximate analysis of stability and apply it to the Benard problem.

The stability of a system in a stationary state can be tested by studying the response of the particular system to imposed disturbances. Since one does not know the source or the nature of all of the spurious noises which are continually acting on any system, the stability must be tested for all possible disturbances. Such a global study is usually accomplished by assuming that any arbitrary disturbance can be expressed as a sum of normal modes, constituting a complete set over the region of interest, and that the response of the system to any stimulus can be deduced by superimposing the responses to each of the individual normal modes. Of course, the process of superposition is valid only if the physical system is described by linear equations; hence, the study must be limited to small disturbances whose action is considered over a very short time interval.

Under these conditions the response of the system is linear. The problem of stability is then reduced to the determination of the response to a disturbance represented by a normal mode. Stability is assured if the perturbation introduced by each of the individual modes fails to grow. On the other hand, the system is deemed unstable if a single mode gives rise to an unbounded output. The foregoing remarks briefly outline the concepts ordinarily used to assess the stability of a system. Chandrasekhar[1] provides a more complete and precise discussion of these concepts in the first chapter of his treatise on stability. Two facts should be stressed here which are to play an essential role in our analysis: (1) the initial magnitude of the

[1] S. Chandrasekhar, "Hydrodynamic and Hydromagnetic Stability," chap. 1, Clarendon Press, Oxford, 1960.

perturbations should be small, and (2) the time interval of integration should be short.

So far, our attention has been focused on the general concepts underlying the analysis of stability. In applying these principles to a particular problem, one is often faced with the necessity of integrating a system of linear differential equations and the simultaneous determination of a characteristic number which defines the growth rate of the disturbance. It is precisely this step of the analysis which often proves to be so complicated that an exact result is not attainable. In these cases, it is convenient to have a variational statement of the characteristic value problem as an aid in establishing an approximate solution. Chandrasekhar[2] makes use of this approach. However, to date the formulation of a variational principle which has the characteristic value problem as its Euler-Lagrange equations has been heuristic in nature rather than based on clearly defined physical principles. Consequently each problem has represented a different challenge.

We shall attempt to present a generalized approach to the analysis of stability using the general principles outlined here. However, the calculations will be based on a variational formulation describing the particular hydrodynamic system to be studied. Clearly, such a study must include time dependence, and for this reason we must extend the concepts presented in Chap. 4 to include time-dependent processes. This particular problem will be considered in the following section. The development of a general stability criterion is presented in Sec. 7.3, and an example is solved in the subsequent section.

7.2 TIME-DEPENDENT PROCESSES

There have been several different methods proposed whereby time-dependent processes are represented in variational form. We shall discuss these techniques in the following paragraphs. However, it should be noted at the onset of our work that variational principles in the classical sense probably do not exist for the unsteady state. Thus, as in much of Chaps. 4 and 6, we shall find that many of the formulations do not give rise to bounds. This is indeed a disadvantage; however, this loss seems to be the price to be paid if one is to preserve the other computational aspects stemming from the integral representation.

The work of Biot[1,2] will be considered first, and his method of solving

[2] S. Chandrasekhar, "Hydrodynamic and Hydromagnetic Stability," chap. 2, Clarendon Press, Oxford, 1960.

[1] M. A. Biot, "New Methods in Heat Flow Analysis with Application to Flight Structure," *J. Aeron. Sci.*, vol. 24, p. 857, 1959.

[2] M. A. Biot, "Further Developments of New Methods of Heat Flow Analysis," *Aero/space Sci.*, vol. 26, p. 367, 1959.

(approximately) problems of unsteady-state heat conduction will be presented. It will then be shown that image systems (Chap. 6.4) can be constructed for transient dissipative processes in much the same fashion as the steady state. Associated functions will be constructed for unsteady-state conduction, but owing to the tentative nature of the applications of this structure, we will not attempt to show examples of its use.

Finally, the local potential (Chap. 4) will be extended to include transient problems, and several examples will be given. It will be noted that the work of Rosen[3,4] and Chambers[5] is closely related to this extended principle.

Let us consider the flow of heat in a solid. The temperature is defined by the energy balance

$$\rho C_p \frac{\partial T}{\partial t} = k \frac{\partial^2 T}{\partial x_i \, \partial x_i} \quad \text{in } V \tag{7.2.1}$$

and on the surface by

$$-kn_i \frac{\partial T}{\partial x_i} = hT \quad \text{on } S \tag{7.2.2}$$

where h is a heat-transfer coefficient. In writing these equations, it has been assumed that k is a constant and ρ, C_p, and h will be constants in the analysis to follow.

To find a functional representation for this problem, Biot defines a heat-flux vector H_i so that

$$\frac{\partial H_i}{\partial x_i} = -\rho C_p T \tag{7.2.3}$$

The physical importance of H_i is difficult to assess. One criticism of Biot's arguments involves the loss of physical interpretation which compounds the difficulty of finding good approximations. It is important to remember that Eq. (7.2.3) defines H_i (at least partially) and that variations of T and H_i are not independent. Eq. (7.2.1) can be written as

$$\frac{\partial}{\partial x_i} \left(\frac{1}{k} \frac{\partial H_i}{\partial t} + \frac{\partial T}{\partial x_i} \right) = 0 \tag{7.2.4}$$

[3] P. Rosen, "On Variational Principles for Irreversible Processes," *J. Chem. Phys.*, vol. 21, p. 1220, 1953.

[4] P. Rosen, "Use of Restricted Variational Principles for Solution of Differential Equations," *J. Appl. Phys.*, vol. 25, p. 336, 1954.

[5] L. C. Chambers, "A Variational Principle for the Conduction of Heat," *Quart. J. Mech. Appl. Math.*, vol. 9, p. 234, 1956.

and is satisfied if

$$\frac{1}{k}\frac{\partial H_i}{\partial t} + \frac{\partial T}{\partial x_i} = 0 \tag{7.2.5}$$

We shall call this the transformed energy balance.   The boundary condition can also be put in terms of H_i as follows:

$$n_i \frac{\partial H_i}{\partial t} = hT \tag{7.2.6}$$

Biot suggests that the temperature distribution in the solid body will be the one satisfying the variation equation

$$\delta \int_V \tfrac{1}{2}\rho C_p T^2\, dV + \int_V \frac{1}{k}\frac{\partial H_i}{\partial t}\, \delta H_i\, dV + \int_S \frac{1}{h} n_i \frac{\partial H_i}{\partial t} n_j\, \delta H_j\, dS = 0 \tag{7.2.7}$$

This can easily be shown to be true if one notes that

$$\rho C_p\, \delta T = -\frac{\partial}{\partial x_i}\, \delta H_i \tag{7.2.8}$$

It will be left as an exercise for the reader to check.   One essential feature of Biot's analysis is that he has not been able to find the functional whose variation gives Eq. (7.2.7).   In other words the variational principle is not stated and, indeed, does not exist in the classical sense.   Thus we find, as suggested in the first paragraph of this section, that one cannot use this method to fix bounds.   On the other hand, Biot's formulation can be used in developing approximate solutions.   His arguments in this regard are interesting and we shall indicate a few of the essential steps.

Expand H_i

$$H_i = \sum_{\alpha=1}^{N} q_\alpha(t) H_i^{(\alpha)} \tag{7.2.9}$$

where the $H_i^{(\alpha)}$ are N vectors ($\alpha = 1, 2, \ldots, N$) selected a priori.   The $q_\alpha(t)$ are called "generalized coordinates" by Biot.   Using Eqs. (7.2.3) and (7.2.8), the temperature can be eliminated from Eq. (7.2.7) to give

$$\int_V \left(+ \frac{1}{\rho C_p}\frac{\partial H_i}{\partial x_i}\frac{\partial}{\partial x_j}\, \delta H_j + \frac{1}{k}\frac{\partial H_i}{\partial t}\, \delta H_i \right) dV + \int_S \frac{1}{h} n_i \frac{\partial H_i}{\partial t} n_j\, \delta H_j\, dS = 0 \tag{7.2.10}$$

The generalized coordinates are independent, so that

$$\delta H_i = \sum_{\alpha=1}^{N} \delta q_\alpha H_i^{(\alpha)}$$

with all N of the q's being independent.   Thus on substituting Eq. (7.2.9) into Eq. (7.2.10), we find the N equations

$$\sum_{\gamma=1}^{N} A_{\gamma\alpha}q_\gamma + \frac{dq_\gamma}{dt} B_{\gamma\alpha} = 0 \qquad \alpha = 1, 2, \dots, N \tag{7.2.11}$$

where

$$A_{\gamma\alpha} = + \int_V \frac{1}{\rho C_p} \frac{\partial H_i^{(\gamma)}}{\partial x_i} \frac{\partial H_j^{(\alpha)}}{\partial x_j} dV$$

and

$$B_{\gamma\alpha} = \int_V \frac{1}{k} H_i^{(\gamma)} H_i^{(\alpha)} dV + \int_S \frac{1}{h} n_i H_i^{(\gamma)} n_j H_j^{(\alpha)} dS$$

The N differential equations are solved to find the q_α, the initial values being selected so that the initial temperature configuration is satisfied.   Biot has given a number of examples to demonstrate the application of his method. Moreover, Nigam and Agrawal[6] and Agrawal[7] have applied this technique to the problem of determining heat transfer from the walls of a duct to a fluid flowing in fully developed laminar flow.   Thus this technique has a range of applications.   However, it is difficult to see how to generalize Biot's method and include a broader class of problems.   Thus we conclude that the method is useful in obtaining approximations to a certain class of problems.

The image system can be used to develop variational principles for the unsteady state.   Indeed, Stattery[8] has proposed that

$$J_T = \int_0^{t_1} \int_V \left[\frac{\rho C_p}{2} \left(T \frac{\partial T^*}{\partial t} - T^* \frac{\partial T}{\partial t} \right) - k \frac{\partial T}{\partial x_j} \frac{\partial T^*}{\partial x_j} \right] dV \, dt$$

$$- \int_V \left(\frac{\rho C_p}{2} TT^* \right)_{t=0} dV \tag{7.2.12}$$

will be stationary when the actual temperature distribution is used.   The associated function T^* is defined by the Euler-Lagrange equation found by requiring that the variation of J_T with respect to T vanish.   This structure is much the same as that found in Sec. 6.4.   The reader is referred to this chapter for examples as to its applications.

[6] S. D. Nigam and H. C. Agrawal, "A Variational Principle for the Convection of Heat," *J. Math. Mech.*, vol. 9, p. 869, 1960.

[7] H. C. Agrawal, "A Variational Method for Laminar Heat Transfer in Channels," *ASME Paper* 60-WA-98, 1960.

[8] J. C. Stattery, "A Widely Applicable Type of Variational Integral I: Development," *Chem. Engr. Sci.*, vol. 19, p. 801, 1964.

Two other authors, Rosen and Chambers, have reported methods of representing time-dependent processes in variational form. Their ideas are closely related to the local potential as it will be extended here. Thus we shall defer our discussion of their method until we have discussed the inclusion of unsteady-state process into the formalism introduced in Chap. 4. It should be remembered that the analysis given in Chap. 4 is applicable only to the stationary state. To work problems in stability, it is necessary to relax this restriction so as to include time-dependent processes.

In Chap. 4 we distinguished between two kinds of functions appearing in the integrand of the variational principle. One type of function was said to be evaluated at the stationary state and hence, not subject to variation. This kind of function is denoted by a superscript zero. The second class of variable was subject to variation. By making such a distinction, we were able to deduce a very general variational principle having the structure

$$E^* = E^*[J_{(1)}, \ldots, J_{(N)}; J^0_{(1)}, \ldots, J^0_{(N)}] \tag{7.2.13a}$$

such that the functions $J_{(1)}, J_{(2)}, \ldots, J_{(N)}$ which make E^* stationary and satisfy the auxiliary condition

$$J_{(\alpha)} = J^0_{(\alpha)} \tag{7.2.13b}$$

are the local thermodynamic variables defining the spatial variation at the stationary state. The function J could represent the temperature, a component of fluid velocity, etc. Of course, in this structure the $J^0_{(\alpha)}$ are presumed to be known functions of position not subject to variation. Moreover, neither $J_{(\alpha)}$ nor $J^0_{(\alpha)}$ were functions of time in our previous work.

To include the time-dependent processes in a variational principle, one must extend one's concept of the local potential. The quantities $J_{(\alpha)}$ and $J^0_{(\alpha)}$ must both be visualized as functions of time. However, the distinction between the two classes of functions must be preserved. The $J^0_{(\alpha)}$ are now assumed to be known functions of both time and position. As such, they are not subject to variation. Prigogine and Glansdorff[9] have shown that this distinction has physical significance within the framework of fluctuation theory. In their development the $J_{(\alpha)}(x,t)$ are microscopic fluctuations about some ensemble average, $J^0_{(\alpha)}(x,t)$. If we adopt this broader viewpoint then it can be shown that all time-dependent processes defined by the macroscopic balance equations (see Sec. 4.2) are expressible as the extremal of a functional having the form

$$L = \int_0^\epsilon E^*(t)\,dt + \int_0^\epsilon \int_V \left[\sum_{\alpha=1}^N a^0_{(\alpha)} \frac{\partial J^0_{(\alpha)}}{\partial t} J_{(\alpha)} \right] dV\,dt \tag{7.2.14}$$

[9] I. Prigogine and P. Glansdorff, "Variational Properties and Fluctuation Theory," *Physica*, vol. 31, p. 1242, 1965.

where the a^0 are physical properties such as the density, thermal conductivity, heat capacity, etc.

The form of Eq. (7.2.14) is not surprising, since the effect of the last term on the right-hand side is to generate a term $a_{(\alpha)}^0 \, \partial J^0/\partial t$ in the Euler-Lagrange equations. This is precisely the first-order derivative with respect to time which appears in all of the balance equations. To illustrate further the terms in this variational principle, let us consider an example.

EXAMPLE 7.2.1   As an example, let us consider the temperature distribution in a finite insulated rod[10] of length 2 as shown in Fig. 7.2.1. The ends of the rod are maintained at a constant temperature, say 0. Assume that the initial temperature is given by $T_0(1 - x^2)$ where T_0 is a constant. If the physical properties of the rod are independent of the temperature, then the process of cooling is determined by the partial differential equation

$$\frac{1}{\kappa} \frac{\partial T}{\partial t} = \frac{\partial^2 T}{\partial x^2} \tag{7.2.15}$$

subject to the initial and boundary conditions

$$T = T_0(1 - x^2) \qquad \text{at } t = 0 \text{ for } -1 \leq x \leq 1 \tag{7.2.16}$$

$$T = 0 \text{ at } x = \pm 1 \qquad \text{for } t \geq 0 \tag{7.2.17}$$

Here κ is the thermal diffusivity. This equation can be expressed in variational form. Indeed it is a trivial matter to verify that the functional L defined as

$$L = \int_0^{-\epsilon} \int_{-1}^{1} \left[\frac{1}{2} \left(\frac{\partial T}{\partial x} \right)^2 + \frac{1}{\kappa} T \frac{\partial T^0}{\partial t} \right] dx \, dt \tag{7.2.18}$$

is stationary if and only if Eq. (7.2.15) is identically satisfied. The correspondence between Eq. (7.2.18), written for the special case of linear heat flow in a rod, and the general structure as given by Eq. (7.2.14) is evident.

[10] J. J. Reynaud, "Application of the Local Potential Concept to Time-Dependent Diffusion Problems," Master's thesis, Department of Chemical Engineering, The University of Texas, Austin, Tex., 1962.

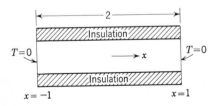

Fig. 7.2.1   Heat flow in an insulated rod.

The local temperature is the only thermodynamic variable needed to specify the state of the system.   Moreover, the quantity

$$\int_{-1}^{1} \frac{1}{2}\left(\frac{\partial T}{\partial x}\right)^2 dx \qquad (7.2.19)$$

is proportional to the generalized rate of entropy production E^*, as shown in Sec. 4.2, and a^0 is identified as the reciprocal of the thermal diffusivity—a physical property of the particular rod studied.   To continue the example, let us use the method of partial integration and develop an approximation to the temperature distribution which depends on both time and position. Assume

$$T = T_0(1 - x^2)f(t) \qquad (7.2.20)$$

where

$$f(0) = 1$$

so that the assumed temperature satisfies the stated initial condition. Similarly

$$T^0 = T_0(1 - x^2)f^0(t) \qquad (7.2.21)$$

Substituting Eqs. (7.2.20) and (7.2.21) into Eq. (7.2.18)

$$L = \int_0^\epsilon \int_{-1}^{1}\left[2x^2f^2 + \frac{1}{\kappa}(1 - 2x^2 + x^4)f\dot{f}^0\right] dx\, dt \qquad (7.2.22)$$

where

$$\dot{f}^0 \equiv \frac{\partial f^0}{\partial t}$$

Hence

$$L = \int_0^\epsilon\left(\frac{4}{3}f^2 + \frac{1}{\kappa}\frac{16}{15}f\dot{f}^0\right) dt$$

The $f(t)$ is to be selected so that L is stationary.   Thus applying the Euler-Lagrange equation, we find that $f(t)$ must satisfy the differential equation

$$\frac{8}{3}f + \frac{16}{15\kappa}\dot{f}^0 = 0 \qquad (7.2.23)$$

Let

$$f = f^0 \qquad (7.2.24)$$

and integrate Eq. (7.2.23) to obtain

$$f = \text{const } e^{-5/2\kappa t}$$

Since $f(0) = 1$,

$$\frac{T}{T_0} = (1 - x^2)\, e^{-5/2\kappa t} \qquad (7.2.25)$$

This approximation is compared with the exact solution[11] of the linear heat-flow problem

$$T = \frac{32}{\pi^3} T_0 \sum_{n=0}^{\infty} \frac{(-1)^n}{(2n+1)^3} \exp\left[-\frac{(2n+1)^2\pi^2\kappa t}{4} \right] \cos\frac{2n+1}{2} x \qquad (7.2.26)$$

in Table 7.2.1.   A brief study of this table will reveal that the approximate solution, even though a first approximation, is in excellent agreement with the exact solution.   A better approximation can be developed by using a more complex expression for the spatial variation—perhaps one having arbitrary parameters as well as being an arbitrary function of time.

In the preceding example, we have approximated the time-dependent temperature by allowing an unknown function of time to be determined by its Euler-Lagrange equation—the method of partial integration.   If we had assumed an explicit form for the time dependence of the temperature, leaving free parameters to be manipulated to make the integral stationary, then these free parameters would, in general, depend on the upper limit of the time integration.   This important fact is illustrated by the following example.

EXAMPLE 7.2.2   As a trial function applicable to the problem of Example 7.2.1, consider

$$T = \frac{T_0(1 - x^2)}{1 + \alpha t} \qquad (7.2.27)$$

[11] H. S. Carslaw and J. C. Jaeger, "Conduction of Heat in Solids," 2d ed., p. 98, Clarendon Press, Oxford, 1959.

TABLE 7.2.1   COMPARISON OF SOLUTIONS FOR LINEAR HEAT FLOW†

x \ κt	0.01		0.1		1.0	
	T/T_0 ‡analytic	T/T_0 §approximate	T/T_0 analytic	T/T_0 approximate	T/T_0 analytic	T/T_0 approximate
0.0	0.968	0.975	0.792	0.779	0.0850	0.0820
0.2	0.927	0.936	0.755	0.747	0.0823	0.0787
0.4	0.804	0.819	0.640	0.654	0.0696	0.0689
0.6	0.612	0.624	0.472	0.498	0.0509	0.0525
0.8	0.336	0.355	0.249	0.280	0.0267	0.0295
1.0	0.000	0.000	0.000	0.000	0.0000	0.0000

† This table taken from reference 10.
‡ These values computed by using Eq. (7.2.26).
§ These values computed by using Eq. (7.2.25).

where α is a parameter to be determined.   Substituting into the L of Eq. (7.2.18), we obtain

$$L = T_0^2 \int_0^\varepsilon \int_{-1}^1 \left[\frac{2x^2}{(1 + \alpha t)^2} - \frac{\alpha^0}{\kappa} \frac{1 - 2x^2 + x^4}{(1 + \alpha t)(1 + \alpha^0 t)^2} \right] dx\, dt \qquad (7.2.28)$$

where we have replaced the infinite upper limit on the time integration by a finite one.   We justify this step by asserting that our aim is to find the best possible value of α over the time interval 0 to ϵ.   We are not concerned with the accuracy of the trial function for times in excess of ϵ.   On integrating Eq. (7.2.28), differentiating with respect to α (holding α^0 fixed), and equating α^0 to α, one gets

$$0 = -\frac{4}{3} \frac{\epsilon^2}{(1 + \alpha\epsilon)^2} + \frac{1}{\kappa\alpha} \frac{16}{15} \left[\frac{1}{6} - \frac{\alpha\epsilon}{3} \left(\frac{1}{1 + \alpha\epsilon} \right)^3 - \frac{1}{6} \left(\frac{1}{1 + \alpha\epsilon} \right)^2 \right] \qquad (7.2.29)$$

This equation determines the proper value of α for a given ϵ.   Clearly, α depends on the ϵ selected.   For very long times ($\epsilon \to \infty$),

$$\alpha = {}^{15}\!/_2\, \kappa \qquad (7.2.30)$$

For short times ($\epsilon \to 0$), Eq. (7.2.29) is indeterminate, but on expanding

$$\frac{1}{(1 + \alpha\epsilon)^2} \cong 1 - 2\alpha\epsilon + 3\alpha^2\epsilon^2$$

and

$$\frac{1}{(1 + \alpha\epsilon)^3} \cong 1 - 3\alpha\epsilon + 6\alpha^2\epsilon^2$$

and retaining terms of order (ϵ^2), we find

$$\alpha \to {}^5\!/_6\, \kappa \qquad \text{as } \epsilon \to 0 \qquad (7.2.31)$$

The fact that the free parameter depends on the upper limit of integration is not surprising.   Indeed, this is also the case with position variables; that is, if one changes the domain of integration, then the approximating function becomes appropriately modified.   However, the region of integration is generally dictated by physical considerations.   Time, on the other hand, "flows" through all values beginning when an experiment is initiated and ending when it is terminated.   The time of termination, however, should not influence the previous results.   Thus it is generally annoying to find that the approximate solution gives an answer at time t which depends on the length of the experiment ϵ.   Unless there is a reason for selecting a particular value of ϵ, one usually avoids this difficulty by using the method of partial integration.   In studies of stability, one is interested in examining the *initial* growth of a disturbance; we know very well that a growth cannot continue indefinitely, since the unstable system will seek a new stationary or quasi-stationary state.   Here we impose the condition that ϵ be small and focus our attention on the time-dependent nature of system behavior during the small time interval ϵ. This will be discussed in greater detail in the following section.

So that we may develop a better understanding of the treatment of time-dependent problems in such a way that the answer is unchanged by the duration of integration, let us consider a second example.

EXAMPLE 7.2.3   Our task in this example is to calculate the rate of heat or mass transfer to a fluid in ideal stagnation flow toward a flat interface. The process is time dependent if we visualize an "eddy" current suddenly sweeping fluid toward an interface, as shown in Fig. 7.2.2. The velocity for planar case is given by

$$v_1 = ax_1 \tag{7.2.32a}$$

and

$$v_2 = -ax_2 \tag{7.2.32b}$$

The transport equation is (applicable to either energy or matter)

$$\frac{\partial T}{\partial t} + v_1 \frac{\partial T}{\partial x_1} + v_2 \frac{\partial T}{\partial x_2} = \alpha \left(\frac{\partial^2 T}{\partial x_1{}^2} + \frac{\partial^2 T}{\partial x_2{}^2} \right) \tag{7.2.33}$$

where α is either the thermal or molecular diffusivity (κ or D). The boundary and initial conditions are

$$T = 0 \qquad \text{at} \quad t = 0 \tag{7.2.34a}$$

$$T = 1 \qquad \text{at } x_2 = 0 \tag{7.2.34b}$$

$$T \to 0 \qquad \text{as } x_2 \to \infty \tag{7.2.34c}$$

Let us begin by putting the problem into dimensionless form. The quantity a determines the intensity of flow and has the dimensions of

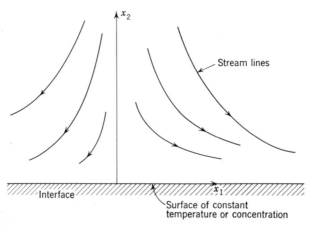

Fig. 7.2.2   Eddy current impinging on plane interface.

reciprocal time.   With this in mind, defining l to be a characteristic length, we can form the following dimensionless variables:

$$\theta = \frac{t\alpha}{l^2}$$

$$x = \frac{x_1}{l}$$

$$y = \frac{x_2}{l}$$

Substituting into Eq. (7.2.33) for the independent variables,

$$\frac{\partial T}{\partial \theta} + 2N_{\text{Pe}}x\frac{\partial T}{\partial x} - 2N_{\text{Pe}}y\frac{\partial T}{\partial y} = \frac{\partial^2 T}{\partial x^2} + \frac{\partial^2 T}{\partial y^2} \qquad (7.2.35)$$

where the Peclet number, defined as

$$N_{\text{Pe}} = \frac{al^2}{2\alpha}$$

is the sole remaining parameter in the differential equation and the associated boundary and initial conditions.   The flux from the wall is given in terms of a Nusselt number as follows:

$$N_{\text{Nu}} = -\left(\frac{\partial T}{\partial y}\right)_{y=0} \qquad (7.2.36)$$

so that

$$\frac{k}{l}N_{\text{Nu}} = \text{heat flux from interface}$$

or

$$\frac{D}{l}N_{\text{Nu}} = \text{mass flux from interface}$$

(T must be interpreted as a concentration in case of mass transfer.)

To obtain a simple approximation, let us first try a boundary-layer approach in which we define some depth of penetration $q(\theta)$† so that

$$T = 1 + \sum_{i=1}^{N} a_i\left(\frac{y}{q}\right)^i \qquad \text{for } 0 \leq y \leq q \qquad (7.2.37)$$

---

† This procedure seems to be quite effective in treating such problems.   We have already used it in the treatment of the thermal entry region (Sec. 5.5); Biot[1] and Agrawal[7] have also employed a similar technique.   Finlayson and Scriven[12] have studied the same problem posed in this example.   They also used a penetration concept.

[12] B. A. Finlayson and L. E. Scriven, "The Method of Weighted Residuals and Its Relation to Certain Variational Principles for Transport Process," *Chem. Engr. Sci.*, vol. 20, p. 395, 1965.

and

$$T = 0 \quad \text{for } y \geq q \tag{7.2.38}$$

The constants a_i must be selected so that T vanishes at the edge of the boundary layer. Thus we must have

$$1 + \sum_{i=1}^{N} a_i = 0 \tag{7.2.39}$$

Finally, let us impose a "smooth-fit condition" at the edge of the boundary layer

$$\frac{\partial T}{\partial y} = 0 \quad \text{at } y = q \tag{7.2.40}$$

A simple polynomial satisfying Eqs. (7.2.39) and (7.2.40) is

$$T = 1 - 2\frac{y}{q} + \left(\frac{y}{q}\right)^2 \tag{7.2.41}$$

It should be remarked that a T (temperature or concentration) which depends on θ and on y, but not on x, can be made to satisfy the differential equation and boundary and initial conditions. Thus we conclude that the T does not depend on x. Hence, the flux from the interface to the fluid will depend only on time.

A variational principle describing the problem is

$$L = \int_0^\epsilon \int_0^\infty \left[T\frac{\partial T^0}{\partial \theta} - 2N_{\text{Pe}} yT\frac{\partial T^0}{\partial y} + \frac{1}{2}\left(\frac{\partial T}{\partial y}\right)^2 \right] dy \, d\theta \tag{7.2.42}$$

We shall select the boundary-layer thickness such that L is stationary. This, in fact, is a method of partial integration, and the $q(\theta)$ so derived will not depend on the upper limit of the time integration ϵ.

Proceeding in the usual way,

$$L = \int_0^\epsilon \int_0^{q^0} \left\{ \left[1 - 2\frac{y}{q} + \left(\frac{y}{q}\right)^2 \right] \left[2\frac{y}{q^0} - 2\left(\frac{y}{q^0}\right)^2 \right] \right.$$
$$\left. \times \left(\frac{1}{q^0}\frac{dq^0}{d\theta} + 2N_{\text{Pe}}\right) + 2\frac{1}{q^2}\left(1 - \frac{y}{q}\right)^2 \right\} dy \, d\theta \tag{7.2.43}$$

The q^0 refers to the boundary-layer thickness which is associated with the unvaried function T^0. Hence, q^0 is not to be varied.

Integrating on y,

$$L = \int_0^\epsilon q^0 \left\{ \left(\frac{dq^0}{d\theta}\frac{1}{q^0} + 2N_{\text{Pe}} \right) \left[\frac{1}{3} - \frac{1}{3}\frac{q^0}{q} + \frac{1}{10}\left(\frac{q^0}{q}\right)^2 \right] \right.$$
$$\left. + \frac{2}{q^2}\left[1 - \frac{q^0}{q} + \frac{1}{3}\left(\frac{q^0}{q}\right)^2 \right] \right\} d\theta \tag{7.2.44}$$

Next we wish to select $q(\theta)$ so that the variation equation $\delta L = 0$ is satisfied for all q.   This leads to the Euler-Lagrange equation

$$\left(\frac{1}{q}\frac{dq}{d\theta} + 2N_{\text{Pe}}\right)\frac{2}{15} - \frac{2}{3}\frac{1}{q^2} = 0 \tag{7.2.45}$$

on setting $q^0 = q$ after taking the variation.
Solving for q, we find

$$q = \left[\frac{10}{4N_{\text{Pe}}}(1 - e^{-4N_{\text{Pe}}\theta})\right]^{\frac{1}{2}} \tag{7.2.46}$$

The Nusselt number is given by

$$N_{\text{Nu}} = -\left(\frac{\partial T}{\partial y}\right)_{y=0} = +2\frac{1}{q}$$

Thus

$$N_{\text{Nu}} = +2\left[\frac{10}{4N_{\text{Pe}}}(1 - e^{-4N_{\text{Pe}}\theta})\right]^{-\frac{1}{2}} \tag{7.2.47}$$

This answer can be checked, for Finlayson and Scriven[12] have reported that Chan has found the following expression to be the exact solution of the problem under consideration:

$$T = \text{erfc}\,[yN_{\text{Pe}}^{\frac{1}{2}}(1 - e^{-4N_{\text{Pe}}\theta})^{-\frac{1}{2}}] \tag{7.2.48}†$$

Differentiating, we find for the exact Nusselt number

$$N_{\text{Nu}} = \frac{2}{\sqrt{\pi}}N_{\text{Pe}}^{\frac{1}{2}}(1 - e^{-4N_{\text{Pe}}\theta})^{-\frac{1}{2}} \tag{7.2.49}$$

If we compare Eqs. (7.2.47) and (7.2.49), we see that the structure is the same—the difference being a numerical coefficient.   The ratio of the two expressions gives the error as

$$\frac{(N_{\text{Nu}})\text{ approx}}{(N_{\text{Nu}})\text{ exact}} = \frac{\sqrt{\pi}}{\sqrt{2.5}} \cong 1.13$$

or an error of roughly 13 percent.
We have examined one method of approximation, a very simple calculation, and found an error of about 13 percent.   Finlayson and Scriven[12] used the Galerkin method (Sec. 6.2) in connection with the boundary-layer approximation and developed a very similar expression.   In a rather intensive piece of work, these two authors also compared the solutions obtained by several other methods to the exact solution.

† The erfc is the complementary error function defined as

$$\text{erfc}(x) = 1 - \text{erf}(x) = 1 - \frac{2}{\sqrt{\pi}}\int_0^x e^{-\lambda^2}\,d\lambda$$

In the case of problems having structure

$$\frac{DT}{D\theta} = \frac{\partial^2 T}{\partial y^2} \tag{7.2.50}$$

one can often obtain a good approximation by assuming a solution of the form

$$T = \text{erfc}\,[f(\theta)y] \tag{7.2.51}$$

provided the boundary and initial conditions can be satisfied. Such an approximation was used in our study of boundary flows (Sec. 5.4) where we interpret $DT/D\theta$ as the material derivative of a component of velocity giving the boundary-layer momentum balance the appearance of Eq. (7.2.50). This was our justification for assuming the particular trial function used in the boundary-layer analysis. We see that Eq. (7.2.35) has the same form as Eq. (7.2.50) when the derivatives with respect to x are discarded. Thus we take Eq. (7.2.51) as a trial function and note that this expression satisfies the initial condition (Eq. 7.2.34a) provided

$$f(\theta) \rightarrow \infty \quad \text{as} \quad \theta \rightarrow 0 \tag{7.2.52}$$

The boundary conditions are satisfied by Eq. (7.2.51). We shall again use the method of partial integration and determine $f(\theta)$ so that the L of Eq. (7.2.42) is stationary. At the onset, we note that the exact solution, Eq. (7.2.48), is included in this trial function and, indeed, this is the solution that we would then expect to find.

We note the following relations starting with Eq. (7.2.51),

$$\frac{\partial T^0}{\partial \theta} = -\frac{2}{\sqrt{\pi}} \frac{df^0}{d\theta} y e^{-(f^0 y)^2}$$

$$\frac{\partial T^0}{\partial y} = -\frac{2}{\sqrt{\pi}} f^0 e^{-(f^0 y)^2}$$

Putting these relations into Eq. (7.2.42),

$$L = \int_0^\epsilon \int_0^\infty \left\{ -[\text{erfc}\,(fy)]\left[\frac{2y}{\sqrt{\pi}} e^{-(f^0 y)^2}\right]\left(\frac{df^0}{d\theta} - 2N_{\text{Pe}} f^0\right)\right.$$
$$\left. + \frac{2}{\pi} f^2 e^{-2(fy)^2}\right\} dy\, d\theta \tag{7.2.53}$$

Thus

$$\delta L = \int_0^\epsilon \int_0^\infty \left\{\left[\frac{4}{\pi} y^2 e^{-2(fy)^2}\right]\left(\frac{df}{d\theta} - 2N_{\text{Pe}} f\right) + \frac{4}{\pi}\,[e^{-2(fy)^2}](f - 2f^3 y^2)\right\} \delta f\, dy\, d\theta$$

Integrating with respect to y,

$$\delta L = \int_0^\epsilon \left[\left(\frac{1}{f^3}\frac{df}{d\theta} - \frac{2N_{\text{Pe}}}{f^2}\right)\frac{1}{2} + 1\right] \delta f \frac{1}{\sqrt{2\pi}}\, d\theta$$

Here we have used the following expressions:

$$\int_0^\infty y^2 e^{-2(fy)^2} \, dy = \frac{1}{f^3} \int_0^\infty \lambda^2 e^{-2\lambda^2} \, d\lambda = \frac{1}{8f^3} \frac{\sqrt{\pi}}{2}$$

$$\int_0^\infty e^{-2(fy)^2} \, dy = \frac{1}{f} \int_0^\infty e^{-2\lambda^2} \, d\lambda = \frac{1}{2f} \frac{\sqrt{\pi}}{2}$$

Since $\delta L = 0$, then

$$\frac{1}{f^3} \frac{df}{d\theta} - \frac{2N_{\text{Pe}}}{f^2} = -2 \tag{7.2.54}$$

Let

$$g(\theta) = \frac{1}{f}$$

so that

$$\frac{dg}{d\theta} = -\frac{1}{f^2} \frac{df}{d\theta}$$

Equation (7.2.54) is then

$$+ g \frac{dg}{d\theta} + 2g N_{\text{Pe}} = +2$$

or, solving for g, we find [since $g \to 0$ as $\theta \to 0$, see Eq. (7.2.52)]

$$g = \left[\frac{1}{N_{\text{Pe}}} (1 - e^{-4N_{\text{Pe}}\theta}) \right]^{\frac{1}{2}}$$

Or, substituting into the trial function, Eq. (7.2.51), we see that our calculation has given the exact solution to the problem. This was expected, since our original trial function "contained" the exact solution.

Example 7.2.3 has been a rather extensive one, in which various methods of solving unsteady-state problems have been discussed. In a sense, they are all summarized by noting that the trial functions have the form

$$T(x_j, \theta) = \sum_\alpha f_\alpha(\theta) v_\alpha(x_i)$$

in which the $f_\alpha(\theta)$ are to be determined by the method of partial integration. In this way, the resulting approximation does not depend on ϵ.

Before embarking on our study of stability, we should note that Rosen and Chambers have suggested variational principles in which one has both varied and unvaried functions, just as in the local potential. Indeed, Rosen defines the temperature of a solid body in a transient state as the function T which renders

$$I(t) = -\int_V \left(\rho C_p T \frac{\partial T}{\partial t} + \frac{1}{2} k \frac{\partial T}{\partial x_i} \frac{\partial T}{\partial x_i} \right) dv + \int_S Tk \frac{\partial T}{\partial x_i} n_i \, ds$$

stationary with the restriction that the heat flux be given on S and that $\partial T/\partial t$ *is fixed in V.* If we integrate Rosen's equations with respect to time and identify the fixed temperature as unvaried by appending the superscript zero, then we would find a typical variational principle of the type that has already been studied. Chambers has proposed a similar functional to define the process of unsteady-state heat conduction. Because of the similarity between these methods and those already studied, we will not discuss them further.

7.3 GENERAL STABILITY CRITERION[1]

Our analysis depends on the existence of a functional such as that defined by Eq. (7.2.14). We shall select a particular form for the time-dependent terms to be used. This then yields a situation in which the result depends on the duration of the integration on time. However, in the analysis of stability, we are only interested in initial behavior and thus are willing to focus our attention on time intervals ϵ which are very short in duration.

The reader is again reminded that stability is measured by the initial growth or decay of imposed disturbances. To give this concept mathematical substance, we assume

$$J_{(\alpha)}(x_i, t) = J_{(\alpha)}^s(x_i) + j_{(\alpha)}(x_i) e^{-\sigma t} \tag{7.3.1}$$

where the $J_{(\alpha)}^s$ are the local thermodynamic state variables evaluated at the stationary state being tested for stability, $j_{(\alpha)}(x_i)$ are the spatial perturbations about this state, and the parameter σ measures the stability of the system. Clearly the existence of a negative σ results in an exponential growth of the perturbation. The system is then deemed unstable. On the other hand, if σ is not negative, then the perturbation does not grow and the system is stable with respect to perturbations $j_{(\alpha)}(x_i)$. Thus σ is an indicator of stability, and our task is to determine its value for all possible $j_\alpha(x_i)$.

Before pursuing the calculation of σ, it should be noted that Eq. (7.3.1) is not generally an exact solution of the problem, since we have selected the time dependence without regard to the equations governing the transient state. However, we justify this by noting that we intend to develop some approximate ideas regarding system stability by finding the best value of σ

[1] R. S. Schechter and D. M. Himmelblau, "The Local Potential and Hydrodynamic Stability," *Phys. of Fluids*, vol. 8, p. 1431, 1965.

(in a variational sense) that describes the system over a very short time interval.

As in our previous work, the unvaried functions are represented in a self-consistent fashion as

$$J^0_{(\alpha)}(x_i,t) = J^s_{(\alpha)}(x_i) + j^0_{(\alpha)}(x_i)e^{-\sigma^0 t} \tag{7.3.2}$$

Substituting Eqs. (7.3.1) and (7.3.2) into Eq. (7.2.14) yields

$$L = \int_0^\epsilon E^*\, dt - \sigma^0 \int_0^\epsilon \int_V \left\{ \sum_{\alpha=1}^N a^0_\alpha j^0_{(\alpha)} e^{-\sigma^0 t}[J^s_{(\alpha)} + j_{(\alpha)}\, e^{-\sigma t}] \right\} dV\, dt \tag{7.3.3}$$

In principle the integration on time can be performed, since the time appears explicitly; however, it is usually too complex to be attempted. Fortunately, we are primarily interested in the *initial growth* of the perturbation, and hence we can restrict our study to small ϵ. Expanding the integrand of Eq. (7.3.3) into a Taylor series, we write

$$L = \int_0^\epsilon \left\{ E^*\Big|_{t=0} + \frac{\partial E^*}{\partial t}\Big|_{t=0} t + \cdots + \right\} dt$$
$$- \sigma^0 \int_0^\epsilon \int_V \sum_{\alpha=1}^N a_\alpha{}^0 \Big|_{t=0} j^0_{(\alpha)}[J^s_{(\alpha)} + j_{(\alpha)}]\, dV\, dt$$
$$- \sigma^0 \int_0^\epsilon t\, dt \left\{ \frac{\partial}{\partial t} \int_V \sum_{\alpha=1}^N a_\alpha{}^0 j^0_{(\alpha)} e^{-\sigma^0 t}[J^s_{(\alpha)} + j_{(\alpha)}\, e^{-\sigma t}]\, dV \right\}_{t=0} - \cdots \tag{7.3.4}$$

To the second order in ϵ, the functional reduces to

$$L \cong \epsilon P_1 + \frac{\epsilon^2}{2} P_2 \equiv L_A \tag{7.3.5}$$

where

$$P_1 = E^*\Big|_{t=0} - \sigma^0 \int_V \sum_{\alpha=1}^N a_\alpha{}^0 \Big|_{t=0} j^0_{(\alpha)}(J^s_{(\alpha)} + j_{(\alpha)})\, dV \tag{7.3.6}$$

and

$$P_2 = \left(\frac{\partial E^*}{\partial t} \right)\Big|_{t=0} - \sigma^0 \left\{ \frac{\partial}{\partial t} \int_V \sum_{\alpha=1}^N a_\alpha{}^0 j^0_{(\alpha)}\, e^{-\sigma^0 t}[J^s_{(\alpha)} + j_{(\alpha)}e^{-\sigma t}]\, dV \right\}_{t=0} \tag{7.3.7}$$

As noted above, Eq. (7.3.1) is generally not the extremalizing function of either L or L_A. However, upon substituting these approximate functions into the integrand defining L or L_A, it is natural to choose both the constant σ and the functions $j_{(\alpha)}(x_i)$ such that L (or L_A) is stationary.

If the $j_{(\alpha)}(x_j)$ and σ are to be chosen so that L_A is rendered stationary, we have

$$\delta L_A = \epsilon \sum_{\alpha=1}^N \frac{\delta P_1}{\delta j_{(\alpha)}} \delta j_{(\alpha)} + \frac{\epsilon^2}{2} \sum_{\alpha=1}^N \frac{\delta P_2}{\delta j_{(\alpha)}} \delta j_{(\alpha)} + \frac{\epsilon^2}{2} \frac{\partial P_2}{\partial \sigma} \delta \sigma \tag{7.3.8}$$

The quantity $\partial P_1/\partial\sigma$ vanishes and, consequently, is omitted from Eq. (7.3.8). If L_A is to be stationary, then it is necessary for

$$\frac{\delta P_1}{\delta j_{(\alpha)}} = 0 \qquad \alpha = 1, \ldots, N \tag{7.3.9}$$

and

$$\frac{\partial P_2}{\partial\sigma} = 0 \tag{7.3.10}$$

This system of equations defines the N functions $j_{(\alpha)}$ and the decay-rate parameter σ. It is interesting to note that Eq. (7.3.9) can be used to determine the stability of some systems without further calculation. If the limits of integration are independent of time, that is, the volume V fixed in space, then one of the parameters σ or σ^0 appears as a coefficient of time in the expression for E^*; that is,

$$E^*(t) = E^*(\sigma t, \sigma^0 t) \tag{7.3.11}$$

Equation (7.3.11) is easily understood if we recall that the state variables are not differentiated with respect to time in forming E^* and the time does not appear explicitly in $E^*(t)$, since the generalized rate of entropy production depends on time only through the dependence of $J_{(\alpha)}(x_i,t)$ on time. Thus the derivative of E^* with respect to time can be formed as

$$\frac{\partial E^*}{\partial t} = \sigma\,\frac{\partial E^*}{\partial(\sigma t)} + \sigma^0\,\frac{\partial E^*}{\partial(\sigma^0 t)} \tag{7.3.12}$$

Equation (7.3.11) permits us to conclude that both

$$\frac{\partial E^*}{\partial(\sigma t)}\bigg|_{t=0} \qquad \text{and} \qquad \frac{\partial E^*}{\partial(\sigma^0 t)}\bigg|_{t=0}$$

are independent of σ and σ^0. Therefore $\partial E^*/\partial t\big|_{t=0}$ is linear in σ. If the a_α^0 are constants (constant physical properties), then Eq. (7.3.10) reduces to

$$\frac{\partial P_2}{\partial\sigma} = \frac{\partial E^*}{\partial(\sigma t)}\bigg|_{t=0} + \sigma^0\int_V \sum_{\alpha=1}^N a_\alpha^0 j_{(\alpha)}^0 j_{(\alpha)}\,dV = 0 \tag{7.3.13}$$

Since we have differentiated with respect to σ, it is no longer necessary to distinguish between varied and unvaried functions. Thus, solving Eq. (7.3.13) for σ, we find

$$\sigma = \frac{-\partial E^*/\partial(\sigma t)\big|_{t=0}}{\int_V \sum_{\alpha=1}^N a_\alpha j_\alpha^2\,dV} \tag{7.3.14}$$

It should be remembered that the partial derivative taken with respect to σt implies that $\sigma^0 t$ is held fixed during the process of differentiation. The denominator of Eq. (7.3.14) is always positive if the $a_\alpha > 0$. In some physical problems, the numerator can be shown to take on a fixed sign for all admissible $j_{(\alpha)}(x_i)$. In these cases the sign of σ is established and the question of stability resolved!

Unfortunately, in most cases the sign of σ cannot be determined without specific knowledge of the perturbations $j_{(\alpha)}(x)$, and to study stability, one must investigate the behavior of these functions. To make an exact study, the differential equations generated by taking the variations indicated by Eq. (7.3.9) must be solved. However, the study of stability can also be carried out by constructing approximate solutions for the $j_{(\alpha)}$ using the Ritz method (see Sec. 3.2). Assume

$$j_{(\alpha)} = \sum_{k=1}^{r} b_{(k)}^{(\alpha)} \phi_{(k)}(x_i) \tag{7.3.15}$$

where the $b_{(k)}^{(\alpha)}$ are constants to be determined and the $\phi_{(k)}$ are specified functions of position.

The function P_1 becomes

$$P_1 = E^*(b_{(k)}^{(\alpha)})\big|_{t=0} - \sigma^0 \int_V dV \left\{ \sum_{\alpha=1}^{N} a_\alpha^{\,0}\big|_{t=0} \left[J_{(\alpha)}^s + \sum_{k=1}^{r} b_{(k)}^{(\alpha)} \phi_{(k)} \right] \sum_{l=1}^{r} b_{(l)}^{0(\alpha)} \phi_{(l)} \right\} \tag{7.3.16}$$

where

$$j_\alpha^{\,0} = \sum_{l=1}^{r} b_{(l)}^{0(\alpha)} \phi_{(l)} \tag{7.3.17}$$

The coefficients $b_{(k)}^{(l)}$ are to be selected so that

$$\frac{\partial P_1}{\partial b_{(k)}^{(\alpha)}} = 0 \qquad \alpha = 1, \ldots, N, \, k = 1, \ldots, r \tag{7.3.18}$$

These $N \times r$ equations can be written as

$$0 = \frac{\partial E^*}{\partial b_{(k)}^{(\alpha)}} - \sigma \int_V dV \left[a_{(\alpha)} \phi_k \sum_{l=1}^{r} b_{(l)}^{(\alpha)} \phi_l \right] \tag{7.3.19}$$

This is a characteristic value problem in that there are $N \times r$ homogeneous equations, and the σ must be selected so that a nontrivial solution exists. These values of σ then determine the stability of the system. This problem is identical to that encountered in Sec. 3.4, where we studied the treatment of eigenvalue problems using the Ritz method.

Equation (7.3.19) is the final working equation. In the next section, we shall apply this result to the Benard problem, which should provide an amplification of the general concepts introduced here.

7.4 THE BENARD PROBLEM

The Benard problem is the determination of the stability of a fluid heated from below. The geometric arrangement is shown in Fig. 7.4.1. The lower plate is maintained at a temperature T_h, and the upper plate temperature is fixed at $T_h - \beta l_1$, which gives a temperature gradient of $-\beta$ at the stationary state.

We begin with the following differential equations describing the mass, momentum, and energy balances for an incompressible fluid:

$$\frac{\partial v_j}{\partial x_j} = 0 \tag{7.4.1}$$

$$\frac{\partial T}{\partial t} + v_j \frac{\partial T}{\partial x_j} = \kappa \frac{\partial^2 T}{\partial x_j \, \partial x_j} \tag{7.4.2}$$

$$\rho_h \left(\frac{\partial v_i}{\partial t} + v_j \frac{\partial v_i}{\partial x_j} \right) = -\frac{\partial p}{\partial x_i} + \mu \frac{\partial^2 v_i}{\partial x_j \, \partial x_j} + F_i \rho \tag{7.4.3}$$

where ρ_h is the density at temperature T_h, and ρ is the local density. In writing these equations, we have invoked the "Boussinesq approximation"[1]

[1] S. Chandrasekhar, "Hydrodynamic and Hydromagnetic Stability," chap. 2, Clarendon Press, Oxford, 1960.

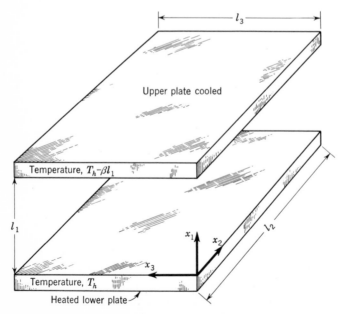

Fig. 7.4.1   Fluid contained between two plates and heated from below—the Benard problem.

in which the variation of density with respect to temperature is ignored in the computation of the inertia terms on the left-hand side of Eq. (7.4.3) and in writing the continuity equation (7.4.1). However, density gradients are not neglected in determining the body force and will be accounted for in the pressure variation. All other physical properties are assumed constant. If we multiply Eq. (7.4.1) by $\partial p/\partial t$, Eq. (7.4.2) by $(\rho_h C_p/T_h)(\partial T/\partial t)$, and Eq. (7.4.3) by $(\partial v_i/\partial t)$, one finds upon summing the resultant equations

$$\psi = \frac{\partial p}{\partial t}\frac{\partial v_i}{\partial x_i} + \rho_h \frac{\partial v_i}{\partial t} v_j \frac{\partial v_i}{\partial x_j} + \frac{\partial v_i}{\partial t}\frac{\partial p}{\partial x_i} - \rho F_i \frac{\partial v_i}{\partial t}$$
$$- \rho_h \nu \frac{\partial v_i}{\partial t}\frac{\partial^2 v_i}{\partial x_j \partial x_j} + \frac{\rho_h C_p v_j}{T_h}\frac{\partial T}{\partial t}\frac{\partial T}{\partial x_j} - \frac{\rho_h \kappa C_p}{T_h}\frac{\partial T}{\partial t}\frac{\partial^2 T}{\partial x_j \partial x_j} \qquad (7.4.4)$$

where ν is the kinematic viscosity ($\nu = \mu/\rho_h$), and ψ is defined as

$$\psi = -\left[\rho_h \frac{\partial v_i}{\partial t}\frac{\partial v_i}{\partial t} + \frac{\rho_h C_p}{T_h}\left(\frac{\partial T}{\partial t}\right)^2\right] \leq 0 \qquad (7.4.5)$$

The quantity ψ has been arranged to be a negative semi-definite function, following the techniques developed in Chap. 4.

Let us consider a volume bounded on the top and the bottom by the cooled and heated surfaces, respectively, and enclosed by lateral surfaces drawn perpendicular to the plates. This configuration is depicted in Fig. 7.4.1. Integrating Eq. (7.4.4) over this volume gives

$$\phi = \int_V \psi \, dV = \int_V \left(\frac{\partial p}{\partial t}\frac{\partial v_i}{\partial x_i} + \rho_h \frac{1}{2} v_j \frac{\partial}{\partial t}\frac{\partial}{\partial x_j} v_i v_i\right.$$
$$- \rho_h v_j v_i \frac{\partial}{\partial t}\frac{\partial v_i}{\partial x_j} + \frac{\partial v_i}{\partial t}\frac{\partial p}{\partial x_i} - \rho F_i \frac{\partial v_i}{\partial t}$$
$$+ \rho_h \frac{\nu}{2}\frac{\partial}{\partial t}\frac{\partial v_i}{\partial x_j}\frac{\partial v_i}{\partial x_j} + \frac{\rho_h C_p v_j}{T_h}\frac{\partial T}{\partial t}\frac{\partial T}{\partial x_j}$$
$$+ \frac{\rho_h \kappa C_p}{T_h 2}\frac{\partial}{\partial t}\frac{\partial T}{\partial x_j}\frac{\partial T}{\partial x_j}\Bigg) dV + \int_{S_L}\left(-\rho_h \nu \frac{\partial v_i}{\partial t}\frac{\partial v_i}{\partial x_j}\right.$$
$$\left.- \frac{\rho_h \kappa C_p}{T_h}\frac{\partial T}{\partial t}\frac{\partial T}{\partial x_j}\right) n_j \, dS \qquad (7.4.6)$$

where the surface integral S_L is taken over the lateral surfaces and the n_j are the components of the outward drawn normal. The surface integrals vanish on both the heated and cooled surfaces because both the velocity and the temperature are time independent on these boundaries.

The local potential can be found by establishing the structure

$$\phi = \frac{\partial}{\partial t}(E_V + E_S) \qquad (7.4.7)$$

where the sum of E_V is the volumetric contribution, and E_S is the surface contribution to the local potential E^*. To develop the structure of Eq. (7.4.7) starting with Eq. (7.4.6), we use the concepts introduced in Sec. 4.3. Thus

$$E^* = E_V + E_S \tag{7.4.8}$$

where

$$
E_V = \int_V \left(p \frac{\partial v_i}{\partial x_i} + \frac{\rho_h}{2} v_j^{\,0} \frac{\partial}{\partial x_j} v_i v_i - \rho_h v_j^{\,0} v_i^{\,0} \frac{\partial v_i}{\partial x_j} \right.
$$

$$
+ v_i \frac{\partial p^0}{\partial x_i} - \rho^0 F_i v_i + \frac{\rho_h \nu}{2} \frac{\partial v_i}{\partial x_j} \frac{\partial v_i}{\partial x_j} + \frac{\rho_h C_p v_j^{\,0}}{T_h} \frac{\partial T^0}{\partial x_j} T
$$

$$
\left. + \frac{\rho_h \kappa C_p}{T_h{}^2} \frac{\partial T}{\partial x_j} \frac{\partial T}{\partial x_j} \right) dV \tag{7.4.9}
$$

and

$$
E_S = \int_{S_L} \left(- \rho_h \nu v_i \frac{\partial v_i^{\,0}}{\partial x_j} - \frac{\rho_h \kappa C_p T}{T_h} \frac{\partial T^0}{\partial x_j} \right) n_j \, dS \tag{7.4.10}
$$

The time-dependent state is defined by the extremal of the functional

$$
L = \int_0^\varepsilon E^* \, dt + \int_0^\varepsilon \int_V \left(\rho_h v_i \frac{\partial v_i^{\,0}}{\partial t} + \frac{\rho_h C_p T}{T_h} \frac{\partial T^0}{\partial t} \right) dV \tag{7.4.11}
$$

subject to the auxiliary conditions

$$v_i^{\,0} = v_i \tag{7.4.12}$$

$$T^0 = T \tag{7.4.13}$$

$$p^0 = p \tag{7.4.14}$$

This equation has the form of the general time-dependent variational principle as expressed by Eq. (7.2.14) and represents the starting point for our stability analysis.

Following the method defined in Sec. 7.3, we write

$$v_i = \xi_i e^{-\sigma t} \tag{7.4.15a}$$

$$T = T_h - \beta x_1 + \theta e^{-\sigma t} \tag{7.4.15b}$$

$$p = p^* - g\rho_h(x_1 + \tfrac{1}{2}\gamma\beta x_1{}^2) + \eta e^{-\sigma t} \tag{7.4.15c}$$

corresponding to Eq. (7.3.1). The density variation has been assumed to be linear with temperature, so that

$$\rho = \rho_h + \rho_h \gamma (T_h - T) \tag{7.4.16}$$

The stationary state to be tested for stability is that of a stagnant fluid with an imposed linear temperature gradient and a pressure determined from the momentum balance

$$-\frac{\partial p^s}{\partial x_1} = g\rho = g[\rho_h + \rho_h\gamma(T_h - T)] \tag{7.4.17}$$

Thus the pressure at the stationary state is

$$p^s = -\rho_h g(x_1 + \tfrac{1}{2}\gamma\beta x_1{}^2) + p^*$$

where p^s = pressure distribution evaluated at the stationary state

$\quad\quad p^*$ = constant

$\quad\quad g$ = acceleration due to gravity ($F_1 = -g$, $F_2 = 0$, $F_3 = 0$)

The functions ξ_i, θ, and η represent the perturbations about the stationary state. These functions depend on position, but not on time.

Following the development presented in Sec. 7.3, we find for the P_1 defined by Eq. (7.3.6), reduced appropriately for the Benard problem,

$$
\begin{aligned}
P_1 = \int_V &\left[\left(p^* - g\rho_h x_1 - \frac{g\rho_h\gamma\beta}{2}x_1{}^2 + \eta \right)\frac{\partial \xi_i{}^0}{\partial x_i} + \frac{\rho_h}{2}\xi_j{}^0\frac{\partial}{\partial x_j}\xi_i\xi_i \right. \\
&- \rho_h\xi_j{}^0\xi_i{}^0\frac{\partial \xi_i}{\partial x_j} + \xi_i\frac{\partial \eta^0}{\partial x_i} - g\rho_h\gamma\theta^0\xi_1 + \frac{\rho_h v}{2}\frac{\partial \xi_i}{\partial x_j}\frac{\partial \xi_i}{\partial x_j} \\
&- \frac{\rho_h C_p \beta \xi_1{}^0}{T_h}(T_h - \beta x_1 + \theta) + \frac{\rho_h C_p \xi_j{}^0}{T_h}\frac{\partial \theta^0}{\partial x_j}(T_h - \beta x_1 + \theta) \\
&\left. + \frac{\rho_h \kappa C_p}{2T_h}\left(\beta^2 - 2\beta\frac{\partial \theta}{\partial x_1} + \frac{\partial \theta}{\partial x_i}\frac{\partial \theta}{\partial x_i} \right) \right] dV + \int_{S_L}\left[-\rho_h v\xi_j\frac{\partial \xi_i{}^0}{\partial x_j} \right. \\
&\left. - \frac{\rho_h \kappa C_p}{T_h}(T_h - \beta x_1 + \theta)\left(-\beta\delta_{1j} + \frac{\partial \theta^0}{\partial x_j} \right) \right] n_j\, dS \\
&- \sigma^0\int_V\left[\rho_h\xi_i{}^0\xi_i + \frac{\rho_h C_p}{T_h}(T_h - \beta x_1 + \theta)\theta^0 \right] dV
\end{aligned} \tag{7.4.18}
$$

Here the unvaried perturbations have been defined to be

$$v_i{}^0 = \xi_i{}^0 e^{-\sigma^0 t} \tag{7.4.19a}$$

$$T^0 = T_h - \beta x_1 + \theta^0 e^{-\sigma^0 t} \tag{7.4.19b}$$

$$p^0 = p^* - g\rho_h(x_1 + \tfrac{1}{2}\gamma\beta x_1{}^2) + \eta^0 e^{-\sigma^0 t} \tag{7.4.19c}$$

It was noted in Sec. 7.1 that one must establish stability against all possible disturbances before the stability of a stationary state is assured. The strategy used to accomplish this task is to study the response to a single mode of a complete expansion. For example, an arbitrary temperature perturbation in the volume V can be expressed in the form of a Fourier series

$$\theta = \sum_{n,m=0}^{\infty} \beta l_1 \lambda_{mn}(x_1) \cos \frac{k_2^{(n)} x_2}{l_1} \cos \frac{k_3^{(m)} x_3}{l_1} \tag{7.4.20}$$

in which $\lambda_{mn}(x_1)$ is a function of x_1.

The response of the system to a single mode can be studied; that is, we will assume the temperature perturbation is of the form

$$\theta = \beta l_1 \lambda(x_1) \cos \frac{k_2 x_2}{l_1} \cos \frac{k_3 x_3}{l_1} \tag{7.4.21}$$

If the system is linear, the response to an arbitrary disturbance can be determined by summing the individual responses. Of course, k_2 and k_3 are not specified so that the analysis is, in fact, valid for each of the individual modes. Thus far in our analysis, we have not restricted the results to linear systems. Indeed Eq. (7.4.18) still contains terms which are third order in the perturbation [for example, $(\rho_h/2)\xi_j^0 \, \partial/\partial x_j \xi_i \xi_i$] corresponding to nonlinear terms in the Euler-Lagrange equations. It should be noted that we could determine the stability of a nonlinear system with respect to disturbances having the form given by Eq. (7.4.21), for there is nothing in the technique of analysis which requires that the equations be linear. However, if the system is not linear, the superposition principle is not applicable and one can no longer be assured that the test of stability is for all possible disturbances. Thus we have a mechanism for testing system stability against a specified disturbance; but unless the superposition principle is valid, we have no way of computing the response to an arbitrary disturbance.

Let us also assume that

$$\xi_1 = \frac{\nu}{l_1} G \cos \frac{k_2 x_2}{l_1} \cos \frac{k_3 x_3}{l_1} \tag{7.4.22a}$$

$$\xi_2 = -\frac{\nu k_2}{k^2} \frac{dG}{dx_1} \sin \frac{k_2 x_2}{l_1} \cos \frac{k_3 x_3}{l_1} \tag{7.4.22b}$$

$$\xi_3 = -\frac{\nu k_2}{k^2} \frac{dG}{dx_1} \cos \frac{k_2 x_2}{l_1} \sin \frac{k_3 x_3}{l_1} \tag{7.4.22c}$$

in which k is the wave number ($k^2 = k_2^2 + k_3^2$) and G is a function of x_1. The k_2 and k_3 are selected so that

$$\sin \frac{k_2 l_2}{l_1} = \sin \frac{k_3 l_3}{l_1} = 0 \tag{7.4.23}$$

The velocities have been selected so that the continuity equation is satisfied,

$$\frac{\partial \xi_i}{\partial x_i} = 0 \tag{7.4.24}$$

We assume for the pressure perturbation

$$\eta = \Delta \sin \frac{k_2 x_2}{l_1} \sin \frac{k_3 x_3}{l_1} \tag{7.4.25}$$

with Δ being a function of x_1.

Substitute Eqs. (7.4.21), (7.4.22), and (7.4.25) into Eq. (7.4.18) and integrate with respect to both x_2 and x_3.   These calculations give

$$
P_1 = \frac{l_2 l_3}{4} \int_0^{l_1} \left\{ -g \rho_h \gamma \beta \nu G \lambda^0 + \frac{\rho_h \nu^3}{2} \left[\frac{1}{k^2} \left(\frac{d^2 G}{dx_1^2} \right)^2 + \frac{2}{l_1^2} \left(\frac{dG}{dx_1} \right)^2 + \frac{k^2}{l_1^4} G^2 \right] \right.
$$
$$
- \frac{\rho_h C_p \beta^2 \nu}{T_h} G^0 \lambda + \frac{\rho_h \kappa C_p \beta^2}{2 T_h} \left[l_1^2 \left(\frac{d\lambda}{dx_1} \right)^2 + k^2 \lambda^2 \right]
$$
$$
\left. - \sigma^0 \nu^2 \left(\rho_h \frac{1}{l_1^2} G G^0 + \rho_h \frac{1}{k^2} \frac{dG}{dx_1} \frac{dG^0}{dx_1} + \frac{\beta^2 l_1^2}{\nu^2} \frac{\rho_h C_p}{T_h} \lambda \lambda^0 \right) \right\} dx_1 \tag{7.4.26}
$$

In writing Eq. (7.4.26), we have discarded all terms which are third order in the perturbations and terms which do not contain at least one function subject to variation.   Thus, terms such as

$$\frac{\rho_h}{2} \xi_j^0 \frac{\partial}{\partial x_j} \xi_i \xi_i$$

$$\rho_h \xi_j^0 \xi_i^0 \frac{\partial \xi_i}{\partial x_j}$$

and

$$\rho_h C_p \xi_j^0 \frac{\partial \theta^0}{\partial x_j} \theta$$

are clearly third order (containing ξ^3, $\xi\theta^2$, etc.) and have been neglected. It should be again noted that such terms correspond to nonlinearities in the Euler-Lagrange equations and neglecting these terms is equivalent to linearizing the differential equations. The terms omitted in writing Eq. (7.4.26) because they do not contain functions subject to variation are

$$(T_h - \beta x_1) \rho_h C_p \beta \xi_1^0$$

$$\rho_h C_p \xi_j^0 \frac{\partial \theta^0}{\partial x_j} (T_h - \beta x_1)$$

$$\frac{\rho_h \kappa C_p}{2} \beta^2$$

and

$$\rho_h C_p(T_h - \beta x_1)\theta^0$$

Certainly these terms cannot contribute to the variational principle, since they vanish with respect to variations in pressure, velocities, or temperature and can be discarded without loss of information.

The pressure perturbation Δ does not appear in Eq. (7.4.26). This is not surprising, since the continuity equation is automatically satisfied owing to our choice of ξ_1, ξ_2, and ξ_3 and as a consequence, we would expect P_1 to lose a degree of freedom. It should be noted that the pressure perturbation will vanish regardless of the functional form which is selected; that is, another choice of Eq. (7.4.25) would not have changed Eq. (7.4.26).

Finally, it is noted that the surface integration has not contributed to Eq. (7.4.26). This is true because the terms involved vanish identically on the surface.

It is perhaps worth stating again that linearization was not a necessary step. Although the calculations are simplified by the assumption, the general method is applicable to nonlinear processes. The only unsolved problem is the question of how to study the response of a nonlinear system to an arbitrary disturbance.

The stability condition of the Benard problem can be approximated by assuming

$$G = A\left(1 - \frac{x_1}{l_1}\right)^2 \left(\frac{x_1}{l_1}\right)^2 \tag{7.4.27}$$

and

$$\lambda = B\left(1 - \frac{x_1}{l_1}\right)\frac{x_1}{l_1} \tag{7.4.28}$$

These approximations have been selected to satisfy the boundary conditions ($\lambda = 0$, for $x_1 = 0$ or l_1, and $G = dG/dx_1 = 0$, for $x_1 = 0$ or l_1) for all values of A and B. Also the functions given by Eqs. (7.4.27) and (7.4.28) are easily integrated when substituted into Eq. (7.4.26). Apart from these features, no other consideration dictated the choice of these approximations.

Substituting Eqs. (7.4.27) and (7.4.28) into Eq. (7.4.26) yields after integration

$$P_1 = \frac{l_1 l_2 l_3}{4}\left(\frac{-g\rho_h\gamma\beta\nu AB^0}{140} + \frac{2\rho_h\nu^3 A^2}{5k^2 l_1^4} + \frac{2\rho_h\nu^3 A^2}{105 l_1^4} + \frac{\rho_h\nu^3 k^2 A^2}{1260 l_1^4}\right.$$

$$- \frac{\rho_h C_p\beta^2\nu A^0 B}{140 T_h} + \frac{\rho_h\kappa C_p\beta^2 B^2}{6T_h} + \frac{\rho_h\kappa C_p\beta^2 k^2 B^2}{60T_h}$$

$$\left. - \frac{\sigma^0\nu^2\rho_h A A^0}{630 l_1^2} - \frac{2\sigma^0\nu^2\rho_h A A^0}{105 l_1^2 k^2} - \frac{\sigma^0\beta^2 l_1^2\rho_h C_p BB^0}{30 T_h}\right) \tag{7.4.29}$$

Of course, in developing Eq. (7.4.29), we have used the self-consistent definition of the unvaried functions; that is,

$$G^0 = A^0 \left(\frac{x_1}{l_1}\right)^2 \left(1 - \frac{x_1}{l_1}\right)^2 \tag{7.4.30}$$

and

$$\lambda^0 = B^0 \frac{x_1}{l_1}\left(1 - \frac{x_1}{l_1}\right) \tag{7.4.31}$$

The constants A and B are to be selected so that

$$\left(\frac{\partial P_1}{\partial A}\right)_{B,A^0,B^0} = 0 \tag{7.4.32}$$

and

$$\left(\frac{\partial P_1}{\partial B}\right)_{A,A^0,B^0} = 0 \tag{7.4.33}$$

Thus we find

$$-\frac{N_R}{140}B^0 + N_{Pr}\left(\frac{4}{5k^2} + \frac{4}{105} + \frac{k^2}{630} - \frac{2\sigma^0 l_1^2}{105\nu k^2} - \frac{\sigma^0 l_1^2}{630\nu}\right)A = 0 \tag{7.4.34}$$

and

$$-\frac{A^0 N_{Pr}}{140} + \left(\frac{1}{3} + \frac{k^2}{30} - \frac{\sigma^0 l_1^2 N_{Pr}}{30\nu}\right)B = 0 \tag{7.4.35}$$

where

N_R = Rayleigh number, $\gamma g \beta l_1^4 / \nu \kappa$

N_{Pr} = Prandtl number, ν / κ

Settling $A^0 = A$, $B^0 = B$, and $\sigma^0 = \sigma$, Eqs. (7.4.34) and (7.4.35) are simultaneous, linear, homogeneous algebraic equations having a nontrivial solution if and only if

$$\left(\frac{4}{5k^2} + \frac{4}{105} + \frac{k^2}{630} - \frac{2\zeta}{105k^2} - \frac{\zeta}{630}\right)\left(\frac{1}{3} + \frac{k^2}{30} - \frac{\zeta N_{Pr}}{30}\right) = \frac{N_R}{140}\frac{1}{140} \tag{7.4.36}$$

where ζ is a dimensionless decay rate ($\zeta = \sigma l_1^2 / \nu$). Equation (7.4.36) defines the decay rate for given wave, Rayleigh, and Prandtl numbers. Under certain conditions, the decay rate will be negative indicating an unstable configuration. The locus of Rayleigh numbers giving marginal stability ($\zeta \equiv 0$) can be computed as a function of the wave number. At the critical wave number, the Rayleigh number giving marginal stability is less than that associated with all other wave numbers. The minimum

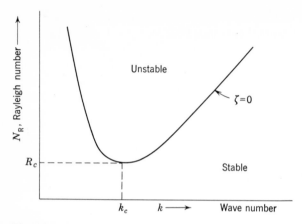

Fig. 7.4.2   Marginal stability.

Rayleigh number evaluated at the critical wave number is called the critical Rayleigh number and represents the largest value of the Rayleigh number which can be imposed without making the system unstable. The position of the critical Rayleigh number is depicted in Fig. 7.4.2. Let us determine the critical wave number using Eq. (7.4.36). Let $\zeta = 0$ and differentiate the equation with respect to the wave number k. This step gives

$$\left(-\frac{8}{5k^3} + \frac{k}{315}\right)\left(\frac{1}{3} + \frac{k^2}{30}\right) + \left(\frac{4}{5k^2} + \frac{4}{105} + \frac{k^2}{630}\right)\left(\frac{k}{15}\right) = \frac{1}{(140)^2}\frac{\partial N_R}{\partial k}$$

(7.4.37)

The critical wave number is defined as the wave number giving $\partial N_R/\partial k = 0$ (necessary, but not sufficient to prove N_R is a minimum). Solving Eq. (7.4.37) for the critical wave number, we find that $k_c = 3.117$ is the critical wave number. Using Eq. (7.4.36), we find the critical Rayleigh number to be 1,750. These two values are remarkably close to the more precise values of 3.117 and 1,708 given by Chandrasekhar.[1] This approximation, although stemming from very crude velocity and temperature perturbations, is quite satisfactory for most engineering purposes.

The next question one might pose regards the possibility of improving the answer. Of course, a better approximation should be achieved by increasing the number of parameters in the perturbations. For example, let

$$G = A\left(1 - \frac{x_1}{l_1}\right)^2\left(\frac{x_1}{l_1}\right)^2 + C\left(1 - \frac{x_1}{l_1}\right)^3\left(\frac{x_1}{l_1}\right)^3$$

(7.4.38)

and

$$\lambda = B\left(1 - \frac{x_1}{l_1}\right)\frac{x_1}{l_1} + D\left(1 - \frac{x_1}{l_1}\right)^2\left(\frac{x_1}{l_1}\right)^2$$

(7.4.39)

instead of using Eqs. (7.4.27) and (7.4.28).   Note that the new forms satisfy the boundary conditions so that they are admissible forms.   These equations can be substituted into Eq. (7.4.26) and the integrations over x_1 again performed.   The requirement that P_1 be stationary now leads to four simultaneous homogeneous equations.   The determinate of the coefficients must again vanish if A, C, B, and D are to have nontrivial solutions.   These calculations have been made[2] but would add little to our understanding if presented here.   It is interesting to note, however, that the critical wave number and critical Rayleigh number are 3.117 and 1,731, respectively. These values are, of course, more nearly correct than the previous numbers obtained by using the two-constant expansion (one for the velocity and one for the temperature perturbations).

One must also wonder what the effect on the answer is of assuming a completely different form for the trial functions.   The only restraint imposed on the choice is that the boundary conditions be satisfied.   (One should also endeavor to select members of a complete set where possible.)   For example, an acceptable choice is

$$G = A\left(\sin\frac{\pi x_1}{l_1}\right)^2 \tag{7.4.40}$$

and

$$\lambda = B\sin\frac{\pi x_1}{l_1} \tag{7.4.41}$$

These give a critical Rayleigh number of 1,824 at the critical wave number of 3.117.   Thus the values are not as good as those obtained with the polynomial expansion.   However, the Rayleigh number is too large by about 5 percent and is still entirely satisfactory for most purposes.

This example has been selected to illustrate the concepts of our general stability analysis.   The results achieved here are, of course, not unique. Indeed we have imposed the same assumption as invoked by Chandrasekhar and we have approximated his more precise result.   It should be noted that Chandrasekhar[1] has given a variational principle for the Benard problem. His principle is of classical structure and hence can be used to place limits on the error.   Therefore the use of Chandrasekhar's variational principle is much to be preferred over the local potential, which has been used here. However, there are many cases, even in linear problems, for which one cannot make a separation of variables and split away the time-dependent part of the solution in the form $e^{-\sigma t}$.   In these cases, the stability problem cannot exactly be represented as an eigenvalue problem.   To find the stability, one

[2] J. G. Ball, "Mass Transfer in Two-phase Co-current Flow in Circular Ducts," doctoral dissertation, University of Texas, Austin, Tex., 1965.

must treat time-dependent equations. An example of such a problem would be the stability of a diffusional system in which a gas is adsorbed at a plane interface and diffuses into the bulk liquid. Suppose that the density of the liquid is increased by the presence of the solute (dissolved gas). Is there some point in time, measured from the start of diffusion, at which the system is unstable? This question has been considered by Ball[2] using the methods outlined here. It was not possible to find a classical variational principle which governs the problem, so the local potential was used.

Finally, it is interesting to note that Eq. (7.3.14) does not yield an answer to the question of stability in the Benard problem, since this equation has the following structure:

$$\sigma = \frac{f_2 - f_3}{f_1} \tag{7.4.42}$$

where

$$0 < f_2 = \int_0^{l_1} \left\{ \frac{\rho_h v^3}{T_h} \left[\frac{1}{k^2} \left(\frac{d^2 G}{dx_1^2} \right)^2 + \frac{2}{l_1^2} \left(\frac{dG}{dx_1} \right)^2 + \frac{k^2 G^2}{l_1^4} \right] \right.$$
$$\left. + \frac{\rho_h \kappa C_p \beta^2}{T_h^2} \left[l_1^2 \left(\frac{d\lambda}{dx_1} \right)^2 + k^2 \lambda^2 \right] \right\} dx_1$$

$$0 < f_1 = v^2 \int_0^{l_1} \left[\rho_h \frac{G^2}{l_1^2} + \rho_h \frac{1}{k^2} \left(\frac{dG}{dx_1} \right)^2 + \frac{\beta^2 l_1^2}{v^2} \rho_h C_p \lambda^2 \right] dx_1$$

$$f_3 = \left(\frac{\rho_h C_p \beta^2 v}{T_h} + v g \rho_h \gamma \beta \right) \int_0^{l_1} G \lambda \, dx_1$$

Thus the sign of σ can be determined only if the sign and magnitude of f_3 is known. This quantity is turn depends on the distribution of temperature and velocity perturbations which must satisfy the balance equations. We see that Eq. (7.3.14) does not contain enough information to completely define stability in the Benard problem. Further calculations were required. However, as noted above, there do exist cases when the sign of σ is determined by Eq. (7.3.14) without requiring further knowledge regarding the behavior of the perturbations.

INDEX